I. McKenzie Smith

B.Sc., Dip.A.Ed., C.Eng., M.I.E.E., M.I.E.R.E., F.I.T.E.

Electrical and electronic principles

Level 2

Longman London and New York

Longman Group Limited
Longman House
Burnt Mill, Harlow,
Essex, U.K.

*Published in the United States of America
by Longman Inc., New York*

First published 1978
Second impression 1981

British Library Cataloguing in Publication Data

Smith, Ian McKenzie
    Electrical and electronic principles, level 2.
    — (Longman technician series : electrical and
    electronic engineering).
    1. Electric engineering
    I. Title
    621.3   TK145   78–40026

    ISBN 0–582–41170–X

Printed in Singapore by Four Strong Printing Co

Longman Technician Series

Electrical and Electronic Engineering

General Editor – Electrical and Electronic Engineering

I. McKenzie Smith, B.Sc., Dip.A.Ed., C.Eng., M.I.E.E., M.I.E.R.E., F.I.T.E.
Head of the Department of Electrical Engineering, Stow College, Glasgow

Books to be published in this sector of the series:

Electrical drawing and communication   **E. J. Pollard, I. Mckenzie Smith and J. McMaster**
Electrical and electronic applications Level 2   **E. Boyle**
Heavy current applications Level 4   **K Roots**

Books already published in this sector of the series:

Electrical principles and measurements Level 2   **I. McKenzie Smith**
Electrical principles and measurements Level 3   **I. McKenzie Smith**
Electrical and elecronic principles Level 2   **I. McKenzie Smith**
Electrical and electronic principles Level 3   **I. McKenzie Smith**
Electronics Level 1   **B. F. Gray**
Electronics Level 2   **B. F. Gray**
Electronics Level 3   **B. F. Gray**
Computer technology for technicians and technician engineers
R V Watkin

To Martin and Graham

Contents

Chapter 4   Capacitors and capacitance   105

Chapter 5   Alternating voltages and currents   141

Chapter 6   Single-phase a.c. circuits   182

Chapter 7   Measuring instruments and measurements   226

Chapter 8   Semi-conductor Diodes   247

Chapter 9   Transistors   262

Preface

Yet my classic lore aggresive
If you'll pardon the possessive
Is exceedingly impressive
When you're passing an exam.

W. S. Gilbert

One of the most exciting developments in technical education has been the introduction of new courses under the guidance of the Technician Education Council (T.E.C.). These courses take into account the educational requirements of technicians and shall fulfil their needs possibly for the remainder of this century.

The aim of this book is to cover the studies of a student presenting himself for the Electrical and Electronic Principles 2 unit of T.E.C. (U76/359). The text is based on this programme and is liberally illustrated by means of worked examples. The content is such that the text will also prove useful to students following other technician courses in electrical and electronic engineering, e.g. those of the Scottish Technical Education Council.

The International System of Units (SI) is used throughout the text. The student may therefore concern himself with that system only, it being the system generally recognised in engineering.

The symbols and abbreviations generally conform to those recommended in BS 1991, BS 3939 and PD 5686 published by the British Standards Institute. Use is also made of the current recommendation of the Institution of Electrical Engineers. To avoid confusion, symbols and abbreviations are not mixed together.

Finally the author wishes to thank his wife for checking the manuscript and for putting up with the trials and tribulations of its being typed. Also he wishes to thank his friends and colleagues both in Stow College and in the Institution of Electrical and Electronics Engineers for their advice and assistance. In particular, the help of Mr. N. E. Logan and of Mr. M. Gibson, both of Stow College, has been much appreciated.

Milngavie,
December 1977

Symbols and abbreviations

	Symbol	Unit abbreviation
Acceleration, linear	a	m/s^2
Area	A	m^2
Capacitance	C	F
Charge	Q	C
Current	I	A
Efficiency	η (eta)	—
Electrical field strength	E	V/m
Electric flux	Ψ (psi)	C
Electric flux density	D	C/m^2
Electric potential	V	V
Electromotive force	E	V
Energy	W	J
Force	F, f	N
Form factor	k_f	—
Frequency	f	Hz
Frequency, angular	ω (omega)	rad/s
Frequency, resonant	f_r	Hz
Impedance	Z	Ω (omega)
Inductance	L	H
Inductance, mutual	M	H
Length	l	m
Magnetic field strength	H	At/m
Magnetic flux	Φ (phi)	Wb
Magnetic flux density	B	T
Magnetic flux linkage	Ψ (psi)	Wb t
Magnetic potential difference	F	At
Magnetomotive force	F	At
Period	T	s
Mass	m	kg
Permeability	μ (mu)	H/m
Permittivity	ϵ (epsilon)	F/m

	Symbol	Unit abbreviation
Phase angle	ϕ (phi)	rad
Power, active	P	W
Power, apparent	S	VA
Power, reactive	Q	var
Reactance, capacitive	X_C	Ω (omega)
Reactance, inductive	X_L	Ω (omega)
Reluctance	S	/H
Resistance	R	Ω (omega)
Resistivity	ρ (rho)	Ω m
Temperature coefficient	α (alpha)	/°C
Temperature difference	θ (theta)	°C
Time	t	s
Torque	T	Nm
Work	W	J
Velocity, angular	ω (omega)	rad/s
	n	rev/s
Velocity, linear	u	m/s
Volume	V	m^3

Chapter 1

Direct-current networks

Resistance in an electrical circuit should be familiar to you; in practice, however, it is rare that the resistance is concentrated into one component section which is called a resistor. Instead, it is usual to find complicated arrangements of two or more resistors and these arrangements may have the resistors connected in series or in parallel. However, there are other network arrangements that can neither be described as series nor as parallel connections and this chapter is intended to extend the study of circuit analysis to the introduction of techniques whereby it is possible to calculate the performance of such networks.

1.1 Series circuits and parallel networks

It is possible to connect two resistors either in series or in parallel. Before proceeding to more advanced circuitry, it would be well to be sure that these two forms of connection are thoroughly appreciated. A comparison between series circuits and parallel networks is given in Table 1.1.

It will be observed that in the series connection, the current has no choice but to pass through all the series-connected components. In the parallel connection, the current has the choice of passing through all of the parallel-connected components, with the result that the supply current divides into the various branch currents which come together again having passed through the parallel arrangement. This is the essential condition of parallel connection in that the branch currents immediately come together again.

For generality, Table 1.1 is based on three resistors and not two. This section commenced with only two forms of connection for simplicity, there being a third possible connection for three resistors which will be introduced in para. 1.2.

Table 1.1

	Series Circuit	Parallel Network
Diagram		

	Series Circuit	Parallel Network
Current	The current is the same in all parts of the circuit	The total current supplied to the network equals the sum of the currents in the various branches
	$I = I_1 = I_2 = I_3$	$I = I_1 + I_2 + I_3$
Voltage	The total voltage equals the sum of the voltages across the different parts of the circuit	The voltage across a parallel combination is the same as the voltage across each branch
	$V = V_1 + V_2 + V_3$	$V = V_1 = V_2 = V_3$
Resistance	The total resistance equals the sum of the separate resistances	The reciprocal of the equivalent resistance equals the sum of the reciprocals of the branch resistances
	$R = R_1 + R_2 + R_3$	$\dfrac{1}{R} = \dfrac{1}{R_1} + \dfrac{1}{R_2} + \dfrac{1}{R_3}$

Example 1.1 A current of 20 A flows in the network shown in Fig. 1.1. Determine the current in each branch.

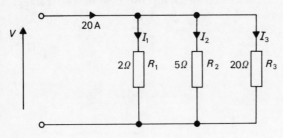

Fig. 1.1

$$\frac{1}{R} = \frac{1}{R_1} + \frac{1}{R_2} + \frac{1}{R_3} = \frac{1}{2} + \frac{1}{5} + \frac{1}{20} = \frac{10 + 4 + 1}{20} = \frac{15}{20}$$

$$R = \frac{20}{15} = 1.33 \ \Omega$$

$$V = IR = 20 \times 1.33 = 26.67 \ V$$

$$I_1 = \frac{V}{R_1} = \frac{26.67}{2} = \underline{13.33 \ A}$$

$$I_2 = \frac{V}{R_2} = \frac{26.67}{5} = \underline{5.33 \ A}$$

$$I_3 = \frac{V}{R_3} = \frac{26.67}{20} = \underline{1.33 \ A}$$

In the case of two resistors in series, it is particularly helpful to remember that, for the circuit shown in Fig. 1.2,

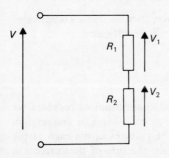

Fig. 1.2 Series-connected resistors

$$V_1 = \frac{R_1}{R_1 + R_2} \cdot V \quad \text{and } V_2 = \frac{R_2}{R_1 + R_2} \cdot V \tag{1.1}$$

Similarly, it is helpful to remember that, for the case of two parallel-connected resistors as shown in Fig. 1.3,

$$I_1 = \frac{R_2}{R_1 + R_2} \cdot I \quad \text{and } I_2 = \frac{R_1}{R_1 + R_2} \cdot I \tag{1.2}$$

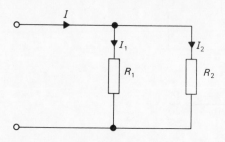

Fig. 1.3 Parallel-connected resistors

Relations 1.1 and 1.2 are most useful when dealing with more complicated networks because it often happens that we can deal with two components at a time and thus steadily progress through the analysis.

Finally there are certain principles to bear in mind so that as our analysis progresses, we may be sure that no careless errors have crept in. These principles may be listed as:

1. In a series circuit, the total resistance is always greater than the greatest individual resistance in the circuit.
2. The greater the resistance in a series-connected circuit, the greater is the potential difference (p.d.) across the resistance.
3. In a parallel network, the total resistance is always less than the smallest resistance in the network.
4. The less the resistance in a parallel network, the greater is the branch current in the resistance.

If these principles are used for your guidance, then the more complicated network arrangements should give you relatively little difficulty.

1.2 Kirchhoff's laws

From our consideration of series and of parallel connections of resistors, we have observed certain conditions appertaining to each form of connection. For instance, in a series circuit, the sum of the voltages across each of the components is equal to the applied voltage; again the sum of the currents in the branches of a parallel network is equal to the supply current.

Gustav Kirchhoff, a German physicist, observed that these were particular instances of two general conditions fundamental to the analysis of any electrical network. These conditions may be stated as follows:

First (current) law. At any instant, the algebraic sum of the currents at a junction in a network is zero. Different signs are allocated to currents held to flow toward the junction and to those away from it.

Second (voltage) law. At any instant in a closed loop, the algebraic sum of the e.m.f.s acting round the loop is equal to the algebraic sum of the p.d.s round the loop.

Stated in such words, the concepts are difficult to grasp and they are more readily appreciated by example. In Fig. 1.4, the currents flowing toward the junction have been considered positive whilst those flowing away from the junction negative. (Had the opposite convention been taken, the algebraic expression would have remained the same since the application of −1 to all terms does not change its validity.)

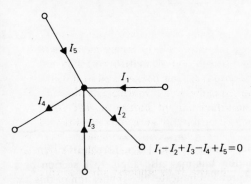

$$I_1 - I_2 + I_3 - I_4 + I_5 = 0$$

Fig. 1.4 Kirchhoff's first (current) law

Example 1.2 For the network junction shown in Fig. 1.5, calculate the current I_3, given that $I_1 = 3$ A, $I_2 = -4$ A and $I_4 = 2$ A.

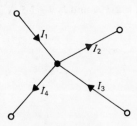

Fig. 1.5

$$I_1 - I_2 + I_3 - I_4 = 0$$
$$I_3 = -I_1 + I_2 + I_4 = -3 - 4 + 2 = \underline{-5\ \text{A}}$$

Example 1.3 With reference to the network shown in Fig. 1.6, determine the relationship between the currents I_1, I_2, I_4 and I_5.

For the junction a,

$$I_1 + I_4 - I_3 = 0$$

hence $\qquad I_3 = I_1 + I_4$

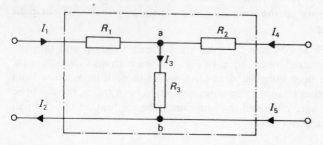

Fig. 1.6

For junction b,

$$I_3 + I_5 - I_2 = 0$$
$$I_3 = I_2 - I_5$$

therefore $\qquad I_1 + I_4 = I_2 - I_5$

and $\underline{I_1 - I_2 + I_4 + I_5 = 0}$

From the result of this example, it may be noted that Kirchhoff's first law need not only apply to a junction but may also apply to a section of a network. The result of the above problem indicates the application of this law to the dotted box indicated in Fig. 1.6. It follows that the performance of quite a complicated network may not require to be known if only the input and output quantities are to be investigated. This is illustrated by the following problem.

Example 1.4 For the network shown in Fig. 1.7, $I_1 = 2\cdot5$ A and $I_2 = -1\cdot5$ A. Calculate the current I_3.

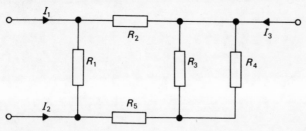

Fig. 1.7

By Kirchhoff's first law,

$I_1 + I_2 + I_3 = 0$

$\qquad I_3 = -I_1 - I_2 = -2 \cdot 5 + 1 \cdot 5 = \underline{-1 \cdot 0 \text{ A}}$

___

Kirchhoff's first law may be applied at any point within a network. This is illustrated by Example 1.5.

___

Example 1.5 Write down the current relationships for junctions a, b and c of the network shown in Fig. 1.8 and hence determine the currents I_2, I_4 and I_5.

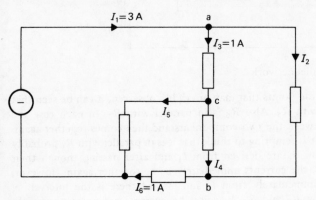

Fig. 1.8

For junction a,

$I_1 - I_2 - I_3 = 0$

$\qquad I_2 = I_1 - I_3 = 3 - 1 = \underline{2 \text{ A}}$

For junction b,

$I_2 + I_4 - I_6 = 0$

$\qquad I_4 = I_6 - I_2 = 1 - 2 = \underline{-1 \text{ A}}$

For junction c,

$I_3 - I_4 - I_5 = 0$

$\qquad I_5 = I_3 - I_4 = 1 + 1 = \underline{2 \text{A}}$

___

The examples chosen so far have permitted the addition and subtraction of the currents at junctions. Parallel arrangements require the division of currents, a point that has already been noted. However, it may also have been observed from the examples given that with more than two resistors, it is possible to make considerably more complicated networks. And these networks need not fit into either the series or the parallel classifications. The network shown in Fig. 1.9 illustrates this observation.

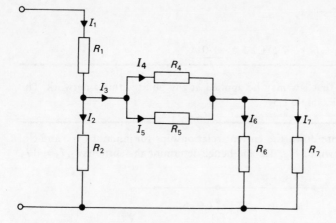

Fig. 1.9 Series-parallel network

Starting with the points that may be readily observed, it can be seen that R_4 is in parallel with R_5. Also R_6 is in parallel with R_7. In each case the current divides between the two components and then comes together again.

What of R_2? It is tempting to think that it is in parallel with R_6 probably because both I_2 and I_6 are derived from I_1 and after passing though their respective resistors, the currents immediately come together again. However, I_6 is not derived immediately from I_1 and instead there is the intervening network comprising R_4 and R_5. Because the currents are not immediately derived from I_1, then their respective branches are not in parallel.

R_2 is in parallel with the network comprising R_4, R_5, R_6 and R_7. In this case it should be remembered that this specified network takes the current I_3, and I_3 and I_2 are directly derived from I_1.

Finally it may be observed that the network comprising R_4 and R_5 is in series with the network comprising R_6 and R_7. In this case, the current in the one network has no choice but to then pass through the other network, this being the condition of series connection. It is, however, the networks that are in series and not the individual resistors, thus you cannot describe R_6 alone as being in series with, say, R_5. This would only apply if you could be sure that only the current in R_5 then passed to R_6, which cannot be said in the given arrangement.

Example 1.6 For the network shown in Fig. 1.10, determine I_1 and I_2.

$$I_3 = \frac{R_2}{R_2 + R_3} \cdot I_1$$

$$I_1 = \frac{R_2 + R_3}{R_2} \cdot I_3 = \frac{60 + 30}{60} \times 1 = \underline{1 \cdot 5 \text{ A}}$$

$$0 = I_2 + I_3 - I_1$$

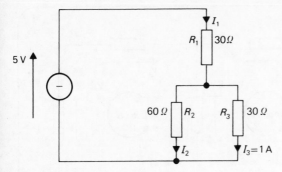

Fig. 1.10

$$I_2 = I_1 - I_3 = 1 \cdot 5 - 1 = \underline{0 \cdot 5 \text{ A}}$$

This example illustrates the third arrangement of connection of three resistors, the other arrangements being the three resistors all in series or all in parallel. The network shown in Fig. 1.10 is termed a series-parallel network, i.e. R_1 is in series with the network comprising R_2 in parallel with R_3.

Kirchhoff's second (voltage) law is most readily exemplified by consideration of a simple series circuit as shown in Fig. 1.11.

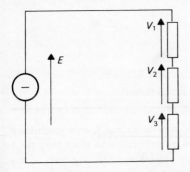

Fig. 1.11 Kirchhoff's second (voltage) law

In this circuit,

$$E = V_1 + V_2 + V_3$$

In even the most simple parallel network, there are three possible loops that may be considered. Figure 1.12 shows a reasonably simple arrangement in which the three loops are indicated.

Example 1.7 For the network shown in Fig. 1.12, determine the voltages V_1 and V_3.

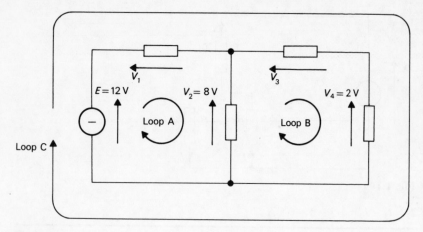

Fig. 1.12

For loop A,

$E = V_1 + V_2$
$V_1 = E - V_2 = 12 - 8 = \underline{4\ V}$

For loop B,

$0 = -V_2 + V_3 + V_4$
$V_3 = V_2 - V_4 = 8 - 2 = \underline{6\ V}$

For loop C,

$E = V_1 + V_3 + V_4$
$12 = 4 + 6 + 2 = 12$ thus confirming the results obtained.

It is important to note that there need not be an e.m.f. in a given loop and this was instanced by loop B. Also it is important to note that p.d.s acting in a clockwise direction round a loop are taken to be negative, which compares with the treatment of currents flowing out from a junction.

The application of Kirchhoff's second law need not be restricted to actual circuits. Instead, part of a circuit may be imagined, as instanced by Fig. 1.13. In this case, we wish to find the total p.d. across three series-connected resistors, i.e. to determine V. Let V be the p.d. across the imaginary section shown by dotted lines and apply Kirchhoff's second law to the loop thus formed.

$0 = -V + V_1 + V_2 + V_3$
and $V = V_1 + V_2 + V_3$

This is a result that was observed when first investigating series circuits but now we may appreciate it as yet another instance of the principle described as Kirchhoff's second law.

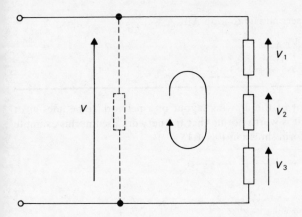

Fig. 1.13 Potential difference across series-connected resistors

Example 1.8 Calculate V_{AB} for the network shown in Fig. 1.14.

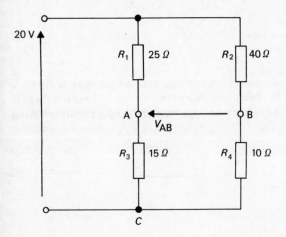

Fig. 1.14

For branch A, let V_{AC} be the voltage at A with respect to C.

$$V_{AC} = \frac{R_3}{R_1 + R_3} \cdot V = \frac{15}{25 + 15} \times 20 = 7 \cdot 5 \text{ V}$$

For branch B,

$$V_{BC} = \frac{R_4}{R_2 + R_4} \cdot V = \frac{10}{40 + 10} \times 20 = 4 \cdot 0 \text{ V}$$

Applying Kirchhoff's second law to loop ABC,

$$0 = V_{AB} + V_{BC} + V_{CA}$$
$$= V_{AB} + V_{BC} - V_{AC}$$
$$V_{AB} = V_{AC} - V_{BC} = 7 \cdot 5 - 4 \cdot 0 = \underline{3 \cdot 5 \text{ V}}$$

The rearrangement of the drawing layout of a network sometimes gives rise to confusion and it is worth noting that the network used in this example is often drawn in the form shown in Fig. 1.15.

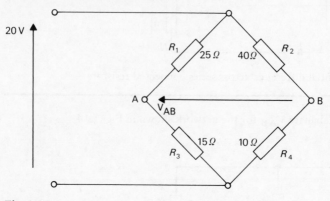

Fig. 1.15

The illustrations of Kirchoff's second law have so far only dealt with networks in which there has been only one source of e.m.f. However, there is no reason to limit a system to only one source and a simple circuit involving three sources is shown in Fig. 1.16. Applying Kirchhoff's second law to this circuit,

$$E_1 + E_2 - E_3 = V$$

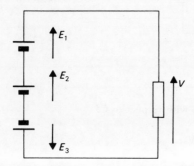

Fig. 1.16 Circuit loop with three sources

Example 1.9 Figure 1.17 shows a network with two sources of e.m.f. Calculate the voltage V_1 and the e.m.f. E_2.

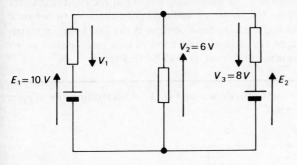

Fig. 1.17

Applying Kirchhoff's second law to the left-hand loop,

$E_1 = V_1 + V_2$
$V_1 = E_1 - V_2 = 10 - 6 = \underline{4\ V}$

The right-hand loop gives

$-E_2 = -V_2 - V_3$
$E_2 = V_2 + V_3 = 6 + 8 = \underline{14\ V}$

These results may be checked by considering the outside loop,

$E_1 - E_2 = V_1 - V_3$
$10 - 14 = 4 - 8$ which confirms the earlier results.

Finally it may be observed that this section has merely stated Kirchhoff's laws and illustrated each in terms of its isolated application. Every time a problem requires that currents be added then the addition conforms to the principle described by the first law whilst all voltage additions conform to the principle described by the second law. Kirchhoff's laws need not be complicated affairs and nine times out of ten they apply to two currents or two voltages being added together. Nevertheless, the laws may be applied jointly to the solution of complicated networks.

1.3 Kirchhoff's laws and network solution

Kirchhoff's laws may be applied to network solution in any of the following ways:

(a) by direct application to the network in conjunction with Ohm's law;
(b) by indirect application to the network in conjunction with the manipulation of the component resistances;

14 (c) by direct application to the network resulting in solution by simultaneous equations.

These statements appear to be most complicated but the following series of examples will illustrate the forms of application of the laws to network solution. The form that ought to be most obvious is the first form, in which the laws are directly applied; curiously this form of solution tends to be so obvious that it is all too often neglected, as shall be illustrated.

Example 1.10 For the network shown in Fig. 1.18, determine the supply current and the source e.m.f.

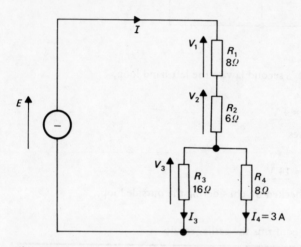

Fig. 1.18

Since R_3 and R_4 are in parallel,

$$V_3 = I_4 R_4 = 3 \times 8 = 24 \text{ V}$$
$$= I_3 R_3 = I_3 \times 16$$

$$I_3 = \frac{24}{16} = 1 \cdot 5 \text{ A}$$

By Kirchhoff's first law,

$$I = I_3 + I_4 = 1 \cdot 5 + 3 = \underline{4 \cdot 5 \text{ A}}$$

Also $V_1 = IR_1 = 4 \cdot 5 \times 8 = 36 \text{ V}$
$V_2 = IR_2 = 4 \cdot 5 \times 6 = 27 \text{ V}$

By Kirchhoff's second law,

$$E = V_1 + V_2 + V_3 = 36 + 27 + 24 = \underline{87 \text{ V}}$$

This is not the only form of solution to the given problem. For instance, the supply current could have been derived directly from I_3 by applying the current-sharing rule, or the source e.m.f. could have been derived from the product of the supply current and the total effective resistance which could have been determined — but the direct solution is readily available without the need to resort to such devices. The following two examples illustrate again the availability of a direct approach to network problems.

Example 1.11 Given the network shown in Fig. 1.19, determine I_1, E, I_3 and I.

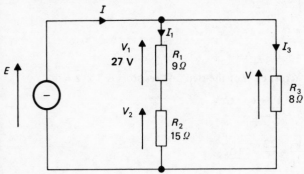

Fig. 1.19

$$I_1 = \frac{V_1}{R_1} = \frac{27}{9} = \underline{3\ A}$$

$$V_2 = I_1 R_2 = 3 \times 15 = 45\ V$$

$$E = V = V_1 + V_2 = 27 + 45 = \underline{72\ V}$$

$$I_3 = \frac{V}{R_3} = \frac{72}{8} = \underline{9\ A}$$

$$I = I_1 + I_3 = 3 + 9 = \underline{12\ A}$$

Example 1.12 For the network shown in Fig. 1.20, the power dissipated in R_3 is 20 W. Calculate the current I_3 and hence evaluate R_1, R_3, I_1, I_2 and V.

Potential difference across the 10-Ω resistor is $1 \times 10 = 10$ V

For resistor R_3, $P = 20$ W

$$= 10 \times I_3$$

Hence $$I_3 = \frac{20}{10} = 2\ A$$

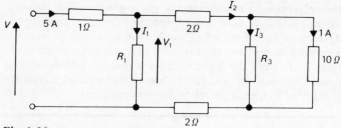

Fig. 1.20

$$P = I_3^2 R_3 = 20$$
hence
$$20 = 2^2 \times R_3$$
$$R_3 = \underline{5\ \Omega}$$

$$I_2 = 2 + 1 = \underline{3\ A}$$

Potential difference across each of the two 2-Ω resistors is $3 \times 2 = 6$ V

Thus
$$V_1 = 6 + 10 + 6 = 22\ V$$
$$I_1 = 5 - 3 = \underline{2\ A}$$

$$R_1 = \frac{V_1}{I_1} = \frac{22}{2} = \underline{11\ \Omega}$$

Potential difference across the 1-Ω resistor is $5 \times 1 = 5$ V

hence
$$V = 5 + 22 = \underline{27\ V}$$

This last example in particular illustrates that a quite complicated network may readily be analysed by this direct approach. However, it is not always possible to proceed in this way, either because most of the information given relates to the resistances or because there is insufficient information concerning any one component of the network.

An instance of the information being presented mainly in terms of resistance is given in Example 1.13 and it also brings us to the second form of application of Kirchhoff's laws.

Example 1.13 For the network shown in Fig. 1.21, determine the supply current and current I_4.

Essentially this network consists of three parts in series but one of them comprises R_3 and R_4 in parallel. These may be replaced by an equivalent resistance, thus

$$R_e = \frac{R_3 R_4}{R_3 + R_4} = \frac{16 \times 8}{16 + 8} = 5 \cdot 33\ \Omega$$

Replacing R_3 and R_4 by R_e, the network becomes that shown in Fig. 1.22.

Now that the network has been reduced to a simple series circuit, the total effective resistance is

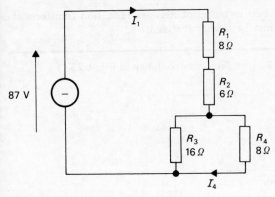

Fig. 1.21

$$R = R_1 + R_2 + R_e = 8 + 6 + 5 \cdot 33 = 19 \cdot 33 \ \Omega$$

$$I = \frac{V}{R} = \frac{87}{19 \cdot 33} = \underline{4 \cdot 5 \text{ A}}$$

Reverting now to the original network,

$$I_4 = \frac{R_3}{R_3 + R_4} \cdot I = \frac{16}{16 + 8} \times 4 \cdot 5 = \underline{3 \text{ A}}$$

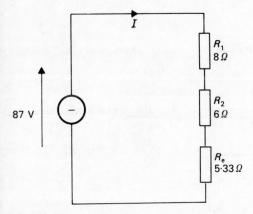

Fig. 1.22

This example compares with Example 1.10 and the figures are in fact the same. However, in this second instance the given voltage and current information stemmed from the source and not from the load, hence the emphasis of the calculation lay in dealing with the resistances of the network. The calculation was based on network reduction, i.e. by replacing two or more resistors by one equivalent resistor. A further example of this approach is given below, in which two instances of network reduction transform the problem into a form that may be readily analysed.

Example 1.14 Determine V_{AB} in the network shown in Fig. 1.23.

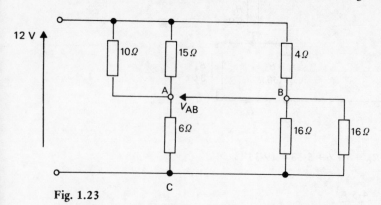

Fig. 1.23

This is quite a complex network. However, there are two instances of parallel resistors that may be replaced by equivalent resistors. For the 10-Ω and 15-Ω resistors.

$$R = \frac{10 \times 15}{10 + 15} = 6 \ \Omega$$

For the two 16-Ω resistors in parallel,

$$R = \frac{16 \times 16}{16 + 16} = 8 \ \Omega$$

If these equivalent values are inserted into the network, the network transforms into that shown in Fig. 1.24.

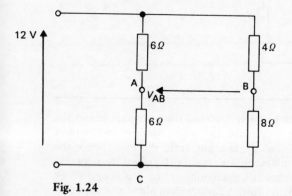

Fig. 1.24

In this form, the network compares with that analysed in Example 1.8.

Thus $V_{AC} = \dfrac{6}{6+6} \times 12 = 6$ V

and $V_{BC} = \dfrac{8}{4+8} \times 12 = 8$ V

$V_{AB} = V_{AC} - V_{BC} = 6 - 8 = \underline{-2 \text{ V}}$

Having now observed the two methods of analysis being demonstrated, you may well wonder how to tell when each should be used. As a general rule, if the information given concerns the voltage or the current associated with one or more components of the network, then you would apply the first form of approach. However, if the information given concerns the supply voltage or current, then you would try to apply the second form of approach by network reduction. This is not always possible because resistors may be connected in a manner that is neither series nor parallel — such an arrangement is shown in Fig. 1.25.

Example 1.15 For the network shown in Fig. 1.25, calculate the currents in each of the resistors.

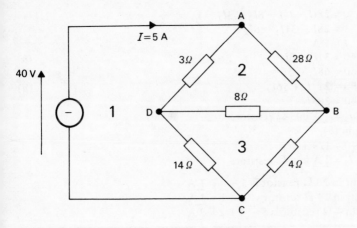

Fig. 1.25

In this network the resistors are neither in series nor in parallel and therefore a more difficult method of analysis must be employed. Let the current in the 3-Ω resistor be I_1 and therefore by Kirchhoff's first law, the current in the 28-Ω resistor is $I - I_1$. Further let the current in the 8-Ω resistor flowing from D to B be I_2. It follows that the current in the 14-Ω resistor is $I_1 - I_2$ whilst that in the 4-Ω resistor is $I - I_1 + I_2$. The resulting voltage drops are shown in Fig. 1.26.

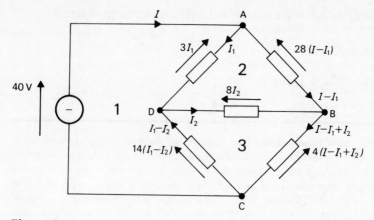

Fig. 1.26

Applying Kirchhoff's second law to loop 1 (comprising source to ADC)

$$40 = 3I_1 + 14(I_1 - I_2)$$
$$40 = 17I_1 - 14I_2 \qquad (a)$$

Applying Kirchhoff's second law to loop 2 (ABD)

$$0 = 28(I - I_1) - 8I_2 - 3I_1$$
$$= 28I - 31I_1 - 8I_2$$

But $\qquad I = 5$ A

Therefore $140 = 31I_1 + 8I_2 \qquad (b)$

$(a) \times 4 \qquad 160 = 68I_1 - 56I_2 \qquad (c)$

$(b) \times 7 \qquad 980 = 217I_1 + 56I_2 \qquad (d)$

$(c) + (d) \qquad 1140 = 285I_1$

$\qquad I_1 = \underline{4\ A}$ in 3-Ω resistor.

Substituting in (b),

$$140 = 124 + 8I_2$$
$$I_2 = \underline{2\ A}\ \text{in 8-}\Omega\ \text{resistor.}$$

Hence current in 28-Ω resistor is $5 - 4 = \underline{1\ A}$

current in 14-Ω resistor is $4 - 1 = \underline{3\ A}$

and current in 4-Ω resistor is $5 - 4 + 2 = \underline{3\ A}$

This form of solution requires that you proceed with great caution otherwise it is a simple matter to make mistakes during the mathematical processes. However, in the instance given, it is necessary to involve such an analysis; had a different current been given in this example, such a solution would not have been required since it would then have been possible to achieve a solution by applying the first approach, i.e. directly applying Kirchhoff's laws.

If two parallel e.m.f.s appear in a network as exemplified by Fig. 1.27, it

may again be necessary to employ the approach using simultaneous equations
resulting from the application of Kirchhoff's laws.

Example 1.16 Calculate the currents in the network shown in Fig. 1.27

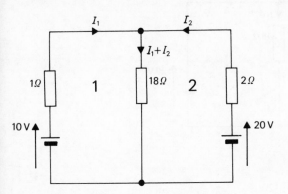

Fig. 1.27

Applying Kirchhoff's second law to loop 1,

$$10 = 1I_1 + 18(I_1 + I_2)$$
$$10 = 19I_1 + 18I_2 \qquad (a)$$

Applying Kirchhoff's second law to loop 2,

$$20 = 2I_2 + 18(I_1 + I_2)$$
$$20 = 18I_1 + 20I_2 \qquad (b)$$

$$(a) \times 10 \quad 100 = 190I_1 + 180I_2 \qquad (c)$$
$$(b) \times 9 \quad 180 = 162I_1 + 180I_2 \qquad (d)$$
$$(d) - (c) \quad 80 = -28I_1$$
$$I_1 = \underline{-2 \cdot 85 \text{ A}}$$

Substituting in (a),

$$10 = -54 \cdot 34 + 18I_2$$
$$I_2 = \underline{3 \cdot 57 \text{ A}}$$

Current in 18-Ω resistor is $3 \cdot 57 - 2 \cdot 85 = \underline{0 \cdot 72 \text{ A}}$

This form of solution is fraught with the danger of mathematical mistakes and therefore should only be employed when all else fails. This section commenced by stating that the obvious solution is all too easily ignored. Thus if the 2-Ω resistor were removed from the network shown in Fig. 1.27, it may be overlooked that the 20-V battery is now directly applied to the 18-Ω resistor and so knowing the voltage drop across one of the components, it is possible to revert to the first form of analysis as shown in Example 1.17.

Example 1.17 Calculate the currents in the network shown in Fig. 1.28.

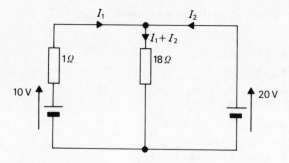

Fig. 1.28

Current in 18-Ω resistor is $\dfrac{20}{18}$ = <u>1·11 A</u>

Applying Kirchhoff's second law to the outside loop,

$$20 - 10 = -I_1 \times 1$$
$$I_1 = \underline{-10 \text{ A}}$$
$$I_2 = -(-10) + 1\cdot11 = \underline{11\cdot11 \text{ A}}$$

To summarise therefore, the approach to network analysis should be to determine whether component voltages and currents are known, in which case a direct approach to the analysis may be made using the principles observed by Kirchhoff's laws. If this is not possible then network reduction should be tried in order that the network is sufficiently simplified that it becomes manageable. Should all else fail, then Kirchhoff's laws should be applied to derive loop simultaneous equations from which the solution may be obtained.

Even so, there are other forms of more specialised solution that may be applied. One such form is described as the Superposition theorem.

1.4 Superposition theorem

The Superposition theorem states that in any network containing more than one source, the current in, or the p.d. across, any branch can be found by considering each source separately and adding their effects: omitted sources of e.m.f. are replaced by resistances equal to their interval resistances.

This sounds very complicated but is really quite simple when demonstrated by example. Example 1.18 illustrates the manner in which Example 1.16 would be solved by means of the Superposition theorem.

Example 1.18 By means of the Superposition theorem, calculate the currents in the network shown in Fig. 1.29(*a*).

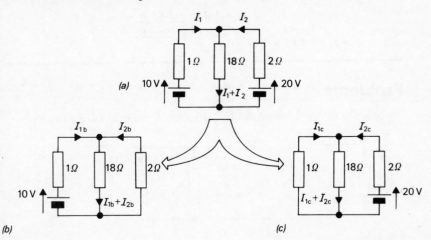

Fig. 1.29

Because there are two sources of e.m.f. in the network, then two separate networks need to be considered, each having one source of e.m.f. Fig. 1.29(*b*) shows the network with the 20-V source replaced by a short-circuit, there being zero internal resistance indicated. Also Fig. 1.29(*c*) shows the network with the 10-V source similarly replaced.

For the (*b*) arrangement, the total resistance is

$$1 + \frac{2 \times 18}{2 + 18} = 2 \cdot 8 \ \Omega$$

thus $\qquad I_{1b} = \frac{10}{2 \cdot 8} = 3 \cdot 57 \ A$

and $\qquad I_{2b} = -\frac{18}{2 + 18} \times 3 \cdot 57 = -3 \cdot 21 \ A$

also $I_{1b} + I_{2b} = 3 \cdot 57 - 3 \cdot 21 = 0 \cdot 36 \ A$

N.B. The current I_{2b} is negative due to the direction in which it has been shown.

For the (*c*) arrangement, the total resistance is

$$2 + \frac{1 \times 18}{1 + 18} = 2 \cdot 95 \ \Omega$$

thus $\qquad I_{2c} = \frac{20}{2 \cdot 95} = 6 \cdot 78 \ A$

and $\qquad I_{1c} = \dfrac{18}{-1 + 18} \times 6{\cdot}78 = -6{\cdot}42 \text{ A}$

$\qquad I_{2c} + I_{1c} = 6{\cdot}78 - 6{\cdot}42 = 0{\cdot}36 \text{ A}$

Thus $\qquad I_1 = I_{1b} + I_{1c} = 3{\cdot}57 - 6{\cdot}42 = \underline{-2{\cdot}85 \text{ A}}$

and $\qquad I_2 = I_{2b} + I_{2c} = -3{\cdot}21 + 6{\cdot}78 = \underline{3{\cdot}57 \text{ A}}$

also $\qquad I_1 + I_2 = -2{\cdot}85 + 3{\cdot}57 = \underline{0{\cdot}72 \text{ A}}$

Problems

1. For the network shown in Fig. 1.30, find the values of I, R_1 and R_2.

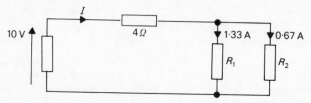

Fig. 1.30

2. A current of 20 A flows into a network comprising four resistors connected in parallel. If the resistances of the resistors are 4 Ω, 8 Ω, 10 Ω and 40 Ω, calculate the current in each resistor.

3. For the network shown in Fig. 1.31, find the values of the branch and the supply currents.

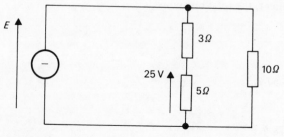

Fig. 1.31

4. Two resistances have an effective resistance of 10 Ω when connected in series and 2·4 Ω when connected in parallel. Determine the values of the resistances.

5. A battery is formed from five cells connected in series. When a load of resistance 4 Ω is connected across the battery, the current is 1·5 A. If the load resistance is changed to 9 Ω, the current falls to 0·75 A. Determine the e.m.f. of the battery and the internal resistance of each cell.

6. For the network shown in Fig. 1.32, the power dissipated in R_2 is 25 W. Determine the current in R_2 and hence calculate the currents in the other components of the network. What is the supply voltage?

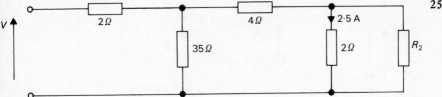

Fig. 1.32

7. For the network shown in Fig. 1.33, find I.

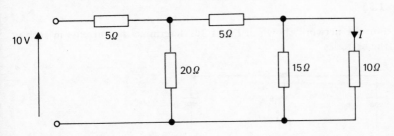

Fig. 1.33

8. Three resistances of 3 Ω, 5 Ω and 8 Ω are connected in parallel and this arrangement is then connected in series with a 1·68-Ω resistance. The resulting network is connected to a battery of e.m.f. 12 V and internal resistance 0·23 Ω. Determine the current in each of the resistors.

9. Two 1-kΩ resistors are connected in series across a constant-voltage supply. A resistor is to be connected in parallel with one of the 1-kΩ resistors so that the voltage across its terminals is reduced by 5 per cent. Determine the resistance of the resistor.

10. For the network shown in Fig. 1.34, determine the remaining input currents and the remaining branch currents.

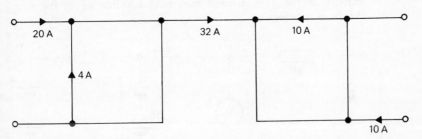

Fig. 1.34

11. For the network shown in Fig. 1.35, determine, V_{AB}, V_{BC} and V_{AC}. Hence calculate the currents in each of the batteries and the resistance of resistor R.

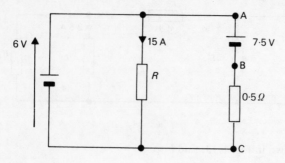

Fig. 1.35

12. For the network shown in Fig. 1.36, determine the currents in each of the batteries.

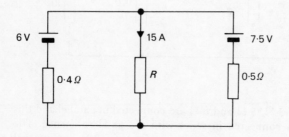

Fig. 1.36

13. In the network shown in Fig. 1.37, no current passes through the voltmeter shown. Calculate:
    (a) the current in the 15-V battery;
    (b) the voltmeter indication;
    (c) the resistance of a resistor to replace the 3-Ω resistor such that the current in the 15-V battery rises to 1·2 A flowing in the same direction as before.

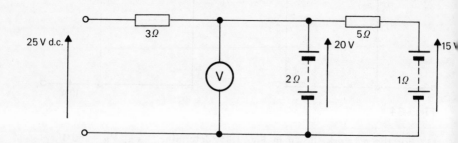

Fig. 1.37

14. The sides of a triangle ABC are made up as follows:
    AB is a resistor of 2 Ω;
    AC is a resistor of 3 Ω;
    BC is a 12-V battery of internal resistance 1 Ω.
    The points A, B and C are joined to a common point D by resistors such that BD is 4 Ω, CD is R ohms and AD is r ohms. Find the value of resistance R if the current in AD is zero and also calculate the battery current.

15. Four resistances AB (= 3 Ω), BC (= 4 Ω), CD (= 6 Ω) and DA (= 6 Ω) are connected in series to form a closed square ABCD. A d.c. supply of 70 V is connected across A and C so that the current flows into the network at A; a high-resistance voltmeter is connected between B and D. What is the voltmeter indication and what is the direction of the current flow in the voltmeter?

    Find the value of a further resistance R to be connected in parallel with DA so that the voltmeter indication is zero.

16. For the network shown in Fig. 1.38, calculate the magnitude and direction of the current in the indicating instrument which has a resistance of 80 Ω.

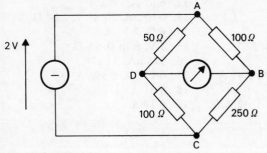

Fig. 1.38

17. For the network shown in Fig. 1.39, determine the current in each branch of the network.

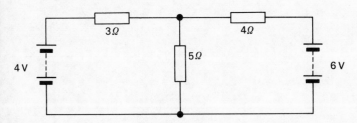

Fig. 1.39

18. By application of the Superposition theorem, determine the current in the 10-Ω resistor shown in Fig. 1.40.

28

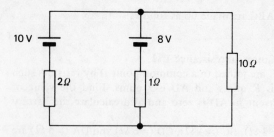

Fig. 1.40

19. If the polarity of the 8-V battery were reversed in Fig. 1.40, again determine the current in the 10-Ω resistor.

Answers

1. 2·0 A, 1·5 Ω, 3·0 Ω
2. 10 A, 5 A, 4 A, 1 A
3. 5 A, 4 A, 9 A
4. 4 Ω, 6 Ω
5. 7·5 V, 0·2 Ω
6. 5 A, 7·5 A, 1 A, 8·5 A, 52 V
7. 0·32 A
8. 1·77 A, 1·06 A, 0·66 A, 3·49 A
9. 17 237 Ω
10. 12 A, −42 A, 24 A, 8 A, 42 A, 52 A

11. 7·5 V, −1·5 V, 6 V, 3 A, 12 A, 0·4 Ω
12. 6·67 A, 8·33 A
13. 0·972 A, 20·83 V, 2·04 Ω
14. 6 Ω, 2·77 A
15. 5 V, B to D, 18 Ω
16. 515 µA, B to D
17. 0·127 A, 0·596 A
18. 0·81 A
19. 0·19 A

Chapter 2

The magnetic field

Electromagnetism is the study of magnetic fields set up by the passage of electric currents through a system of conductors. This study leads, in the first instance, to an understanding of most electrical machines, and it is also important when considering electronic networks, particularly with respect to communications.

This chapter has the objective of defining the terms of electromagnetic theory required for a basic understanding of electrical engineering.

2.1 Magnetic field displays

A picture of a magnetic field can be obtained if a compass needle is moved progressively in the direction of its north pole through the magnetic field. If this is done, without deviation, it is found that a complete path is traced out; the path is therefore a complete loop when surrounding a current-carrying conductor and the path is said to link the conductor.

These paths are termed lines of flux. Typical field displays are shown in Fig. 2.1 for different arrangements of current-carrying conductors. From these diagrams, certain properties may be given to the lines of flux:

1. In an electromagnetic field, each line of magnetic flux forms a complete

loop round at least one current-carrying conductor, which it is said to link. This forms a flux linkage.

2. The direction of the line is that of the force experienced by the north pole of a compass needle placed at that point in the electromagnetic field.

3. The lines of flux never intersect since the resultant force at any point in an electromagnetic field can have only one direction.

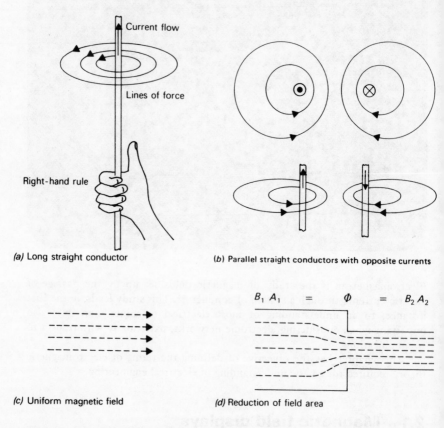

(a) Long straight conductor

(b) Parallel straight conductors with opposite currents

(c) Uniform magnetic field

(d) Reduction of field area

Fig. 2.1 Typical lines of force in electromagnetic fields

The line of magnetic flux is a useful convention to describe magnetic fields. However, it must be remembered that it has no real existence and is purely imaginary.

It is helpful to remember the right-hand grip rule which relates the direction of the field to the direction of current flow. This rule is illustrated in Fig. 2.1(a): if a conductor is gripped by the right hand in such a manner that the thumb indicates the direction of the flow of current, then the fingers indicate the direction of the lines of flux about the conductor.

2.2 Magnetic flux and flux density

The total magnetic effect of a system as described by the lines of magnetic flux is termed the magnetic flux linking the system. The unit of magnetic flux is the weber.

Magnetic flux   Symbol: Φ Unit: weber (Wb)

When a circuit moves relative to a magnetic field so that the amount of magnetic field enclosed by its conductors changes, an e.m.f. is induced in it. This concept is further discussed in Chapter 3 but it is used to define the weber as that flux change which, when experienced within a closed path in one second, causes an average e.m.f. of one volt to be induced in the circuit formed by the closed path. This is a rather difficult definition to understand at this stage but it becomes clearer when reviewed after further studies of electromagetism.

The flux tells little of the distribution of the magnetic field. For instance, is it uniformly spread about? Or is it mainly concentrated together, with a wide, weaker fringe section? The distribution or concentration of the field is described by the flux density. The flux density B is given by the flux Φ passing uniformly and normally (i.e. at right angles) through a surface of area A; at each point on the surface, flux density is given by

$$B = \frac{\Phi}{A} \tag{2.1}$$

hence $\Phi = BA$ $\tag{2.2}$

Flux density   Symbol: B Unit: tesla (T)

For many years, the unit of flux density was the weber per square metre (Wb/m^2) and this unit is still to be found in various technical information publications.

A plane cutting the flux normally (i.e. at right angles) is shown in Fig. 2.2(a). If the plane is not taken at right angles to the direction of the

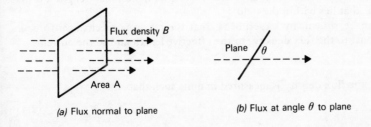

(a) Flux normal to plane   (b) Flux at angle θ to plane

Fig. 2.2 Effect of the angle between the plane and the direction of flux

field, then, by the geometry of the diagram shown in Fig. 2.2(b), the flux through the plane is given by

$$\Phi = BA \sin \theta \qquad (2.3)$$

It follows that when the plane is parallel to the direction of the flux, no flux will pass through the plane.

Example 2.1 A rectangular coil measuring 200 mm by 100 mm is mounted such that it can be rotated about the midpoints of the 100-mm sides. The axis of rotation is at right angles to a magnetic field of uniform flux density 0·05 T. Calculate the flux in the coil for the following conditions:

(a) The maximum flux through the coil and the position at which it occurs.
(b) The flux through the coil when the 100-mm sides are inclined at 45° to the direction of the flux.

Fig. 2.3

(a) The maximum flux will pass through the coil when the plane of the coil is at right angles to the direction of the flux.

$$\Phi = BA = 0.05 \times 200 \times 10^{-3} \times 100 \times 10^{-3} = 1 \times 10^{-3} \text{ Wb}$$
$$= \underline{1 \text{ mWb}}$$

(b) $\Phi = BA \sin \theta = 1 \times 10^{-3} \times \sin 45° = 0.71 \times 10^{-3} \text{ Wb}$
$$= \underline{0.71 \text{ mWb}}$$

The definition of the ampere depends on the principle that a current-carrying conductor situated in a magnetic field experiences a mechanical force. Consider a straight uniform conductor placed in and normally to a magnetic field of uniform flux density B, as shown in Fig. 2.4. The conductor carries a current I and has an effective length l, i.e. that length of the conductor that lies within the field.

It can be shown, by experiment, that the resulting mechanical force is proportional to the flux density, to the effective length and to the current.

$$F \propto BIl$$

However, the flux density is measured in units such that

$$F = BIl \qquad (2.4)$$

Thus the unit of flux density is that density of magnetic flux such that a conductor carrying a current of one ampere and placed at right angles to the

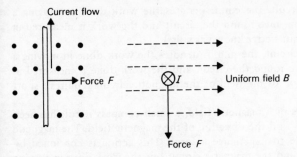

Fig. 2.4 Current-carrying conductor in a uniform magnetic field

flux has a force of one newton acting on it per metre of its length. This unit is the tesla.

2.3 Magnetomotive force and magnetic field strength

It is a characteristic of lines of flux that each line is a closed loop. The complete closed path followed by any group of flux lines is termed a magnetic circuit. Whilst it is possible to have magnetic circuits in air, they tend to be comparatively weak, and most practical applications have circuits comprising a material such as steel in which most of the field is created. A simple form of magnetic circuit is the toroid shown in Fig. 2.5.

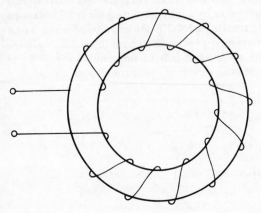

Fig. 2.5 A magnetic circuit made from a steel toroid

The magnetic circuit has similar properties to those of an electric circuit. The electric circuit requires an e.m.f. to create the current in the circuit. Similarly the magnetic circuit requires a magnetomotive force (m.m.f.) to create the flux in the circuit.

In the electric circuit, the e.m.f. denotes the work done in moving a charge of one coulomb once round the circuit and the work is measured in joules per coulomb (units better known as volts).

In the magnetic circuit, the m.m.f. denotes the work done in moving a flux of one weber once round the circuit and the work done is measured in joules. This investigation of the field of the magnetic circuit requires a short explanation.

In previous studies of a magnetic field, a small compass needle has been introduced in order to find the direction of the magnetic field. The magnetic field caused the needle to experience a force. This action is continued by moving the needle around the magnetic circuit but the work done in moving the north pole of the needle round the magnetic circuit is equal to the work done in moving the south pole of the needle except that the respective energies are of opposite polarity. It follows that to investigate the work done, only one pole of the investigating needle must be considered. Finally let the flux emanating from this pole be one weber, the basic unit of flux; it follows that the pole is described as a unit magnetic pole.

If the unit magnetic pole is made to move in a complete path round N current-carrying conductors then work is done by the pole provided the movement is in opposition to the lines of force. Conversely, if the movement is in the direction of the magnetic field, work will again be done by the magnetic force on whatever force is restraining the movement of the pole. In either case, the unit pole makes one complete loop around the N conductors. The work done is given by the magnetic work law which states that the net work done on or by a unit pole in moving once round any complete path is equal numerically to the product of the current and the number of turns linked within the path. It follows that if there are N conductors each carrying a current I then the work done on or by a unit magnetic pole is IN, measured in joules. In Fig. 2.6 a simple regular path (a) is shown, around which a unit pole may be moved but any irregular path, such as path (b), would yield the same result. Path (c) on the other hand fails to link any conductors and therefore there is no work done in moving a unit pole round such a path.

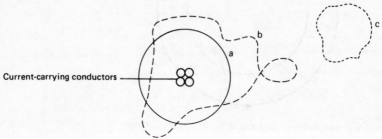

Current-carrying conductors

Fig. 2.6 Work law

The law is applicable to all magnetic fields regardless of the dimensions of the field or any magnetic properties that it may possess. The work law can be proved by developing the concept of the unit magnetic pole but the mathematics involved are unnecessarily complicated to be brought into an introduction to electromagnetism. It is better at this stage to accept that the m.m.f. (magnetomotive force) is a measure of the work related to the creation of a magnetic field similar to that associating an e.m.f. to an electric circuit.

For instance, let the work law be applied to the movement of a unit pole in a circular path about a current-carrying conductor as shown in Fig. 2.7.

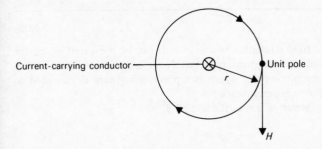

Fig. 2.7 Magnetic field strength about a current-carrying conductor

If a unit pole is placed on the circle, it experiences a force. Let this force be represented by H; when the unit pole is moved around the circle one, the work done is

$$Hl = 2\pi r H$$

By the work law, this is numerically equal to the product of the current and the number of conductors linked. In this case, there is only one conductor hence

$$2\pi r H = I$$

$$H = \frac{I}{2\pi r}$$

Had there been N conductors linked, each carrying a current I, then

$$H = \frac{NI}{2\pi r} \tag{2.5}$$

By observation of this expression, it can be seen that the force, which is termed the magnetic field strength, is measured in ampere turns per metre. The number of turns serves as a dimensionless factor and it may be preferred to describe the unit of measurement as amperes per metre, but engineers generally prefer the practical aspect of maintaining the 'turns' in the unit. The magnetic field strength is a vector quantity since the force has both magnitude and direction.

Magnetic field strength **Symbol:** H **Unit: ampere turns per metre (At/m)**

The work done in moving a unit pole around a magnetic circuit is given by the product IN. This is termed the magnetomotive force and again the number of turns is a dimensionless quantity.

Magnetomotive force **Symbol:** F **Unit: ampere turn (At)**

$$F = IN \qquad (2.6)$$

Since the magnetic field strength and the m.m.f. can be measured in ampere turns per metre and ampere turns respectively, it is no longer necessary to consider the unit magnetic pole, which is a purely imaginary device used to derive the concept of these quantities.

By substituting Relation 2.6 in Relation 2.5,

$$H = \frac{F}{2\pi r}$$

For the general case in which the path length is l, then

$$H = \frac{F}{l} \qquad (2.7)$$

The magnetic field strength is thus seen to be the gradient of the m.m.f. around the magnetic circuit, as its unit of measurement suggests.

Example 2.2 The magnetic field strength of a magnetic field is 40 At/m when measured at a point 80 cm from a current-carrying conductor. Calculate the current in the conductor.

$F = Hl = 40 \times 0.8 = 32$ At
  $= NI = 1 \times I$
$\therefore = I = \dfrac{32}{1} = \underline{32 \text{ A}}$

2.4 Permeability

A magnetic field can be set up by an m.m.f. giving rise to a flux. At any point in the magnetic field, the m.m.f. gradient is given by the magnetic field strength whilst the density of the field is given by the magnetic flux density. It follows that the flux density B is proportional to the magnetic field strength H, i.e.

$B \propto H$

In the case of a magnetic field set up in a free space such as a vacuum, it may be stated that

$$B = \mu_0 H \tag{2.8}$$

where μ_0 is a constant used to relate the flux density to the magnetic field strength. The constant μ_0 is termed the permeability of free space and it can be evaluated from the definition of the ampere.

Consider two long parallel conductors carrying currents I_1 and I_2 spaced a distance d apart in free space. The distance d is much greater than the diameter of either conductor (so that if the field strength due to one conductor is known at the centre of the other conductor, this value will be approximately valid for the remainder of the cross-section of the conductor). The arrangement is shown in Fig. 2.28.

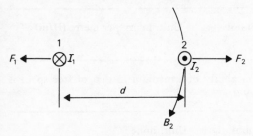

Fig. 2.8 Parallel current-carrying conductors

Let B_2 be the average flux density at the second conductor due to the current I_1 in the first conductor.

$$B_2 = \frac{\mu_0 I_1}{2\pi d}$$

Therefore the force on length l_2 of conductor 2 is given by

$$F_2 = B_2 l_2 I_2$$

Per unit length of conductor 2, the force is given by

$$F_2 = B_2 I_2$$

$$= \frac{\mu_0 I_1 I_2}{2\pi d} \tag{2.9}$$

In the definition of the ampere, it is stated that if such a system of conductors is placed one metre apart and a current of one ampere is passed through each of the conductors then the force experienced by the conductors is 2×10^{-7} newtons per metre run. From Relation 2.9, it follows that

$$\mu_0 = \frac{2\pi d F_2}{I_1 I_2} = \frac{2\pi \times 1 \times 2 \times 10^{-7}}{1 \times 1}$$

$$= 4\pi \times 10^{-7} \text{ H/m}$$

The unit — the henry per metre — in which permeability is measured shall be justified in para. 3.6. Also it should be noted that F_1 and F_2 are mechanical forces in this instance and not magnetomotive forces; it is unfortunate that the standard symbols for both these quantities are the same.

If the flux density due to a magnetising field strength exists in a medium other than free space, the permeability is found to change in value. This new value is termed the absolute permeability μ.

Absolute permeability　　　Symbol: μ　　　Unit: henry per metre (H/m)

The absolute permeability may be expressed as a multiple of that of free space μ_0.

Absolute permeability　　　Symbol: μ_0　　　Unit: henry per metre (H/m)
of free space

The ratio of the absolute permeability of a medium to that of free space is termed the relative permeability μ_r.

Relative permeability　　　Symbol: μ_r　　　Unit: none

$$\mu_r = \frac{\mu}{\mu_0}$$

$$\mu = \mu_0 \mu_r \tag{2.10}$$

It follows that the general case of Relation 2.8 is

$$B = \mu_0 \mu_r H \tag{2.11}$$

For air, μ_r may be taken as unity; most other materials such as wood, plastics, copper and other non-ferrous metals, etc. also have a similar value of μ_r. Ferromagnetic materials, such as iron, cobalt and nickel have very much higher values of relative permeability and μ_r can achieve values as high as 100 000.

Example 2.3 A coil of 250 turns is wound uniformly on to a wooden toroid in a manner similar to that illustrated in Fig. 2.5. The toroid has a mean circumference of 500 mm and a uniform cross-sectional area 300 mm². If the current in the coil is 5·0 A, calculate:

(a)　the magnetic field strength;
(b)　the flux density;
(c)　the total magnetic flux in the ring.

$$F = IN = 5 \times 250 = 1250 \text{ At}$$

$$H = \frac{F}{l} = \frac{1250}{500 \times 10^{-3}} = \underline{2500 \text{ At/m}}$$

$$B = \mu_0\mu_r H = 4\pi \times 10^{-7} \times 1 \times 2500 = 3 \cdot 14 \times 10^{-3} \text{ T}$$
$$= \underline{3 \cdot 14 \text{ mT}}$$
$$\Phi = BA = 3 \cdot 14 \times 10^{-3} \times 300 \times 10^{-6} = 0 \cdot 942 \times 10^{-6} \text{ Wb}$$
$$= \underline{0 \cdot 942 \ \mu\text{Wb}}$$

Example 2.4 A coil of 500 turns is wound uniformly on to a steel toroid of mean circumference 500 mm, uniform cross-sectional area 300 mm^2 and relative permeability 10 000. If the magnetic flux in the ring is 0·3 mWb, calculate:

(a) the magnetic field strength;
(b) the current in the coil.

$$B = \frac{\Phi}{A} = \frac{0 \cdot 3 \times 10^{-3}}{300 \times 10^{-6}} = 1 \cdot 0 \text{ T}$$

$$H = \frac{B}{\mu_0\mu_r} = \frac{1 \cdot 0}{4\pi \times 10^{-7} \times 10 \times 10^3} = \underline{79 \cdot 6 \text{ At/m}}$$

$$F = Hl = 79 \cdot 6 \times 500 \times 10^{-3} = 39.8 \text{ At}$$

$$I = \frac{F}{N} = \frac{39 \cdot 8}{500} = 79 \cdot 6 \times 10^{-3} \text{ A}$$

$$= \underline{79 \cdot 6 \text{ mA}}$$

Comparison of the figures of Examples 2.3 and 2.4 indicates the effect of the ferromagnetic material's presence. A very much larger flux is obtained from a very much reduced current.

Example 2.5 Two parallel conductors P and Q are placed 100 mm apart in air. Conductor P carries a current of 100 A in one direction whilst conductor Q carries a current of 60 A in the other direction. Calculate the magnetic field strength at a point R which is 60 mm from conductor P and 40 mm from conductor Q.

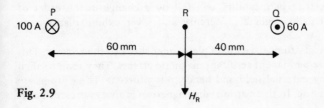

Fig. 2.9

The magnetic field strength at R due to conductor P is

$$H_{RP} = \frac{I_P N_P}{2\pi r_{RP}} = \frac{100 \times 1}{2\pi \times 60 \times 10^{-3}} = 265 \text{ At/m}$$

Similarly

$$H_{RQ} = \frac{I_Q N_Q}{2\pi r_{RQ}} = \frac{60 \times 1}{2\pi \times 40 \times 10^{-3}} = 239 \text{ At/m}$$

Both magnetic field strengths act vertically downwards — this may be confirmed by application of the right-hand grip rule. The resultant magnetic field strength at R is therefore given by

$$H_R = H_{RP} + H_{RQ} = 265 + 239 = \underline{504 \text{ At/m}}$$

This addition is really a vector addition since the magnetic field strengths have direction.

2.5 Ferromagnetic materials

It has been noted that a ferromagnetic material has a very much higher relative permeability than other materials. This important observation requires further investigation.

When a permanent magnet is cut in two, if forms two smaller magnets. If this process is taken to the extreme situation in which only one molecule is left, and then further division results in an isolated atom, the smallest possible magnet is produced from that material. The magnetic field of such an atom is derived from the movement of its electrons and these electrons move in two distinct ways:

1. round the nucleus of the atom;
2. round their own axes.

The resultant magnetic effect of an atom is the resultant of the effects due to the electrons' spins and their orbital motions, and it can be shown that the electron spin is the more important of the two factors. The observation of the resultant magnetic effect is simplified by the fact that complete electron shells have no magnetic effect, due to their symmetry.

Many atoms have no magnetic effect when in the presence of a magnetic field. This is because their symmetry is deformed by the magnetic field. In such a case, the magnetic effect is reduced and the atom is said to be diamagnetic. Its relative permeability will fall by a change in the order of 10^{-6}, which is virtually negligible. Mercury and silver exhibit diamagnetic effects.

Certain groups of atoms have incomplete inner shells to their atoms. This causes them to have permanent resultant magnetic effects. They tend to align themselves with any external field and hence to reinforce it. These atoms are said to be paramagnetic. In these atoms, diamagnetism is always present but is overwhelmed by the greater paramagnetism. A paramagnetic material has a relative permeability greater than unity by the order of 10^{-3}. Platinum and tungsten exhibit paramagnetic effects.

Both groups have values of relative permeability that have scarcely changed from unity and it is for this reason that all non-ferrous materials may be assumed to have a relative permeability of 1.

However, there remains the important group of ferromagnetic materials — principally iron, cobalt and nickel. In these cases, the atoms do not act singly but in groups called domains, each containing between 10^9 and 10^{15} atoms. These domains are smaller than the grains of the material in which they exist. Each atom or ion has a permanent magnetic effect. All the ions in each domain have the axes of their fields pointing in the same direction, being aligned by a permanent intramolecular field which exists over the complete domain. This intramolecular field is the characteristic of ferromagnetism.

The domain structure is dependent on temperature. With increase in temperature, thermal agitation tends to break up the domains and, in the case of iron, finally succeeds at about 750°C.

The reason that iron, cobalt and nickel form domains is complex. The third electron ring from the nucleus is incomplete, which is the condition of paramagnetism. However, the spacing of the ions is such that the orbits of these magnetic electrons can interpenetrate one another in adjacent ions. Intramolecular fields occur in other substances, but only in ferromagnetic materials does the field have the right direction to cause alignment of the magnetic axes of the ions.

When a specimen of ferromagnetic material is placed in a magnetic field, the domains tend to turn into line. It follows that their magnetic fields add to the external field, resulting in a stronger total field. This effect can be observed from the characteristic shown in Fig. 2.10, relating the resulting flux density to the magnetic field strength.

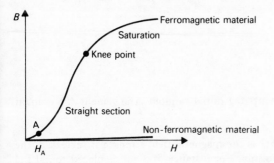

Fig. 2.10 Flux density/magnetic field strength characteristic

Initially the specimen is magnetically neutral. This is caused by the domains having random orientation and the resultant magnetic effect is zero. Any small magnetic field strength up to about H_A produces a flux density which is greater than that due to the magnetic field strength acting alone on the equivalent space. This extra flux is due to the actions of the domains. Up to this value, it is the boundaries of certain domains which change, these domains being those which are more or less parallel to the external field growing at the expense of their immediate neighbours. This growth is reversible and if the magnetic field strength is removed, the flux will also disappear.

As the magnetic field strength increases further, the domains not only continue to grow but many of them are turned round into alignment. This movement will not be reversed by the removal of the magnetic field strength; hence, if the magnetic field strength is removed, a field will remain due to the alignment of the domains which have been rotated.

The process of building the domains up into an aligned condition continues at a reasonably steady rate with increase in magnetic field strength until most of the domains have been aligned. Because of this steady rate, the appropriate part of the characteristic is termed the straight part of the characteristic. When most of the domains are aligned, the material is said to be saturated; strictly speaking saturation is never achieved under normal conditions, and even if saturation were completed, the flux density would still increase with magnetic field strength but at a rate appropriate to a relative permeability of 1. The relative domain positions are indicated in the schematic diagrams of Fig. 2.11.

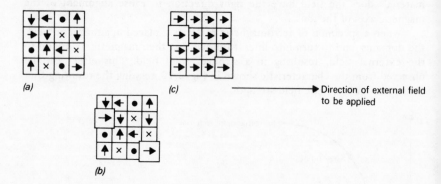

Fig. 2.11 Domain arrangements (*a*) initial random arrangement (*b*) domain growth (*c*) 'saturation'

It should be noted that, as the magnetic field strength is increased, the domains will not turn uniformly. For instance, if a coil is placed round the ferromagnetic specimen, the domain movements will induce e.m.f.s in it which can be amplified and heard on a loudspeaker. The resultant noise either takes the form of a rustling or a series of clicks, thus indicating a discontinuity of movement. This is known as the Barkhausen effect.

Using any magnetisation characteristic, it is possible to derive the values of the relative permeability corresponding to the magnetic field strength or to

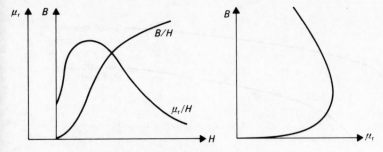

Fig. 2.12 Relative permeability characteristics

the flux density from the relation $B = \mu_0\mu_r H$. The resulting characteristics take the forms shown in Fig. 2.12.

It should be noted that the characteristics indicated throughout this section have been exaggerated. For instance, the part of the magnetisation characteristic before the domains commence turning is very small and the smaller it is, then the more linear is the initial and useful part of the characteristic. It is therefore necessary to now consider the practical effects of the theory that has just been described.

2.6   Magnetisation characteristics of soft magnetic materials

Whilst all magnetisation characteristics take the form described in the previous paragraph, it is found that by comparing the characteristic of one ferromagnetic material with that of another, then the characteristics can vary widely. For practical purposes, magnetic materials fall into two classes:

1.   permanent (or hard) magnetic materials;
2.   temporary (or soft) magnetic materials.

The permanent materials are those which can retain their magnetism to form permanent magnets. For this purpose, it is necessary that their magnetic fields retain a relatively high amount of energy and this will be further discussed in para. 2.9. The temporary or soft materials only exhibit their magnetic properties when influenced by an external m.m.f.

Soft magnetic materials fall into three groups:

(*a*)   alloys based on iron;
(*b*)   nickel-iron alloys;
(*c*)   ferrites.

The magnetisation characteristics of a variety of soft magnetic materials are shown in Fig. 2.13. The most crude material is cast iron, which requires a considerable magnetic field strength to produce a comparatively low flux density. It has an initial part which clearly shows the effect of domain growth

44

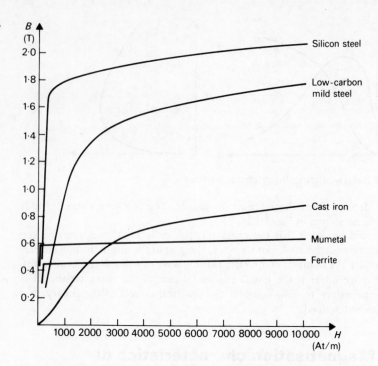

Fig. 2.13 Magnetisation characteristics of soft magnetic materials

at low values of field strength. Due to its low level of saturation, the magnetic applications of cast iron require large volumes of the material and this may be suitable in the manufacture of motor bodies, i.e. motor stators.

For most electric power applications such as a.c. transformers and motors, it is usual to find that the materials used vary from low-carbon, mild steel to oriented silicon steel. The choice of material in this range depends on a number of factors such as cost, required mechanical properties, and working flux density relative to the permeability. The attraction to these steels is the relatively high values of flux density that may be attained and it is possible to magnetise some silicon steels to working densities of over 2·3 T. From Fig. 2.13, it can be seen that the silicon steel requires a low magnetic field strength for densities up to about 1·6 T, but such a steel is costly, so that if a reduction in flux density can be accepted in conjunction with a greater magnetic field strength then the cheaper mild steel could be used.

The nickel-iron alloys have 30–80 per cent nickel in their compositions. The mumetal characteristic shown is typical, requiring very little magnetic field strength to produce the knee-point conditions. Thereafter almost all the further increase in magnetic field density is derived directly from the magnetic field strength acting on the space occupied by the material, hence the very low rate of increase in density with change of field strength. The sharp change of characteristic is useful for applications such as magnetic amplifiers, whilst the low values of magnetic field strength relative to the field make nickel-iron alloys useful for such applications as communication transformers, logic cores, measurement inductors and transformers, recording heads and sensitive relays. Such alloys are expensive and the low saturation levels limit their applications to ones of precision.

Ferrites are formed from a mixture of oxides which come in powder form, are pressed and finally sintered into appropriate shapes. Thus they are effectively ceramics possessing useful magnetic properties but with low saturation levels. Their advantages are that they are lightweight and cheap, giving a good linear characteristic up to the working flux density. Like the nickel-iron alloys, applications include communication inductors and transformers, which can also find general electronic application.

By application of the formula $B = \mu_0\mu_r H$, it is possible to derive the corresponding characteristics relating the relative permeability to magnetic field strength. However, such are the variations of results that, as can be seen from Fig. 2.14, it is not really suitable to make comparison by plotting the characteristics to the same scale on the same graph.

It can be seen from the μ_r/H characteristics shown that the materials with the higher permeabilities achieve saturation at comparatively lower

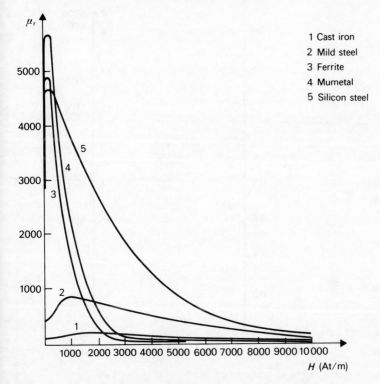

Fig. 2.14 μ_r/H characteristics for soft magnetic materials

values of magnetic field strength. Thus not only do such materials produce better magnetic fields intrinsically, but also they require less magnetising current to induce them to do so.

The characteristics have been chosen so that the differences between the various groups of materials have not been too wide. For instance, the nickel-iron alloys can have relative permeabilities of over 10^6, e.g. one form of mumetal has $\mu_r = 1\ 150\ 000$, a field strength of only 0·55 At/m being required to produce a flux density of 0·77 T. Ferrites also can be in the same range of permeabilities but with slightly reduced flux densities.

The silicon steels operate at much higher flux densities but, coupled with relative permeabilities ranging up to about 50 000, they require greater magnetising currents to compensate the higher field strengths involved. A typical silicon steel would be Alphasil, with $\mu_r = 43\ 000$ and a saturation flux density of 2·0 T.

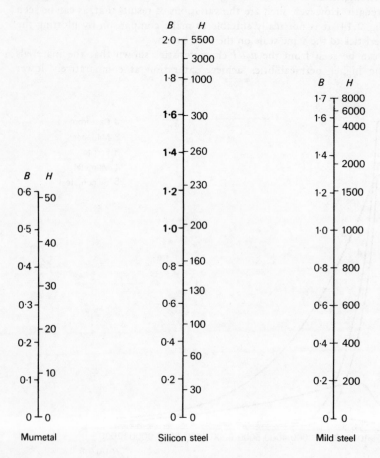

Fig. 2.15 Magnetisation nomograms

Finally it should be noted that the graphical characteristics indicated in Fig. 2.13 and Fig. 2.14 can be replaced by 'nomograms'. Typical nomograms giving the same information as was presented in Fig. 2.13 are shown in Fig. 2.15; it will be noted, however, that nomograms do not clearly indicate the knee-points of the characteristics but they clarify the relations of the flux densities to the field strengths.

It has already been noted that Fig. 2.13 has been limited by giving a comparison within a single diagram, and this has been indicated by some of the much higher values of relative permeability possible. Figure 2.16 shows a typical nomogram of the magnetic characteristics of a commercial mumetal.

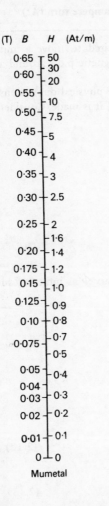

Mumetal

Fig. 2.16 Magnetisation nomogram of a commercial mumetal

2.7 Reluctance

In a complete magnetic circuit, the m.m.f. acting upon the circuit can be related to the flux in the circuit by a constant termed the reluctance of the magnetic circuit. This is comparable to the resistance of an electric circuit.

Just as part of an electric circuit can be considered separately, so can part of a magnetic circuit be considered. In such a section, only the change in magnetic potential is relevant, i.e. the magnetic potential difference as opposed to the magnetomotive force. Magnetic p.d. is comparable with electric p.d. in the same manner that m.m.f. is comparable with e.m.f.

Magnetic potential difference   Symbol: F Unit: ampere turn (At)

The magnetic potential difference is the energy required to move a unit magnetic pole between two points. The sum of the magnetic p.d.s around a circuit is equal to the m.m.f.

The reluctance, like resistance, is dependent on the physical dimensions of the magnetic circuit and on the material from which it is made. Consider part of a uniform magnetic field as shown in Fig. 2.17.

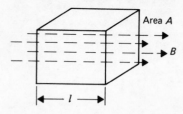

Fig. 2.17 Derivation of reluctance

For the section of the field involving a magnetic flux Φ as indicated in the diagram

$$F = Hl$$

$$= \frac{Bl}{\mu_0 \mu_r}$$

$$= \frac{\Phi l}{\mu_0 \mu_r A}$$

$$= \Phi \cdot \frac{l}{\mu_0 \mu_r A} \qquad (2.12)$$

$$\text{Let } S = \frac{l}{\mu_0 \mu_r A} \qquad (2.13)$$

where S is the reluctance of the magnetic circuit.

Reluctance **Symbol:** S **Unit: reciprocal henry (/H)**

By substituting Relation 2.13 in 2.12,

$$F = \Phi S \tag{2.14}$$

It may be observed that this Relation compares with

$$V = IR$$

and hence reluctance may be defined as the ratio of magnetic p.d. to magnetic flux for part or all of a magnetic circuit.

Example 2.6 Part of a magnetic circuit is made from a piece of steel of length 150 mm, cross-sectional area 1200 mm^2 and relative permeability 1000. Calculate the reluctance of the piece of steel.

$$S = \frac{l}{\mu_0 \mu_r A} = \frac{150 \times 10^{-3}}{4\pi \times 10^{-7} \times 1000 \times 1200 \times 10^{-6}}$$

$$= \underline{100\ 000\ /\text{H}}$$

Example 2.7 A steel ring of mean circumference 400 mm, cross-sectional area 500 mm^2 and relative permeability 1850 has a coil of 250 turns wound uniformly around it as shown in Fig. 2.18. Calculate the reluctance of the ring and hence the current required to produce a flux of 750 μWb in the ring.

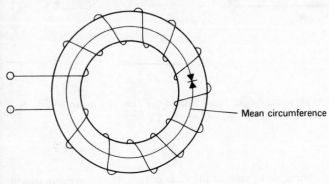

Mean circumference

Fig. 2.18

Figure 2.18 indicates what is meant by the mean circumference.

$$S = \frac{l}{\mu_0 \mu_r A} = \frac{400 \times 10^{-3}}{4\pi \times 10^{-7} \times 1850 \times 500 \times 10^{-6}}$$

$$= \underline{344\ 200\ /\text{H}}$$

$F = \Phi S = 750 \times 10^{-6} \times 344\,200 = 258$ At
$\quad = IN = I \times 250$

$$I = \frac{258}{250} = \underline{1 \cdot 03 \text{ A}}$$

Whilst is makes the arithmetic of the reluctance calculation relatively simple, it would not be practical to think of all magnetic circuits as being made from steel rings or toroids. Most magnetic circuits are rectangular, at least in part, and Example 2.8 indicates the manner in which such a magnetic circuit is analysed.

Example 2.8 A magnetic core is shown in Fig. 2.19. Given that the cross-sectional area of the core is 200 mm^2, and that the relative permeability of the material is 4000, calculate the reluctance of the magnetic circuit.

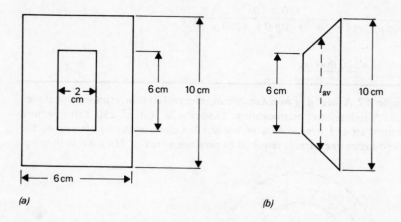

Fig. 2.19

Figure 2.19(*b*) shows the right-hand side of the core. Its mean length, l_{av}, is the average of its shortest and longest lengths, i.e.

$$l_{av} = \frac{10 + 6}{2} = 8 \text{ cm}$$

Applying this principle to each of the sides in turn, the total mean length of the core is $8 + 4 + 8 + 4 = 24$ cm

$$S = \frac{l}{\mu_0 \mu_r A} = \frac{24 \times 10^{-2}}{4\pi \times 10^{-7} \times 4000 \times 200 \times 10^{-6}}$$

$$= \underline{239\,000 \text{ /H}}$$

It should be borne in mind that the reluctance of a magnetic circuit or of part of a magnetic circuit is not a constant but varies with the value of permeability which it has been seen varies in turn with the magnetic field strength. This is illustrated by Example 2.9.

Example 2.9 Part of a magnetic circuit is made from a piece of mild steel, the magnetic characteristics of which are given in Figs. 2.13 and 2.15. The piece of steel is of length 150 mm and cross-sectional area 1200 mm^2. Calculate the reluctance of the piece of steel, given that:

(*a*) the flux density is 0·6 T;
(*b*) the flux density is 1·2 T.

From the magnetic characteristics,

$B = 0·6$ T
$H = 600$ At/m

$B = 1·2$ T
$H = 1450$ At/m

$$\mu_r = \frac{B}{\mu_0 H} = \frac{0·6}{4\pi \times 10^{-7} \times 600}$$

$$\mu_r = \frac{1·2}{4\pi \times 10^{-7} \times 1450}$$

$= 796$

$= 658$

$$S = \frac{l}{\mu_0 \mu_r A}$$

$$S = \frac{150 \times 10^{-3}}{4\pi \times 10^{-7} \times 658 \times 1200 \times 10^{-6}}$$

$$= \frac{150 \times 10^{-3}}{4\pi \times 10^{-7} \times 796 \times 0·0012}$$

$$= \underline{151\ 000\ /\text{H}}$$

$$= \underline{125\ 000\ /\text{H}}$$

Comparison of the two results shows that the reluctance of the material increases once the material has been magnetised beyond the knee-point of the magnetic characteristic.

2.8 Simple magnetic circuits

In the previous paragraphs, the magnetic circuits considered were simple ones, e.g. the toroid, in which the magnetic cores were uniform throughout. Many practical circuits are more complicated, yet it is necessary to be able to analyse them with a view to optimising the use of the core material by possibly utilising the highest possible flux density.

It is of interest therefore to compare a simple magnetic circuit with an equivalent electric circuit as illustrated by Fig. 2.20. The m.m.f. $F = IN$ compares with the e.m.f. E. The magnetic potential difference (m.p.d.)

$F = \Phi S$ compares with the electric p.d. $V = IR$. The reluctance $S = \dfrac{1}{\mu_0 \mu_r} \cdot \dfrac{l}{A}$ compares with $R = \rho \cdot \dfrac{l}{A}$.

It can also be seen that the flux is analogous to current but it would be incorrect to think of flux as moving in any way.

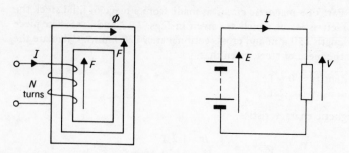

Fig. 2.20 Comparison between magnetic and electric circuits

If the electric circuit were complicated, e.g. a series circuit, it would be necessary to consider the p.d.s or the resistances within the circuit. This would permit the introduction of Kirchhoff's laws to the circuit analysis in their entirety.

Magnetic circuits require an equivalent to p.d. if only parts of the circuit are to be considered. This is the magnetic potential difference, which facilitates the application of Kirchhoff's laws to magnetic circuit analysis. Hence the sum of the m.m.f.s around any closed loop of a magnetic circuit is equal to the sum of the magnetic potential differences. The reluctances of the various sections of a magnetic circuit can also be manipulated in the same manner as resistances in an electric circuit. Figure 2.21 shows a comparison between simple magnetic and electric series circuits.

With reference to Fig. 2.21(a), since the sum of the m.m.f.s around a

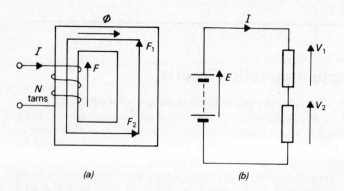

(a)   *(b)*

Fig. 2.21 Comparison between simple magnetic and electric series circuits

magnetic circuit is equal to the sum of the m.p.d.s, then

$$F = F_1 + F_2$$
$$= \Phi S_1 + \Phi S_2$$
$$= \Phi S$$

where, in this instance, S is the total effective reluctance of the circuit, and

$$S = S_1 + S_2 \tag{2.15}$$

Example 2.10 A magnetic circuit comprises two parts, each of uniform cross-sectional area as shown in Fig. 2.22. The parts have:

(a) a length of 160 mm and cross-sectional area 50 mm^2;
(b) a length of 60 mm and cross-sectional area 90 mm^2.

A coil of 4000 turns is wound on part (b) and the flux density in part (a) is 0.9 T. Assuming that all the flux passes through both parts of the magnetic circuit, and that the relative permeability of the core material is 1300, estimate the coil current to produce such a flux density.

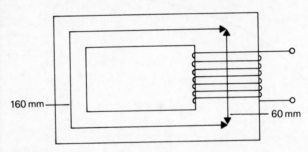

160 mm · 60 mm

Fig. 2.22

$$\Phi = B_a A_a = 0.9 \times 50 \times 10^{-6} = 45 \times 10^{-6}\,\text{Wb}$$

$$S_a = \frac{l_a}{\mu_0\mu_r A_a} = \frac{160 \times 10^{-3}}{4\pi \times 10^{-7} \times 1300 \times 50 \times 10^{-6}} = 1\,959\,000\,/\text{H}$$

$$S_b = \frac{l_b}{\mu_0\mu_r A_b} = \frac{60 \times 10^{-3}}{4\pi \times 10^{-7} \times 1300 \times 90 \times 10^{-6}} = 408\,000\,/\text{H}$$

$$S = S_a + S_b = 1\,959\,000 + 408\,000 = 2\,367\,000\,/\text{H}$$
$$F = \Phi S = 45 \times 10^{-6} \times 2\,367\,000 = 106.5\,\text{At}$$
$$= IN = 4000 \times I$$

$$I = \frac{106.5}{4000} = 0.0266\,\text{A}$$
$$= \underline{26.6\,\text{mA}}$$

It has been shown through the discussion on the magnetisation characteristics of ferromagnetic materials that the assumption of constant relative permeability is an approximation at best. A better estimate of the coil current can be derived by application of the B/H characteristic, as applied in Example 2.11.

Example 2.11 The magnetic circuit of Example 2.10 is made from a material which has the magnetic characteristic shown in Table 2.1.

Table 2.1

Flux density	T	0·2	0·4	0·6	0·8	1·0	1·2
Magnetic field strength	At/m	100	210	340	500	800	1500

From this characteristic, estimate the current which would now be required to produce a flux density of 0·9 T in part (a).

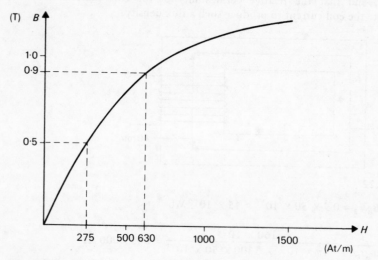

Fig. 2.23

Again $\Phi = B_a A_a = 0.9 \times 50 \times 10^{-6} = 45 \times 10^{-6}$ Wb

$$B_b = \frac{\Phi}{A_b} = \frac{45 \times 10^{-6}}{90 \times 10^{-6}} = 0.5 \text{ T}$$

From the characteristic, $H_a = 630$ At/m and $H_b = 275$ At/m

Thus $\mu_{r_a} = \frac{B_a}{\mu_0 H_a} = \frac{0.9}{4\pi \times 10^{-7} \times 630} = 1137$

$$S_a = \frac{l_a}{\mu_0 \mu_r A_a} = \frac{160 \times 10^{-3}}{4\pi \times 10^{-7} \times 1137 \times 50 \times 10^{-6}} = 2\ 240\ 000\ /\text{H}$$

And $\mu_{rb} = \dfrac{B_b}{\mu_0 H_b} = \dfrac{0\cdot5}{4\pi \times 10^{-7} \times 275} = 1447$

$$S_b = \frac{l_b}{\mu_0 \mu_r A_b} = \frac{60 \times 10^{-3}}{4\pi \times 10^{-7} \times 1447 \times 90 \times 10^{-6}} = 367\ 000\ /\text{H}$$

$$S = S_a + S_b = 2\ 240\ 000 + 367\ 000 = 2\ 607\ 000\ /\text{H}$$

$$F = \Phi S = 45 \times 10^{-6} \times 2\ 607\ 000 = 117\cdot3\ \text{At}$$
$$= IN = 4000 \times I$$

$$I = \frac{117\cdot3}{4000} = 0\cdot0293\ \text{A}$$

$$= 29\cdot3\ \text{mA}$$

An alternative solution to this problem can be based on the relation that the m.m.f. is equal to the sum of the m.p.d.s. Thus again from the characteristic,

$$H_a = 630\ \text{At/m}$$
and $\quad F_a = H_a l_a = 630 \times 160 \times 10^{-3} = 100\cdot8\ \text{At}$
Also $\quad H_b = 275\ \text{At/m}$
and $\quad F_b = H_b l_b = 275 \times 60 \times 10^{-3} = 16\cdot5\ \text{At}$
$$F = F_a + F_b = 100\cdot8 + 16\cdot5 = 117\cdot3\ \text{At}$$
Hence $\quad I = 29\cdot3\ \text{mA}$ as before

The practical significance of series magnetic circuits mainly stems from those into which an air gap has been introduced. The effect of an air gap within a ferromagnetic core can be best considered by means of Example 2.12.

Example 2.12 A magnetic circuit is shown in Fig. 2.24 and is of uniform cross-section throughout. The ferromagnetic core has a mean length of 220 mm and cross-sectional area 50 mm². The air gap has a length of 1·0 mm and the same effective cross-sectional area. A coil of 4000 turns is wound on the core and the magnetic characteristic of the core material is also given in Fig. 2.24. Estimate the current in the coil to produce a flux density of 0·9 T in the air gap, assuming that all the flux passes through both parts of the magnetic circuit.

For the core, $B = 0\cdot9$ T
$$H = 820\ \text{At/m from the nomogram}$$

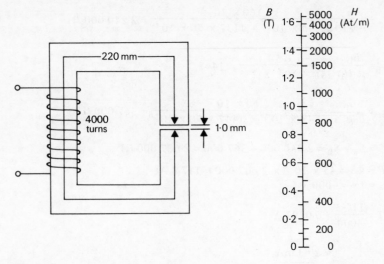

Fig. 2.24

$$\mu_r = \frac{B}{\mu_0 H} = \frac{0 \cdot 9}{4\pi \times 10^{-7} \times 820} = 873$$

$$S_c = \frac{l}{\mu_0 \mu_r A} = \frac{220 \times 10^{-3}}{4\pi \times 10^{-7} \times 873 \times 50 \times 10^{-6}} = 4\,010\,000 \text{ /H}$$

For air gap, $S_a = \dfrac{l}{\mu_0 \mu_r A} = \dfrac{1 \times 10^{-3}}{4\pi \times 10^{-7} \times 1 \times 50 \times 10^{-6}} = 15\,913\,000 \text{ /H}$

$$S = S_a + S_c = 15\,913\,000 + 4\,010\,000 = 19\,923\,000 \text{ /H}$$
$$\Phi = BA = 0 \cdot 9 \times 50 \times 10^{-6} = 45 \times 10^{-6} \text{ Wb}$$
$$F = \Phi S = 45 \times 10^{-6} \times 19\,923\,000 = 896 \cdot 5 \text{ At}$$
$$= IN = 4000 \times I$$
$$I = \frac{896 \cdot 5}{4000} = \underline{0 \cdot 224 \text{ A}}$$

Notice in this example the relative importance of the air gap in the magnetic circuit. The air gap is only 1·0 mm long yet its reluctance is approximately four times that of the steel core which has a length of 220 mm and has also a rather poor relative permeability for a steel. Had a better steel been used, the reluctance of the core would tend toward being negligible.

Notice also that the air gap length was stated as 1·0 mm; this accuracy is required since even a length of 1·1 mm would increase the total reluctance by approximately 1 600 000 /H. As it is, the accuracy of the measurement of the air-gap length is suspect and for this reason it is impossible to calculate the

reluctance of the air gap accurately and hence to calculate the coil current
accurately; instead, it is possible to estimate these values, thereby indicating
that the probability of error is recognised.

A further cause of error has been avoided in the example by stating that
all the flux passes through both parts of the magnetic circuit. In practice, this
would not be the case as some of the flux is set up in the space surrounding
the circuit. Figure 2.25 indicates the leakage flux (its lines of force do not
emanate from the air gap) and the fringing flux (its lines of force bulge out
from the air gap, effectively increasing its cross-sectional area).

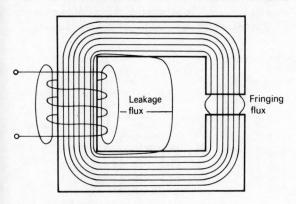

Fig. 2.25 Leakage and fringing fluxes

The introduction of an air gap considerably increases the current in the
coil required to set up the same flux density as there would have been
without the gap. This can be further illustrated by considering the magnetic
p.d.s of Example 2.12 as indicated by Example 2.13.

Example 2.13 Given the information of Example 2.12, calculate the magnetic
p.d. of the core and of the air gap, and hence estimate the coil current to
produce a flux density of 0·9 T in the air gap.

For the core, $B = 0.9$ T

$$H = 820 \text{ At/m}$$

$$F_c = Hl = 820 \times 220 \times 10^{-3} = \underline{180.4 \text{ At}}$$

For the air gap, $B = 0.9$ T

$$H = \frac{B}{\mu_0 \mu_r} = \frac{0.9}{4\pi \times 10^{-7} \times 1} = 716\,100 \text{ At/m}$$

$$F_a = Hl = 716\,100 \times 1 \times 10^{-3} = \underline{716.1 \text{ At}}$$

$$F = F_a + F_c = 716.1 + 180.4 = 896.5 \text{ At}$$

$$= IN = 4000 \times I$$

$$I = \frac{896.5}{4000} = \underline{0.224 \text{ A}} \text{ as before.}$$

The effect of the air gap is therefore that a current of 0·224 A is required instead of 0·045 A, and this represents a considerable increase, which might well have been much greater. This raises the question as to why there should be an air gap at all.

Generally, air gaps appear in magnetic circuits for two purposes. The first is to permit part of the magnetic circuit to move. A simple illustration of this is the magnetic relay shown in Fig. 2.26, in which the closing of the air gap permits the movement of the crank which operates the switching contacts.

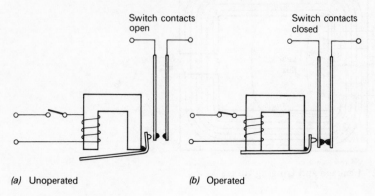

(a) Unoperated   *(b)* Operated

Fig. 2.26 Magnetic relay

The second purpose of an air gap is to make the magnetisation characteristic of the circuit more linear. In electrical machines such as transformers, a linear characteristic is most important in order to maintain a linear relationship between voltage and current. This importance will become apparent after you have read about electromagnetism in Chapter 3 and a.c. circuits in Chapter 6.

Figure 2.27 shows the effect on the Φ/F characteristic of a steel-core magnetic circuit due to the introduction of a 0·2-mm air gap, and the introduction of a 1·0-mm air gap. For a rigid core, the cross-sectional area and the circuit length are constant, therefore the characteristic is similar to that of the B/H characteristic drawn to a different scale.

Because of the much larger m.m.f.s required for the air gaps, it might appear from Fig. 2.27 that all of the characteristics shown are more or less linear and that no advantage is derived from the introduction of an air gap. However, if the characteristics are adjusted to the same horizontal range by plotting each to a base of the ratio of m.m.f. to the corresponding saturation m.m.f. as shown in Fig. 2.28. This diagram now clearly shows how the introduction of even a very small air gap makes the characteristic more linear and that it is not necessary to have a large air gap as this would only make an unnecessary increase in the current required for magnetisation.

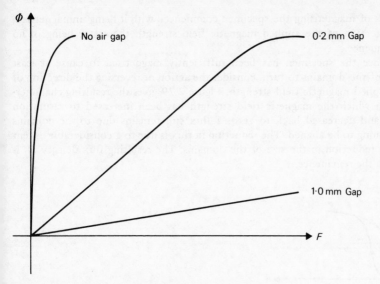

Fig. 2.27 Effect of air gaps on Φ/F characteristic

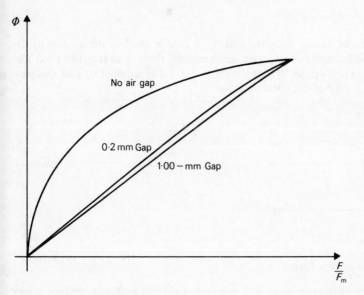

Fig. 2.28 Air gap linearisation

2.9 Hysteresis

In para. 2.5, the magnetisation characteristic was obtained by considering the application of a magnetic field strength to a ferromagnetic material. The process of magnetising the specimen commenced with it being unmagnetised, the direction of the applied magnetic field strength thereafter being of no consequence.

Once the specimen has been sufficiently magnetised to cause at least some of the domains to turn, consider the action of reversing the direction of the applied magnetic field strength. Figure 2.29 gives the resulting characteristic in which the magnetic field strength has been increased to saturation point and decreased back to zero: a flux still remains due to the domains continuing to be aligned. The reduction in flux is due to a considerable extent to the reduction in the size of the domains. The resulting flux density B_2 is termed the remanence.

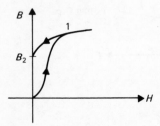

Fig. 2.29 Remanence

If a force of the opposite polarity is then applied to the specimen, the domains will progressively turn until eventually there is no effective flux. The magnetic field strength H_3, as shown in Fig. 2.30, required to give this new condition is termed the coercive force.

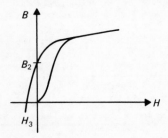

Fig. 2.30 Coercive force

Yet further increase of the magnetic field strength will produce a flux acting in the opposite direction to that formerly noted. Eventually saturation will be achieved in this opposite sense.

If this sequence of events is reversed, a similar magnetic effect is produced and eventually the original point of saturation 1 is achieved, as shown in Fig. 2.31. The resulting characteristic therefore forms a loop, which is termed the hysteresis loop. It follows that when an alternating current gives

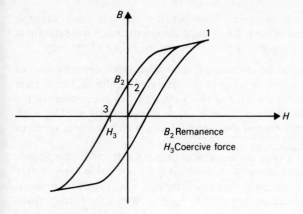

Fig. 2.31 Hysteresis loop

rise to a varying flux in a ferromagnetic material, the corresponding instantaneous values of flux density and magnetic flux are shown by the hysteresis loop.

The hysteresis loop shown in Fig. 2.31 is only one of many possible loops. There are three factors that affect the shape and size:

1. The maximum value of flux density: This can be shown most easily in a diagram. Fig. 2.32(a) shows how the loop area increases as the alternating magnetic field strength has progressively greater peak values.

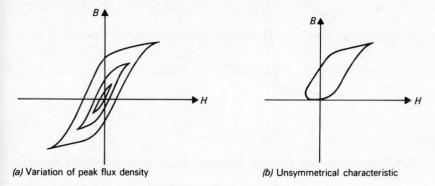

(a) Variation of peak flux density

(b) Unsymmetrical characteristic

Fig. 2.32 Hysteresis loops for varying conditions

2. The initial magnetic state of the specimen: Fig. 2.32(b) shows a hysteresis loop in which the specimen has been saturated, the flux density has been reduced to zero and finally returned to the saturated condition. This could happen if the specimen were magnetised by a direct current with an alternating current superimposed on it.
3. The material: this may magnetise easily in which case the loop will appear narrow whilst, conversely, if the material does not magnetise

easily, the loop will be wide. These are the soft and hard magnetic materials introduced in para. 2.6. Also, different materials will saturate at different values of flux density thus affecting the height of the loop.

Different materials can be compared if their hysteresis loops are drawn to the same scale and each loop is taken to the saturated condition. One feature of particular importance is the area of the loop. The area is a measure of the work done in taking the material through a cycle of magnetisation. This work results in a loss of energy termed the hysteresis loss, which becomes apparent in the form of heat.

Figure 2.33 shows a typical comparison between soft and hard magnetic materials. The soft material tends to have a higher saturation level of flux density coupled with a relatively thin characteristic, whilst the hard material has a lower level of saturation flux density coupled with a fat characteristic. The hysteresis loss for a soft material is about $1-200$ J/m^3 per cycle of magnetisation whilst for a hard magnetic material the loss is about $10-2000$ kJ/m^3. In the former case, it is desirable to have as low a value as possible in a material that is being continuously magnetically cycled, e.g. the core of a transformer or of a motor. In the latter case, the material is used for permanent magnets and high hysteresis losses are an advantage because this tends to give high values of stored magnetic energy.

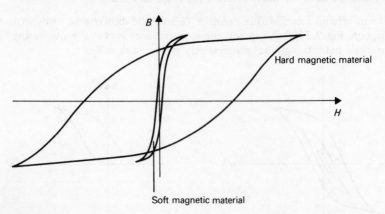

Fig. 2.33 Comparison between hysteresis loops of hard and soft magnetic materials

The two most common forms of hard magnetic materials are the Alnico alloys and the ferrites. As the name suggests, Alnico alloys are made from aluminium, cobalt, nickel and iron. A standard form of Alnico that would be used for the magnets in telephone receivers, energy meters and loudspeakers, has a remanence of about 1·2 T and a coercive force of about 50 kAt/m, with a maximum stored energy density of about 40 kJ/m^3.

Ferrites are now the most popular form of permanent magnet, having similar uses to those stated above as well as in toys and holding devices. They are not as mechanically strong and remanence values are in the region of 0·2—0·4 T, which consequently means lower stored energy densities.

Problems

1. A magnetic field of cross-sectional area 600 cm^2 has a total magnetic flux 30 mWb. Calculate the average flux density.

2. A steel core of cross-sectional area 400 mm^2 maintains a magnetic field of density 0·8 T. Determine the magnetic flux in the core.

3. Determine the m.m.f. of a 500-turn coil carrying a current 1·5 A.

4. A steel core contains a magnetic flux 1·4 mWb and is magnetised by an m.m.f. 850 At. Determine the reluctance of the steel core.

5. A 1000-turn coil carries a current 2·5 A. If the coil surrounds a magnetic 'circuit' of effective length 50 cm and relative permeability 1, calculate:
   (a) the magnetic field strength;
   (b) the magnetic flux density.

6. A ferromagnetic circuit has a uniform cross-sectional area 500 mm^2 and a mean diameter 200 mm. The relative permeability of the ferromagnetic material is 2000 and the flux density in it is 1·5 T. Calculate the reluctance of the magnetic circuit and the m.m.f.

7. A toroid of mean diameter 200 mm has a uniformly wound conductor passed ten times through its centre. The cross-sectional area of the toroid is 100 mm^2 and the relative permeability 850. A current of 1·5 A is passed through the conductor. Calculate the flux in the ring.

8. A coil of insulated wire is wound tightly round a steel ring and with 400 turns. The resistance of the coil is 250 Ω and it is connected to a 4-V d.c. supply. The steel ring is of uniform cross-sectional area 600 mm^2 and of mean diameter 150 mm. The relative permeability of the steel is 9000. Calculate the total flux in the ring.

9. A steel ring has a cross-sectional area 150 mm^2. The ring has a mean diameter 85 mm and is wound with 250 turns of wire. The steel has a relative permeability of 500 and the total flux in the steel is 0·35 mWb. What current is required in the coil to produce this flux?

10. A coil is wound uniformly with 300 turns about a steel ring of relative permeability 900, having a mean circumference 400 mm and cross-sectional area 500 mm^2. If the coil has resistance 8 Ω and is connected to a 20-V d.c. supply, calculate:
    (a) the coil m.m.f.;
    (b) the magnetic field strength;
    (c) the reluctance of the ring.

11. A Perspex toroid has a mean circumference 450 mm and a uniform cross-sectional area 500 mm^2. The coil consists of 900 turns of wire and carries a current 3·0 A. Calculate:
    (a) the m.m.f.;
    (b) the magnetic field strength;
    (c) the reluctance of the magnetic circuit;
    (d) the flux;
    (e) the flux density.

12. A closed steel ring has a mean length 700 mm and the relative permeability of the steel is 540 when the flux density is 1·28 T. Determine the m.m.f. required for such a flux density in the ring.

What additional m.m.f. is required to maintain a flux density of 1·28 T when a radial air gap of 1·6 mm is introduced to the ring?

13. A steel ring 300 mm in diameter has a cross-sectional area 400 mm² for the first one-third of its radial axis, 800 mm² for the middle third, and 1200 mm² for the remainder. The relative permeability of the steel is 3000. Calculate the m.m.f. required to produce a flux of 1·0 mWb.

14. An electromagnet has a magnetic circuit that can be regarded as comprising three parts in series, each of uniform cross-sectional area:
Part a is of length 80 mm and cross-sectional area 50 mm²;
Part b is of length 60 mm and cross-sectional area 90 mm²;
Part c is an air gap of length 0·5 mm and cross-sectional area 150 mm².

Parts a and b are made from a material having the corresponding magnetic characteristic values shown in Table 2.2.

Table 2.2

Magnetic field strength (At/m)	275	620
Flux density (T)	0·5	0·9

Determine the current necessary in a coil of 4000 turns wound on part b to produce an air-gap flux density 0·3 T.

15. A series magnetic circuit has a steel path of length 500 mm and an air gap of length 1·0 mm. The cross-sectional area of the steel is 600 mm² and the excitation coil has 400 turns. Determine the current required to produce a flux 0·9 mWb in the circuit, given that the appropriate section of the magnetisation characteristic for the steel may be taken from Table 2.3.

Table 2.3

Flux density (T)	1·20	1·35	1·45	1·55
Magnetic field strength (At/m)	500	1000	2000	4500

16. A transformer core is made from steel, the magnetisation characteristic of which is indicated in Fig. 2.34. Part of the core is effectively 500 mm long and of cross-sectional area 4000 mm² whilst the other part is effectively 200 mm long and of cross-sectional area 3000 mm². An air gap is introduced into this second part and is 1·0 mm long. Calculate the flux density in the air gap when a current of 1·33 A is passed through a 1000-turn coil wound on the core.

17. The core of a magnetic circuit consists of three parts:
Part a — A = 500 mm², l = 125 mm;
Part b — A = 1250 mm², l = 100 mm;
Part c — A = 500 mm², l = 0·5 mm.

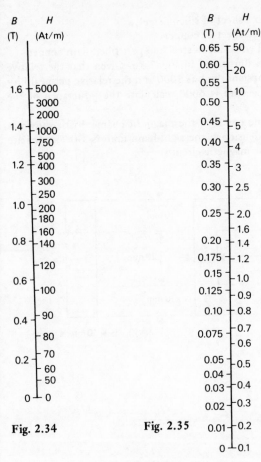

B (T)	H (At/m)
1.6	5000
	3000
	2000
1.4	1000
	750
	500
1.2	400
	300
	250
1.0	200
	180
	160
0.8	140
	120
0.6	100
0.4	90
	80
	70
0.2	60
	50
0	0

Fig. 2.34

B (T)	H (At/m)
0.65	50
0.60	20
0.55	10
0.50	
0.45	5
0.40	4
0.35	3
0.30	2.5
0.25	2.0
0.20	1.6
	1.4
0.175	1.2
0.15	1.0
0.125	0.9
0.10	0.8
0.075	0.7
	0.6
0.05	0.5
0.04	
0.03	0.4
0.02	0.3
0.01	0.2
0	0.1

Fig. 2.35

Parts a and b are made from a material the magnetisation characteristic of which is indicated in Fig. 2.35. Part c is an air gap. A 1000-turn coil is wound on part b. Calculate the coil current to produce a flux density of 0·5 T in part a.

18. A ring of mean diameter 20 cm is made of circular-section steel of 3 cm diameter. The ring is sawn through radially at one point to have a gap 1·0 mm wide, and 1000 turns of wire are wound uniformly about the ring. Calculate the current required to produce a flux density 1·0 T in the air gap. Assume the relative permeability of the steel under these conditions to be 750 and that leakage and fringing may be neglected.

If the magnetising current were doubled, would you expect the flux density to double? Give reasons for your answer.

19. A steel toroid has a radial cut sawn through it to form a gap. A coil is wound around the toroid and a constant current is made to pass through the coil. What is the effect on the magnetic flux in the toroid if:
    (*a*) the gap is filled with plastic;

(b) the gap is filled with a sheet of silicon steel;

(c) the gap is filled with a sheet of copper;

(d) the gap is part filled with silicon steel and part filled with copper.

20. A ferromagnetic core is illustrated in Fig. 2.36. Given that the relative permeability of the right-hand limb is 5000 and the relative permeability of the remainder of the core is 6000, calculate the reluctance of the magnetic circuit.

   If the material of the core had the magnetic characteristic shown in Fig. 2.34 and the flux density in the right-hand limb is 1·0 T, calculate the new reluctance of the magnetic circuit.

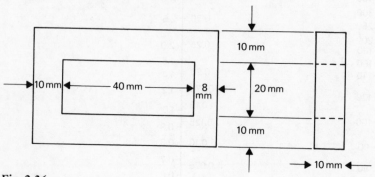

Fig. 2.36

Answers

1. 0·5 T
2. 320 µWb
3. 750 At
4. 607 140 /H
5. 5000 At/m, 6·28 mT
6. 500 000 /H, 375 At
7. 2·55 µWb
8. 92 µWb
9. 3·9 A
10. 750 At, 1875 At/m, 707 000/H
11. 2700 At, 6000 At/m, 716 × 10^6 /H, 3·77 µWb, 7·54 mT
12. 1320 At, 1630 At
13. 382 At
14. 46·4 mA
15. 6·2 A
16. 1·33 T
17. 0·2 A
18. 1·47 A, No — due to 2 T likely to approach saturation
19. None, Greatly increased, None, Increased but not as much as (b)
20. 229 400 /H, 314 500 /H

Chapter 3

Electromagnetic induction

Having introduced some of the physical background to electromagnetism, there remains the need to consider further the concept of induced e.m.f.s which so far have only been mentioned in passing. Induced e.m.f.s play an important part in the transfer of energy to and from electrical systems and it is the objective of this chapter to consider the salient points that concern an engineer with respect to his understanding of the principles of motors, generators and transformers.

3.1 Force on a current-carrying conductor

It has already been noted in para. 2.2 that, due to the flux density of a magnetic field being measured in the appropriate teslas, it follows that the force on a current-carrying conductor is given by

$$F = BIl \tag{3.1}$$

Whilst it is from this relation that the unit of flux measurement is derived, it will be shown that this principle can be related to the resulting induced e.m.f. which permits a simple definition for the unit of flux — the weber.

Nevertheless, Relation 3.1 is important as the basis of all magnetic

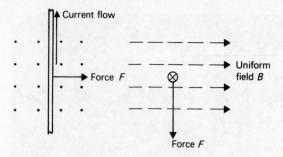

Fig. 3.1 Current-carrying conductor in a uniform magnetic field

measurement. The force BIl, which is measured in newtons, is only obtained when the magnetic field and the conductor are at right angles as shown in Fig. 3.1.

If the conductor and the field make an angle θ with one another then the effective length of the conductor in the field, i.e. the conductor length presented at right angles to the field, is $l \sin \theta$ and the force is given by

$$F = BIl \sin \theta \tag{3.2}$$

The corresponding arrangement is shown in Fig. 3.2.

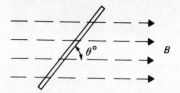

Fig. 3.2 Current-carrying conductor in a uniform magnetic field and at an angle to the field

Thus the mechanical force experienced is proportional to:

(*a*) the field flux density B;
(*b*) the effective length of the conductor $l \sin \theta$;
(*c*) the conductor current I.

Each of these points may be shown experimentally although such experiments require some care. The most simple arrangement would be constructed from ferromagnetic materials in order to obtain strong flux densities but, unless the arrangement is symmetrical, the presence of the ferromagnetic materials may introduce errors as large as 20 per cent. However, the flux densities obtained without ferromagnetic materials are so small that measurements become difficult. The most suitable compromise is a coil free to rotate within a uniform magnetic field as shown in Fig. 3.3. This form of construction is similar to that used on the permanent-magnet,

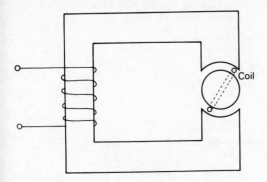

Fig. 3.3 Equipment to demonstrate $F = BIl$

moving-coil meter except that an electromagnet is being used in place of the permanent magnet.

Providing that a relatively low level of flux density is involved, and the electromagnetic core is made from a good ferromagnetic material, then the coil current used to magnetise the system is directly proportional to the flux density. By measuring the torque on the moving coil, it may be observed that $F \propto B$ as indicated in the F/B characteristic shown in Fig. 3.4.

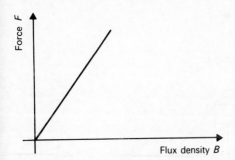

Fig. 3.4 F/B characteristic of experiment

The effective length of the conductor may be changed by switching in different numbers of turns in the moving coil. The more turns, the greater is the effective length, and hence it may be observed that $F \propto l$ as indicated in the F/l characteristic shown in Fig. 3.5.

Finally the torque and hence the force may be observed whilst the current in the moving coil is varied with the result that $F \propto I$ as indicated in the F/I characteristic shown in Fig. 3.6.

By observation of the experiment, it may also be noted that the mechanical force exerted by the conductor always acts in a direction perpendicular to the plane of the conductor and the magnetic field directions. The direction of the force is given by the left-hand rule, which is illustrated in Fig. 3.7.

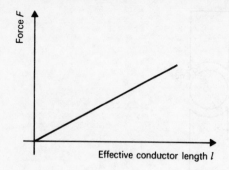

Fig. 3.5 *F/l* characteristic of experiment

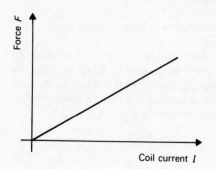

Fig. 3.6 *F/I* characteristic of experiment

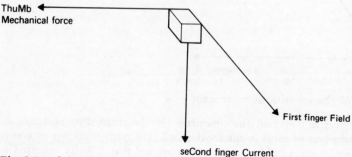

Fig. 3.7 Left-hand rule

Left-hand rule:

1. Hold the thumb, first finger and second finger of the left hand in the manner indicated by Fig. 3.7, whereby they are mutually at right angles.
2. Point the First finger in the Field direction.
3. Point the seCond finger in the Current direction.
4. The thuMb then indicates the direction of the Mechanical force exerted by the conductor.

It follows that if either the current or the direction of the field is reversed, then the direction of the force is also reversed. If both current and field are reversed, the direction of the force remains unchanged.

Example 3.1 A conductor of length 0·5 m is situated in and at right angles to a uniform magnetic field of flux density 1·0 T and carries a current of 100 A. Calculate the force exerted by the conductor when:

(*a*) it lies in the given position;
(*b*) it lies in a position inclined at 30° to the direction of the field.

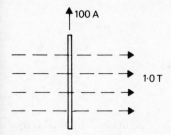

Fig. 3.8

(*a*) $F = BlI = 1 \times 0.5 \times 100 = \underline{50\ N}$

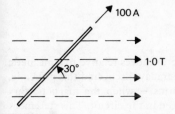

Fig. 3.9

(*b*) $F = BlI \sin \theta = 50 \times \sin 30° = \underline{25\ N}$

Example 3.2 A coil is wound with 30 turns on a rectangular former 8 cm long and 4 cm broad. It is mounted to rotate as shown in Fig. 3.10, the axis of rotation being perpendicular to a uniform magnetic field of 0·5 T. If the coil is inclined at 45° to the magnetic field and passes a current of 0·3 A, calculate the torque on the coil.

By application of the left-hand rule, it will be found that the resultant torque on the coil comes only from the 8-cm sides. The force on the coil ends cancel one another out in terms of producing torque about the axis of rotation. It will also be found that the forces act in the directions shown in the end view given in Fig. 3.10.

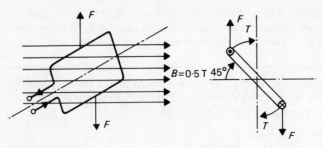

Fig. 3.10

Force on each 8-cm conductor is $BIl \sin \theta$

$= 0.5 \times 0.08 \times 0.3 \times \sin 90°$
$= 0.012$ N

Torque due to each 8-cm conductor is $Fr \cos 45°$

$= 0.012 \times 0.03 \times 0.71$
$= 25.4 \times 10^{-6}$ N m

There being 30 turns, there are therefore 60 conductors and the total torque is $60 \times 25.4 \times 10^{-6} = 1524 \times 10^{-6}$ N m
$$= \underline{1.524 \times 10^{-3} \text{ N m}}$$

3.2 Induced e.m.f.

It has already been stated that when a conductor moves relative to a magnetic field, an e.m.f. is induced in the conductor. Faraday discovered this principle, which may be expressed in more general terms — when the magnetic flux linking a circuit is changing, an e.m.f. is induced in the circuit. This statement is the more appropriate since only the e.m.f. induced in a closed loop can be measured. For instance, if a single conductor is connected to an appropriate voltmeter so that the e.m.f. may be measured, the voltmeter connections complete a loop or circuit.

The manner in which the flux linking a circuit is varied may be achieved in one of three ways:

1. The coil may be moved in and relative to a fixed magnetic field so that the flux established in the coil varies in magnitude.
2. The field may be varied by changing the current that gives rise to it, the coil remaining stationary. Again the flux in the coil will vary.
3. The above conditions may occur simultaneously.

An e.m.f. induced by method 1 is termed a motional e.m.f. whilst an e.m.f. induced by method 2 is termed a transformer e.m.f. Possible arrangements for inducing these e.m.f.s are shown in Fig. 3.11.

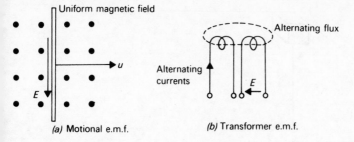

Fig. 3.11 Arrangements for inducing e.m.f.s in coils

The instance of the coil moving through the magnetic field introduces the problem of how the polarity of the induced e.m.f. can be ascertained. To solve this problem, it is necessary to introduce Lenz's law.

3.3 Lenz's law

Lenz's law states that the e.m.f. induced in a circuit by a change of flux linkage will be of a polarity that tends to set up a current which will oppose the change of flux linkage.

As an instance of this law, consider the two coils mounted in close proximity as shown in Fig. 3.12. Coil B has its circuit completed by a resistor. If the current in coil A is increased, the flux in coil B is increased and thus the flux linkage in coil B increases, causing an e.m.f. to be induced in coil B. This e.m.f. will cause a current to flow such that the current will create a flux which will oppose the increase in initial flux. To satisfy this requirement, terminal 2 must be driven positive with respect to terminal 1.

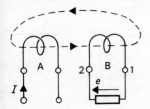

Fig. 3.12 Arrangements of two coils to illustrate Lenz's law

Lenz's law is effectively an extension of the principle of conservation of energy. It is an electrical application of this principle in that for every action there is an equal and opposite reaction. In the case of the two coils, the resistance of circuit B prevents the current attaining a sufficient value to prevent the flux linkage from changing.

From Lenz's law, it can be shown that the polarity of the induced e.m.f. in a moving conductor is given by the right-hand rule. This can be illustrated by Fig. 3.13.

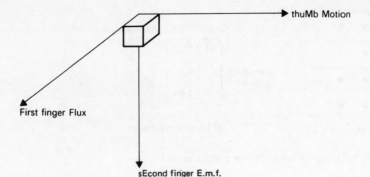

Fig. 3.13 Right-hand rule

Right-hand rule:

1. Hold the thumb, first finger and second finger of the right hand in the
   manner indicated by Fig. 3.13, whereby they are mutually at right
   angles.
2. Point the thuMb in the direction of the conductor Movement normal to
   the field.
3. Point the First finger in the direction of the Field.
4. The sEcond finger indicates the polarity of the resulting E.m.f. with
   respect to the conductor.

3.4 Faraday's law

Consider a single conductor moving at right angles across a uniform magnetic
field as shown in Fig. 3.14.

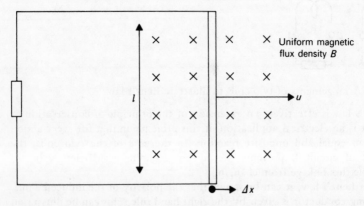

Fig. 3.14 Current-carrying conductor moving across a uniform magnetic field

Since the conductor is carrying a current I, it experiences a force given by

$$F = BlI$$

This is the force which is exerted by the conductor on the mounting. It is also the force that is exerted on the conductor by the mechanical mounting and which will be equal in magnitude but opposite in sense.

If the conductor moves a small distance Δx in a time Δt, then its velocity u is given by

$$u = \frac{\Delta x}{\Delta t}$$

It follows that the average power during the period Δt required to move the conductor is

$$P = Fu$$

$$= BlI \cdot \frac{\Delta x}{\Delta t}$$

However, by the principle of conservation of energy, the power input from the mechanical source must equal the electrical power output from the conductor. If the average induced e.m.f. is E, then

$$P = EI$$

$$= BlI \cdot \frac{\Delta x}{\Delta t}$$

Thus $E = Bl \cdot \dfrac{\Delta x}{\Delta t}$ (3.3)

Let ΔA be the area traced out by the movement of the conductor where

$$\Delta A = l \cdot \Delta x$$

Thus $E = B \cdot \dfrac{\Delta A}{\Delta t}$

Since $\Phi = BA$, then the flux cut by the conductor will be given by

$$\Delta\Phi = B \cdot \Delta A$$

and $E = \dfrac{\Delta\Phi}{\Delta t}$ (3.4)

What does this mathematical expression mean in practical terms? A simple investigation is indicated in Fig. 3.15, in which a coil is connected to a galvanometer that will indicate the passage of current round the circuit. A centre-zero galvanometer is used so that the direction of the indicated deflection shows the direction of current flow. A permanent magnet provides the magnetic field and may be moved in and out of the coil.

The investigation has four stages:

1. The permanent magnet is moved steadily into the coil but not too rapidly. The result observed on the galvanometer is the passage of current in the coil induced by the movement of the permanent magnet.
2. The permanent magnet is withdrawn in a similar manner to the insertion. The result observed is a similar deflection of the galvanometer needle but in the opposite direction. This permits the observation that the polarity of the induced e.m.f. depends on the direction of movement of the magnetic field and will be found to compare with the right-hand rule.
3. The previous stages may be repeated with the movement of the permanent magnet being more rapid. The result observed is that the faster the motion of the permanent magnet, then the greater the current due to increased e.m.f. It may therefore be concluded that Relation 3.4 states that the e.m.f. is given by the rate of change of flux with time.
4. Finally a different coil can be substituted into the experiment, say with a greater number of turns. The previous stages of the experiment are repeated with the new coil and it is found that in all cases, the induced e.m.f. increases. Thus it may be concluded that the greater the number of turns, then the greater the e.m.f.

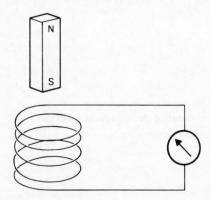

Fig. 3.15 Investigation of induced e.m.f.

Applying the final observation to Relation 3.4, if the conductor in Fig. 3.14 had been formed into a coil of N turns, the induced e.m.f. would have been proportionally increased, hence

$$E = N \cdot \frac{\Delta\Phi}{\Delta t} \qquad (3.5)$$

The use of $\Delta\Phi$ and Δt is merely to indicate that small changes are being considered, but for general changes commencing with zero flux at zero time then

$$E = \frac{N\Phi}{t} \tag{3.6}$$

The product $N\Phi$ is termed the flux linkage of the coil or circuit.

Flux linkage   **Symbol: Ψ**   **Unit: weber turn (Wb t)**

$$\Psi = \Phi N \tag{3.7}$$

and $E = \dfrac{\Psi}{t}$ (3.8)

For small changes of flux linkage $\Delta\Psi$ in time Δt, then

$$E = \frac{\Delta\Psi}{\Delta t} \tag{3.9}$$

This is a mathematical expression for Faraday's second law of electrodynamics. This law is usually termed Faraday's law, and the definition of the weber is obtained from Relation 3.9.

For those readers familiar with the calculus notation,

$$e = N \cdot \frac{d\phi}{dt} = \frac{d\psi}{dt} \tag{3.10}$$

where the lower-case letter e denotes the instantaneous e.m.f.

Example 3.3 A coil of 100 turns is linked by a flux of 20 mWb. If this flux is reversed in a time of 2·0 ms, calculate the average e.m.f. induced in the coil.

$$\Delta\Phi = (20 \times 10^{-3}) - (-20 \times 10^{-3}) = 40 \times 10^{-3} \text{ Wb}$$

$$E = N \cdot \frac{\Delta\Phi}{\Delta t} = 100 \times \frac{40 \times 10^{-3}}{2 \times 10^{-3}} = \underline{2000 \text{ V}}$$

Relations 3.4 and 3.5 may be modified to relate the induced e.m.f. to the velocity at which the conductor is moving in a magnetic field. A conductor is used in this context, rather than a loop or coil, because of its practical implications in electrical machines. Nevertheless, the conductor will eventually form part of a circuit and thus a conductor can be said to have flux linkage. Consider again the conductor in Fig. 3.14; it will be noted that only the conductor lies within the magnetic field.

The conductor is moving with a velocity u. The flux cut by the conductor and therefore entering the circuit loop in a time Δt is given by

$$\Delta\Phi = Bl \cdot \Delta x$$
$$= Blu \cdot \Delta t$$

For a single-turn coil, it follows that the average e.m.f. is given by

$$E = \frac{\Delta \Phi}{\Delta t}$$

$$= \frac{Blu \cdot \Delta t}{\Delta t}$$

$$= Blu \qquad (3.11)$$

Again for those readers familiar with the notation of calculus,

$$e = \frac{d\Phi}{dt}$$

$$= Blu \qquad (3.12)$$

As before, this e.m.f. can be measured using a voltmeter. Provided the connecting wires from the voltmeter to the conductor play no part in the cutting to the flux, Relation 3.11 remains valid. This factor applies to all similar cases in this chapter. If the connections cut the field then an e.m.f. is induced in them which will contribute to the voltmeter reading.

Note the case of a rectangular coil moving through a uniform magnetic field. The rate at which flux enters the loop at one side is equal to the rate at which the flux leaves the loop at the other side. There is therefore no change in the flux linkage with the loop and hence there is no e.m.f. induced in the loop. However, if the loop sides are considered to be separate conductors, then each will have an e.m.f. Blu induced in it. These e.m.f.s act in opposite directions around the loop and so cancel one another out — the total effective e.m.f. is therefore zero as stated before.

The conductor does not actually require to move across the field. Instead the field may sweep past the coil which is then held stationary. Or again the field may be moving while the conductor is moving with a different velocity. In the relation $E = Blu$, the velocity u is that of the conductor relative to the field.

The motion of the conductor must be across the field if the conductor is to cut the field. Any motion parallel with the field therefore will not produce any change in flux linkage and hence will fail to induce an e.m.f. If the conductor is moving at an angle α to the field then the velocity with which the conductor moves across the field is $u \sin \alpha$, hence

$$E = Blu \sin \alpha \qquad (3.13)$$

Example 3.4 A conductor of length 0·5 m is situated in and at right angles to a uniform magnetic field of flux density 1·0 T and moves with a velocity of 40 m/s. Calculate the e.m.f. induced in the conductor when the direction of motion is:

(a) at right angles to the direction of the field;

(b) inclined at 30° to the direction of the field;

(c) as in (b) but with the conductor inclined as 45° to the field.

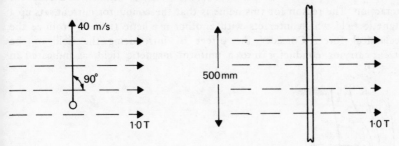

Fig. 3.16

(a) $E = Blu \sin \alpha = 1 \times 0.5 \times 40 \times \sin 90° = \underline{20\ V}$

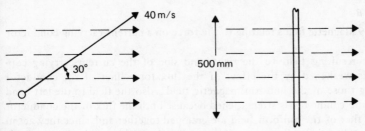

Fig. 3.17

(b) $E = Blu \sin \alpha = 1 \times 0.5 \times 40 \times \sin 30° = \underline{10\ V}$

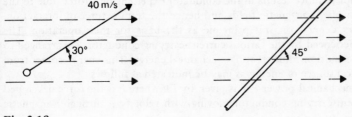

Fig. 3.18

(c) $E = B(l \sin \theta)u \sin \alpha = 10 \times \sin 45° = \underline{7.1\ V}$

3.5 Motor and generator principles

A motor is a device that takes in electrical energy and transfers it into mechanical energy, whilst a generator converts mechanical energy into electrical energy.

80   The mechanical energy system requires that there be a mechanical force (or torque) associated with the displacement of its point of action. Often this force is that described in para. 3.1 and which is known as a force of interaction. The reason for this name is that the conductor current sets up a magnetic field which interacts with another magnetic field to produce the mechanical force. Consider the effect of introducing the field of the current-carrying conductor into a uniform magnetic field, as indicated in Fig. 3.19.

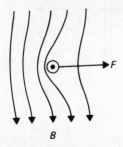

Fig. 3.19 Magnetic fields relating to the force on a current-carrying conductor

The resulting field to the right-hand side of the current-carrying conductor is weakened by the effect of the flux force lines of the conductor opposing those of the uniform magnetic field. Also the field to the left-hand side of the conductor is strengthened because both the flux of the conductor and the flux of the uniform field are cramped together and, since they act in the same direction, they also repel one another. This results in the fields trying to adjust themselves so that the cramped conditions to the left-hand side of the conductor are alleviated by pushing the field of the conductor towards the right into the relatively uncramped conditions that exist there. The attempt to move results in the conductor experiencing a force, due to the interaction of the magnetic fields and hence the term − force of interaction.

Motors depend on this principle as the basis for their operation. The forces experienced by the various current-carrying conductors are arranged to give rise to motion, thus creating mechanical energy. This energy comes from the electrical source of energy as may be indicated as follows.

The mechanical power P_M is given by Fu where F is the force developed on a current-carrying conductor moving with velocity u through a magnetic field of density B, thus

$$P_M = Fu$$
$$= BlI \cdot u$$

But the electrical power P_E is given by EI, where E is the induced e.m.f. in the conductor due to its motion through the magnetic field; thus

$$P_E = EI$$
$$= Blu \cdot I$$
$$= P_M$$

The induced e.m.f. should not be confused with the e.m.f. of the source causing the current to flow. The induced e.m.f. is the reaction indicated by Lenz's law to the action of the conductor moving through the field and attempting to change the flux. By moving, the conductor produces mechanical energy which in a motor is taken out of the machine and transferred to the mechanical system. The e.m.f. is the reaction which attempts to transfer energy into the machine to make good the change, thus $P_E = EI$ indicates the rate at which energy enters the motor and $P_M = Fu$ indicates the rate at which energy leaves the motor.

Generally the above has been based on the assumption of the linear motion considered throughout the present chapter. However, rotational motion would have been just as appropriate, although a bit more difficult to analyse; thus $P_M = T\omega$, where T is torque and ω angular velocity, is an acceptable alternative to $P_M = Fu$.

Also it should be recalled that in earlier consideration of e.m.f., it has been noted that e.m.f.s are associated with energy interchange between systems. Thus in the instance considered above, the electrical power was determined in terms of the induced e.m.f. and not in terms of the potential difference.

Generators are very similar to motors in their action except that the energy flow is from the mechanical input to the electrical output. In these instances, the conductor forming part of an electric circuit is made to move through a magnetic field. This requires a mechanical force to drive it; hence there is an input of mechanical power. By forcing the conductor through a magnetic field, an e.m.f. is induced in it, and thus a source of electrical e.m.f. is created.

Because an electric circuit has been employed, it is reasonable to infer that the e.m.f. causes a current to flow and that this induced current flowing through some circuit load causes electric energy to be dissipated. The rate at which this energy is dissipated depends on the rate of energy being induced into the circuit, which is given by $P_E = EI$. The field produced by the current is in a direction that gives rise to a force on its conductor that opposes the turning action of the prime mover driving the generator. The greater the electric energy rate of dissipation, then the greater is this reaction and thus the greater is the mechanical energy required from the prime mover.

That the induced current gives rise to a force that opposes the driving force is again an instance of the observation stated in Lenz's law, i.e. the induced e.m.f. has caused a current to flow in such a direction that its magnetic effect has opposed the change that has produced it. Since the e.m.f. is the system's answer back to the change brought on it, the e.m.f. is termed a back e.m.f. The back e.m.f. is the reaction described by Lenz's law; by comparison, Faraday's law indicated that an e.m.f. would be induced.

Finally, wherever a current-carrying conductor moves in a magnetic field, both mechanical force and electrical induced e.m.f. will be experienced, no matter whether the resulting action is that of a motor or of a generator. However, it is the function of a motor to produce force whilst it is the function of a generator to induce e.m.f.

Example 3.5 A conductor of effective length 15 cm moves with a velocity 5 m/s perpendicular to a magnetic field of uniform flux density 0·4 T. Calculate:

(a) the e.m.f. induced in the conductor;
(b) the force acting on the conductor when it carries a current of 20 A;
(c) the power required to move the conductor.

Give a diagram of the relative directions of the field, the motion of the conductor, and the induced e.m.f.

$$E = Blu = 0·4 \times 0·15 \times 5 = \underline{0·3 \text{ V}}$$
$$F = Bll = 0·4 \times 0·15 \times 20 = \underline{1·2 \text{ N}}$$
$$P = Fu = 1·2 \times 5 = \underline{6 \text{ W}}$$
$$\text{or} \quad P = EI = 0·3 \times 20 = \underline{6 \text{ W}}$$

The relative directions of field, motion and e.m.f. are shown in Fig. 3.20.

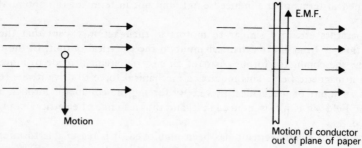

Fig. 3.20

3.6   Self inductance

The process of inducing an e.m.f. into a circuit is termed induction. In any electric circuit, the current in the conductors sets up a magnetic field. Further, whenever this current increases or decreases, the magnetic field increases or decreases. This changing field gives rise to an inductive effect that opposes and therefore delays the change of current. Thus the effect described by Lenz's law is the inductive property which is present to some extent in all circuits and which, whilst not preventing the change of current, at least delays it.

The inductive property of a system is called the inductance. Generally the inductance of the conductors' connecting source to load is negligible compared with the inductance of equipment containing coils, especially those which are wound round ferromagnetic cores. Coils specially wound on such cores for the purpose of providing large values of inductance are called inductors.

As described by Lenz's law, the effect of induction is to induce an e.m.f., which it has been noted is given by:

$$E = \frac{\Delta\Psi}{\Delta t} \text{ or } \frac{\Psi}{t}$$

$$= N \cdot \frac{\Delta\Phi}{\Delta t} \text{ or } \frac{N\Phi}{t} \text{ for small or large changes as appropriate.}$$

The effect of the e.m.f. can be observed from measurements in the electric circuit and since the flux is due to the current, it follows that the e.m.f. is proportional to the rate of change of current, i.e.

$$E \propto \frac{\Delta\Phi}{\Delta t} \text{ or } \frac{\Phi}{t}$$

thus $\quad E \propto \frac{\Delta I}{\Delta t} \text{ or } \frac{I}{t}$

Proportionalities may be replaced by equalities by the introduction of suitable constants. In this case,

$$E = L \cdot \frac{\Delta I}{\Delta t} \text{ or } \frac{LI}{t} \tag{3.13}$$

where L is a constant called the inductance of the system.

Self inductance   Symbol: L Unit: henry (H)

The winding e.m.f. is entirely self-induced, hence the inductance is termed the self inductance. The unit of inductance, called the henry, is the inductance of a closed circuit in which an e.m.f. of 1 volt is produced when the electric current in the circuit varies uniformly at the rate of 1 ampere per second.

It is not the case, however, that the inductance of a winding is an absolute constant; thus Relation 3.13 may be more generally stated in the form

$$E = \frac{\Delta(LI)}{\Delta t} \text{ or } \frac{LI}{t}$$

$$= \frac{\Delta\Psi}{\Delta t} \text{ or } \frac{\Psi}{t}$$

Thus, regardless of whether small or large changes are considered,

$$\Psi = LI$$

and $\quad L = \frac{\Psi}{I} = \frac{N\Phi}{I} \tag{3.14}$

It can thus be said that a circuit has an inductance of 1 henry if 1 weber turn of flux linkage is set up by 1 ampere in the circuit. Regardless of how inductance is defined, it has the important role of relating magnetic and electric systems in terms of the effects on the electric system. It is also a factor of 'goodness' denoting the ability of the system to set up a magnetic field relative to the current required.

Relation 3.14 may be given in instantaneous terms because the inductance of a circuit is not necessarily constant, thus

$$L = \frac{\psi}{i} = \frac{N\phi}{i} \qquad (3.15)$$

where the lower-case letter i denotes the instantaneous current.

The relative values depend on the shape of the magnetisation characteristic, which, in the case of ferromagnetic materials, gives rise to a varying value of relative permeability. In turn, this gives rise to a varying value of the ratio ϕ/i. However, provided the magnetisation characteristic is reasonably linear up to the maximum flux density experienced, the inductance is almost constant.

In cases where there is no ferromagnetic material present, the magnetisation characteristic is a straight line and the self inductance is constant.

The inductance of a circuit depends on the construction of the circuit, the number of turns and the relative permeability of the constituent materials. This may be derived from consideration of a uniform magnetic system such as a toroid in which

$$B = \mu_0\mu_r H$$

$$= \mu_0\mu_r \cdot \frac{NI}{l}$$

$$\Phi = BA$$

$$= \mu_0\mu_r \cdot \frac{NIA}{l}$$

$$L = \frac{N\Phi}{I}$$

$$= \frac{N}{I} \cdot \mu_0\mu_r \cdot \frac{NIA}{l}$$

$$= N^2 \cdot \frac{\mu_0\mu_r A}{l}$$

but $\quad S = \dfrac{l}{\mu_0\mu_r A}$

hence $L = \dfrac{N^2}{S}$ (3.15)

Consideration should be given in passing to some of the units of measurement which have been introduced: by definition

$$L = \frac{N\Phi}{I}$$

It has already been noted that the turn is not a unit of measurement but is a dimensionless factor. Consequently the henry is effectively the weber per ampere.

$$S = \frac{F}{\Phi} = \frac{NI}{\Phi}$$

In the expression for reluctance, it has been seen that the reluctance is equated to current per unit of flux, i.e. it will be measured in amperes per weber. By comparison with the above argument, this unit of measurement is abbreviated to the reciprocal henry.

$$S = \frac{l}{\mu_0 \mu_r A}$$

thus $\mu_r \mu_0 = \mu = \dfrac{l}{SA}$

Hence dimensionally the absolute permeability is measured in metres per square metre per reciprocal henry, which reduces to henrys per metre.

Example 3.6 A wooden toroid of mean diameter 400 mm and cross-sectional area 400 mm^2 is uniformly wound with a coil of 1000 turns, which carries a current of 2·0 A. Determine the self inductance of the coil and the e.m.f. induced in it when the current is uniformly reduced to zero in 10 ms.

$$L = \frac{N^2}{S}$$

where $S = \dfrac{l}{\mu_0 \mu_r A} = \dfrac{0 \cdot 4 \times \pi}{4\pi \times 10^{-7} \times 1 \times 400 \times 10^{-6}}$

$$= 25 \times 10^8 \ /\text{H}$$

$$L = \frac{N^2}{S} = \frac{1000 \times 1000}{25 \times 10^8}$$

$$= 4 \times 10^{-4} \ \text{mH}$$

$$= \underline{0 \cdot 4 \ \text{mH}}$$

$$E = L \cdot \frac{\Delta I}{\Delta t} = 0.4 \times 10^{-3} \times \frac{2}{10 \times 10^{-3}}$$

$$= \underline{0.08 \text{ V}}$$

Example 3.7 A magnetic circuit is shown in Fig. 3.21 and is of uniform cross-sectional area throughout. The ferromagnetic core has a mean length of 220 mm and cross-sectional area 50 mm^2. The air gap has a length of 1·0 mm and the same effective cross-sectional area. A coil of 4000 turns is wound on the core and the magnetic characteristic of the core material is given in Fig. 3.21. Estimate the current in the coil to produce a flux density of 1·0 T in the air gap, assuming that all the flux passes through both parts of the magnetic circuit, and hence determine the inductance of the arrangement.

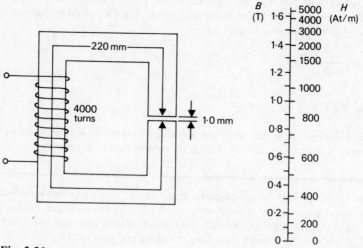

Fig. 3.21

For the core, $B = 1.0$ T
   $H = 905$ At/m from the nomogram
   $F_c = Hl = 905 \times 220 \times 10^{-3} = 199$ At

It will be recalled that for 1·0 T in air, $H = 800\,000$ At/m

thus $F_a = 800\,000 \times 1 \times 10^{-3} = 800$ At
   $F = F_a + F_c = 800 + 199 = 999$ At
   $= IN = 4000 \times I$

$$I = \frac{999}{4000} = \underline{0.25 \text{ A}}$$

$$\Phi = BA = 1 \times 50 \times 10^{-6} = 50 \times 10^{-6} \, \text{Wb}$$

$$L = \frac{N\Phi}{I} = \frac{4000 \times 50 \times 10^{-6}}{0 \cdot 25}$$

$$= \underline{0 \cdot 8 \, \text{H}}$$

It will be noted that in this example, if a different value of flux density had been taken, then the value for inductance obtained would have varied accordingly.

3.7 Induced e.m.f. in a circuit

Whilst the relation

$$E = L \cdot \frac{\Delta I}{\Delta t}$$

gives the magnitude of the e.m.f., there remains the problem of polarity. When a force is applied to a mechanical system, the system reacts by deforming, or by mass-accelerating, or by dissipating or absorbing energy. A comparable state exists when a force (voltage) is applied to an electrical system, which accelerates (accepts magnetic energy in an inductor) or dissipates energy in heat (in a resistor). The comparable state to deformation is the acceptance of potential energy in a capacitor, which is dealt with in Chapter 4. In the case of a series circuit containing resistance and inductance then

$$V = IR + L \cdot \frac{\Delta I}{\Delta t}$$

There are now two schools of thought as to how to proceed. One says

$$V = V_R + E_L$$

The other school says

$$V = V_R - E_L$$
$$= V_R + V_L$$

This recognises that

$$E = -L \cdot \frac{\Delta I}{\Delta t}$$

The idea behind this second interpretation is a wish to identify active circuit components. These include batteries, generators and (because they store energy) inductors and capacitors. A charged capacitor can act like a battery for a short time, and certainly a battery possesses an e.m.f. which, when a battery is part of a circuit fed from a source of voltage, acts against the passage of current through it from the positive terminal to the negative terminal. Similarly an inductor opposes the increase of current in it by acting against the applied voltage with an opposing e.m.f.

The first school of thought would reply that the only voltage to be measured is a component of the voltage applied and this is

$$V_L = +L \cdot \frac{\Delta I}{\Delta t}$$

Both arguments are acceptable and the reader will find both systems have wider application. Although the International Electrotechnical Commission prefer the second method, for the purposes of this text the positive version will be used. The choice is a matter of convention.

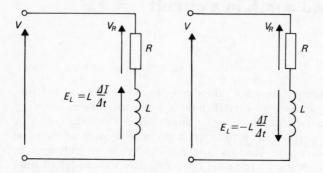

Fig. 3.22 Polarity of e.m.f. in a circuit diagram

It will be noted that the positive version of the relation appears to be more logical in a circuit diagram. In Fig. 3.22, both versions are considered. If the induced e.m.f. is taken as an effective voltage drop, it may be represented by an arrow pointing upwards. If the negative version is used, the arrow must point in the direction of the current flow.

Example 3.8 A coil having a resistance of 4 Ω and an inductance of 0·08 H has a current passed through it which varies as follows:

(a) uniform increase from 0 to 5 A in 0·25 s;
(b) constant at 5 A for 0·5 s;
(c) uniform decrease from 5 to 0 A in 1·0 s.

Plot graphs representing the current, the induced e.m.f. and the applied voltage.

During the period of increasing current,

$$E_a = L \cdot \frac{\Delta I}{\Delta t} = 0 \cdot 8 \times \frac{5}{0 \cdot 25} = 16 \text{ V}$$

During the period of steady current,

$V_b = IR = 5 \times 4 = 20$ V

During the period of decreasing current,

$$E_c = L \cdot \frac{\Delta I}{\Delta t} = 0.8 \times \frac{-5}{1.0} = -4 \text{ V}$$

The graph of the current can now be drawn as shown in Fig. 3.23.

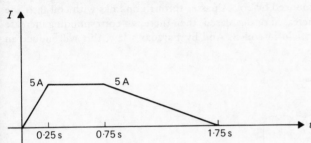

Fig. 3.23

The applied voltage graph is obtained by first drawing the graph of the voltage drop across the resistance. This voltage drop is added to the induced e.m.f. to obtain the applied voltage as shown in Fig. 3.24.

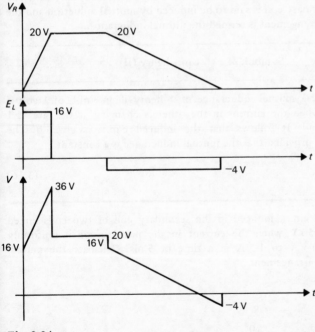

Fig. 3.24

3.8 Mutual inductance

It has been shown that an e.m.f. may be induced in a circuit due to its magnetic field being varied. However, if another coil forming part of a separate circuit also lay in the magnetic field, then it also would have an e.m.f. induced in it due to the change of flux linkage.

If two coils are placed adjacent to one another as shown in Fig. 3.25, a part of the flux produced by coil A passes through on links with coil B. If the field of coil A is increased or decreased, then there is a corresponding increase or decrease in the field in coil B. And by Faraday's law, this will induce an e.m.f. in coil B.

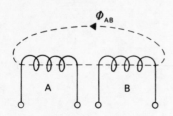

Fig. 3.25 Two coils linked by a mutual flux

Coil A, the coil that is connected to the supply and that produces the original flux, is called the primary coil; coil B is called the secondary coil. The e.m.f. in the secondary coil is said to be induced by mutual induction and the property of the arrangement is termed the mutual inductance.

Mutual inductance   **Symbol:** M **Unit: henry (H)**

Two circuits have a mutual inductance of 1 henry if an e.m.f. of 1 volt is induced in one when the current in the other is changing at the rate of 1 ampere per second. It follows that the induced e.m.f. is given by the following relation provided that the mutual inductance is a constant.

$$E = M \cdot \frac{\Delta I}{\Delta t} \tag{3.16}$$

Example 3.9 The e.m.f. induced in the secondary coil of two coils linked magnetically is 250 V when the current in the primary coil is uniformly increased from 0·5 A to 1·5 A in a time of 5 ms. Calculate the mutual inductance of the arrangement.

$$E = M \cdot \frac{\Delta I}{\Delta t}$$

$$250 = M \times \frac{1 \cdot 5 - 0 \cdot 5}{5 \times 10^{-3}} = M \times \frac{10^3}{5}$$

$$M = \frac{250 \times 5}{10^3} = \underline{1 \cdot 25 \text{ H}}$$

The e.m.f. induced in the secondary coil takes one polarity when the mutual field increases and takes the opposite polarity when the field decreases. These polarities may be obtained by application of the right-hand rule, which is merely an application of Lenz's law in that the e.m.f.s induced will attempt to maintain the existing field.

If the two coils were series-connected, then it would be necessary to know the manner in which one was wound with respect to the other. This could be done pictorially but most electrical diagrams use symbols, in which case a notation is required to indicate the effect of the mutual inductance. Depending on the physical winding of the secondary coil, the direction of any flux it may create may add to or subtract from the flux of the primary coil; thus for two circuits with mutual inductive coupling, the relative directions of the e.m.f.s in each winding depend on the relative directions of the turns and the relative position of the windings.

One system of defining the directions is the dot notation. At any instant, it may be considered that current is entering the first coil at one particular end. This end is indicated by placing a dot beside it. A second dot is placed at the end of the second coil at which current would have to enter at the same instant to give additive flux. These dots are indicated on a diagram as shown in Fig. 3.26.

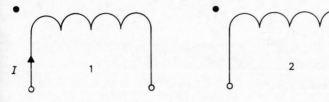

Fig. 3.26 Dot notation

The relative e.m.f. directions can now be derived. Suppose a voltage is applied to the first coil. If this makes the 'dotted' end positive with respect to the 'undotted' end, then current enters at the dotted end and increases in magnitude due to the increase in p.d. across the coil. This change in current causes e.m.f.s to be set up in the first coil due to the self flux linkages increasing, and in the second coil due to the mutual flux linkages increasing. The e.m.f. in the first coil opposes the current and so makes the dotted end positive with respect to the undotted end, i.e. it opposes the change in flux linkages as we would expect from Lenz's law. Also the e.m.f. induced in the second coil will make current leave at the dotted end of this coil. Hence in both coils, both dotted ends are driven simultaneously positive with respect to the undotted ends.

It follows that it would have been possible to connect the two coils in series in two ways such that they would be mutually linked. These ways are

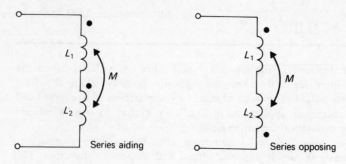

Fig. 3.27 Series connections of mutually-coupled coils

such that the common current enters or leaves both coils at the dotted ends, i.e. both produce flux in the same direction, or such that, while the current enters the dotted end of one coil, it leaves the dotted end of the other. These arrangements are termed series aiding and series opposing respectively. Circuit connection diagrams are shown in Fig. 3.27.

In the first case, suppose the current to be changing with the rate $\Delta I/\Delta t$. The total induced e.m.f. in the circuit is given by the self-induced e.m.f.s plus the mutually-induced e.m.f.s. In the aiding connection, the e.m.f.s are all driving the dotted ends positive with respect to the undotted ends.

$$E = L_1 \cdot \frac{\Delta I}{\Delta t} + L_2 \cdot \frac{\Delta I}{\Delta t} + M \cdot \frac{\Delta I}{\Delta t} + M \cdot \frac{\Delta I}{\Delta t}$$

$$= (L_1 + L_2 + 2M) \cdot \frac{\Delta I}{\Delta t}$$

$$= L \cdot \frac{\Delta I}{\Delta t}$$

where L is the effective inductance of the circuit,

$$L = L_1 + L_2 + 2M \tag{3.17}$$

If the two coils are connected in opposition then the polarity of the mutually-induced e.m.f.s is reversed, hence

$$E = L_1 \cdot \frac{\Delta I}{\Delta t} + L_2 \cdot \frac{\Delta I}{\Delta t} - M \cdot \frac{\Delta I}{\Delta t} - M \cdot \frac{\Delta I}{\Delta t}$$

$$= (L_1 + L_2 - 2M) \cdot \frac{\Delta I}{\Delta t}$$

thus $L = L_1 + L_2 - 2M$ \hfill (3.18)

Example 3.10 Two identical coils are connected in series aiding on the same magnetic former. The self inductance of each coil is 2 H. Assuming that there is not flux leakage between the coils, calculate the total inductance of the arrangement.

Since the coils are identical and there is no leakage of flux between the coils, then the flux of one coil must induce the same e.m.f. in the other coil as it does in itself and therefore

$$L_1 = L_2 = M$$
hence $L = L_1 + L_2 + 2M$
$$= 2 + 2 + (2 \times 2)$$
$$= \underline{8 \text{ H}}$$

The result of this example compares with the relation that $L \propto N^2$. By connecting the two coils in series aiding, the arrangement is similar to that of doubling the number of turns in the coil of an inductor, in which case the inductance becomes four times greater as instanced in this example.

Example 3.11 Two identical coils, when connected in series can either have an effective inductance of 10 H or 2 H. Find the self and mutual inductances of the coils.

$$L = L_1 + L_2 \pm 2M = 2L \pm 2M \text{ since the coils are identical.}$$
$$10 = 2L + 2M$$
and $\qquad 2 = 2L - 2M$
hence $\qquad 12 = 4L$
and $\qquad L = \underline{3 \text{ H}}$
Substituting $10 = 6 + 2M$
thus $\qquad M = \underline{2 \text{ H}}$

Example 3.12 Two coils, A and B, are so placed that 80 per cent of the total flux produced by one links with the other. Both coils are air-cored and are identical, except that coil A has 2000 turns and coil B has 3000 turns. When the current in A is changing at the rate 500 A/s, the flux linking it is changing at the rate 1 mWb/s. Determine:

(a) the corresponding e.m.f. induced in each coil;
(b) the self inductance of each coil;
(c) the mutual inductance between the coils;
(d) the effective inductance of the two coils connected in series opposition.

(a) $\qquad E_A = N_A \cdot \dfrac{\Delta \Phi}{\Delta t} = 2000 \times 1 \times 10^{-3} = \underline{2 \cdot 0 \text{ V}}$

$\qquad E_B = N_B \cdot \dfrac{\Delta \Phi}{\Delta t} = 3000 \times 0 \cdot 8 \times 1 \times 10^{-3} = \underline{2 \cdot 4 \text{ V}}$

(b) $\qquad E_A = L_A \cdot \dfrac{\Delta I_A}{\Delta t} = L_A \times 500 = 2 \cdot 0 \text{ V}$

Thus $L_A = 4 \times 10^{-3}$ H $= 4 \cdot 0$ mH

Since the coils are identical other than the number of turns in each then

$$L \propto N^2$$

$$\frac{L_A}{L_B} = \frac{N_A{}^2}{N_B{}^2} = \frac{4 \times 10^{-3}}{L_B} = \frac{2000^2}{3000^2}$$

Thus $L_B = 9 \times 10^{-3}$ H $= \underline{9 \cdot 0 \text{ mH}}$

(c) $\qquad E_B = M \cdot \dfrac{\Delta I_A}{\Delta t} = 2 \cdot 4 = M \times 500$

$$M = 4 \cdot 8 \times 10^{-3} \text{ H} = \underline{4 \cdot 8 \text{ mH}}$$

(d) $\qquad L = L_A + L_B - 2M = 4 + 9 - (2 \times 4 \cdot 8) = \underline{3 \cdot 4 \text{ mH}}$

If two coils were so mounted that the turns of one coil were as close to those of the other as possible, then it might be reasonable to assume that the whole of the flux produced by the current in one coil would link with all of the turns of the other coil. Let the reluctance of the magnetic circuit be S, which is common, and let the quantities relating to the primary coil have the suffix 1, and those of the secondary coil the suffix 2; thus

$$L_1 = \frac{N_1 \Phi_1}{I_1} = \frac{N_1{}^2}{S}$$

and $L_2 = \dfrac{N_2 \Phi_2}{I_2} = \dfrac{N_2{}^2}{S}$

thus $S = \dfrac{I_1 N_1}{\Phi_1} = \dfrac{I_2 N_2}{\Phi_2}$

Because the whole of flux Φ_1 due to the current I_1 is linked with coil 2, it follows that

$$M = \frac{N_2 \Phi_1}{I_1}$$

$$= \frac{N_1 N_2 \Phi_1}{I_1 N_1}$$

$$= \frac{N_1 N_2}{S} \qquad\qquad (3.19)$$

hence $M^2 = \dfrac{N_1{}^2}{S} \cdot \dfrac{N_2{}^2}{S}$

$$= L_1 L_2$$
$$\text{and} \qquad M = (L_1 L_2)^{1/2} \tag{3.20}$$

The derivation of the above expressions is based on the assumption that all the magnetic flux produced by one coil passes through the other, i.e. there is no magnetic flux leakage. When there is leakage, then

$$M = k(L_1 L_2)^{1/2} \tag{3.21}$$

where k is termed the coupling coefficient. The term indicates the factor of goodness of the coupling between the two coils and the coupling coefficient is often used in electronic work, especially in radio and other communications systems.

Example 3.13 A ferromagnetic-cored coil is in two sections. One section has an inductance of 0·9 H and the other an inductance of 0·1 H. The coefficient of coupling is 0·5. Calculate:

(a) the mutual inductance;
(b) the total inductance, when the sections are connected first in series aiding and then in series opposing.

$$M = k(L_1 L_2)^{1/2} = 0.5(0.9 \times 0.1)^{1/2}$$
$$= \underline{0.15 \text{ H}}$$

Aiding $\qquad L = L_1 + L_2 + 2M = 0.9 + 0.1 + (2 \times 0.15)$
$$= \underline{1.3 \text{ H}}$$

Opposing $\quad L = L_1 + L_2 - 2M = 0.9 + 0.1 - (2 \times 0.15)$
$$= \underline{0.7 \text{ H}}$$

A direct application of coils linked by mutual inductance is that of the transformer, which is a mutual-induction device used to change the value of alternating voltages. The transformer consists of two windings wound on the same ferromagnetic core but the coils are electrically separate. The arrangement is shown in Fig. 3.28.

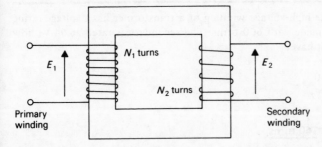

Fig. 3.28 Simple transformer

When an alternating voltage is applied to the primary winding, an alternating current results in the winding. This current gives rise to an alternating flux, i.e. one that increases up to a maximum value then decreases to zero before building up to the same maximum magnitude but acting in the opposite direction; on decreasing, it reduces to zero and commences to repeat the same cycle of events. The varying flux induces an alternating e.m.f. in the secondary winding and this e.m.f. is directly proportional to the number of turns in the secondary winding, since by Lenz's law,

$$E = N \cdot \frac{\Delta \Phi}{\Delta t}$$

The flux linking the coils is the same in each case hence the e.m.f. induced in the primary winding, E_1, is given by

$$E_1 = N_1 \cdot \frac{\Delta \Phi}{\Delta t}$$

Similarly $E_2 = N_2 \cdot \dfrac{\Delta \Phi}{\Delta t}$

Thus $\qquad \dfrac{E_1}{E_2} = \dfrac{N_1}{N_2}$ \hfill (3.22)

The ratio E_1/E_2 is termed the voltage ratio of the transformer and the ratio N_1/N_2 is termed the turns ratio of the transformer. If the secondary voltage is greater than the primary voltage then the transformer is said to be a step-up transformer, since the effect of it is to step up the voltage. This requires that the number of turns in the secondary winding be greater than the primary winding. Conversely a step-down transformer has fewer turns in the secondary winding that in the primary.

Notice that the e.m.f. induced in each turn of each winding is the same, i.e.

$$E = \frac{\Delta \Phi}{\Delta t} = \frac{E_1}{N_1} = \frac{E_2}{N_2}$$

Example 3.14 The high-voltage winding of a transformer has a voltage rating of 240 V and is made with 600 turns. The secondary is rated at 64 V; how many turns does it have?

$$\frac{E_1}{E_2} = \frac{N_1}{N_2} = \frac{240}{64} = \frac{600}{N_2}$$

$$N_2 = 600 \times \frac{64}{240} = \underline{160 \text{ turns}}$$

The transformer provides the basis for one of the main advantages of a.c. transmission and distribution: the ease with which the operating voltage can be increased or decreased. It is usual practice to distribute energy at such voltages as 11 kV and 33 kV whilst bulk transmission from one part of the country to another takes place at 275 kV and 400 kV. At those smaller areas in which the energy is to be applied, the voltage is reduced by transformer to 240 V for household purposes and 415 V for commercial purposes. Transformers have efficiencies of 96—98 per cent so that the energy required for transformation is very small.

Transformers also have a wide range of uses in light-current applications. Apart from changing voltages, they can also be used to induce an e.m.f. into a circuit otherwise completely electrically separate from the primary, which can be most important in certain electronic configurations. Finally the transformer may be used to optimise the power output of a system by matching the source (e.g. a microphone) or the load (e.g. a loudspeaker) to the system.

3.9 Energy storage in inductors

In the circuit shown in Fig. 3.29, the closing of the switch causes a current to flow. In the course of time, the current achieves a steady value given by

$$I = \frac{V}{R}$$

During the period of change, while the current is increasing, an e.m.f. is induced in the inductor due to the change in the flux linkage, caused by the increasing current. This e.m.f. opposes the current, which therefore is flowing against the e.m.f. As the current increases, the rate of change falls in value, so in turn the back e.m.f. falls thus permitting further increase in current.

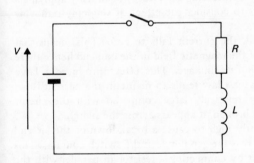

Fig. 3.29 Energy storage

Potential energy is stored by a magnetic field so that when a current grows to a steady value, a definite amount of potential energy is stored in the magnetic field. The power dissipated into the magnetic field at any instant is given by EI. The e.m.f. will equal the applied voltage unless there is a further voltage drop due to resistance in the coil of the inductor. For simplicity, assume that the current rises steadily from zero to a final value I in a time t, thus

$$E = \frac{LI}{t}$$

The mean current during the changing period is $\frac{1}{2}I$ since the current increases at a steady rate. Thus the energy supplied to the field, W_f, is given by

$$W_f = E \cdot \tfrac{1}{2}I \cdot t$$
$$= \tfrac{1}{2}LI^2 \qquad\qquad (3.23)$$

It can be shown that this result holds true no matter the method whereby it is derived.

If two inductors are connected in series and can act mutually then the potential energy stored is again $\frac{1}{2}LI^2$, where L is the effective inductance of the system. In the case of series-opposed coils:

$$L = L_1 + L_2 - 2M$$
$$W_f = \tfrac{1}{2}LI^2$$
$$= \tfrac{1}{2}(L_1 + L_2 - 2M)I^2$$
$$= \tfrac{1}{2}L_1I^2 + \tfrac{1}{2}L_2I^2 - MI^2 \qquad\qquad (3.24)$$

The negative sign may be interpreted as that of potential energy due to the mutual inductance, which is in opposition to the potential energy due to the self inductance. Similarly the expression for series-aiding coils is:

$$W_f = \tfrac{1}{2}L_1I^2 + \tfrac{1}{2}L_2I^2 + MI^2 \qquad\qquad (3.25)$$

This section commenced by considering the effect of suddenly applying a direct p.d. to a coil. It remains to consider the effect of suddenly removing this p.d.

When the switch is opened, the current falls to zero. This means that there will be a rapid collapse of the magnetic field in the coil and hence there will be a rapid change in the flux linkage. This effect produces a large self-induced e.m.f., which by Lenz's law tends to maintain the current flow. The induced e.m.f. is usually relatively large compared with the circuit voltages and, since the circuit is broken, it appears across the switch.

Such an e.m.f. is sufficiently high to cause a breakdown of the air and hence cause a spark to jump across the gap between the switch contacts. This can be avoided to some extent by connecting a resistor in parallel with the inductor as shown in Fig. 3.30. The parallel resistor permits the self-induced e.m.f. to create a current round the closed loop thus dissipating the energy in the magnetic field.

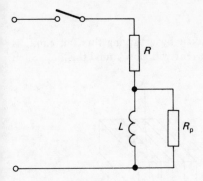

Fig. 3.30 Dissipation of stored energy

Example 3.15 A coil of fixed inductance 4·0 H and effective resistance 30 Ω is suddenly connected to a 100-V, d.c. supply. What is the rate of energy storage in the field of the coil at each of the following instants:

(a) when the current is 1·0 A;

(b) when the current is 2·0 A;

(c) when the current is at its final steady value;

What is the final energy stored in the field?

(a) When the current is 1·0 A, the voltage drop across the resistance is 1 × 30 = 30 V; thus the voltage drop across the inductance is

100 − 30 = 70 V

The rate of energy storage in the field is therefore

$$EI = 70 \times 1 = \underline{70 \text{ W}}$$

(b) When the current is 2·0 A, the voltage drop across the resistance is 2 × 30 = 60 V, thus the voltage drop across the inductance is

100 − 60 = 40 V

The rate of energy storage in the field is therefore

$$EI = 40 \times 2 = \underline{80 \text{ W}}$$

(c) When the current has reached its final steady value, all the voltage drop appears across the resistance and therefore the e.m.f. is zero. This being the case, there is no transfer of energy to the field.

$$I = \frac{V}{R} = \frac{100}{30} = 3 \cdot 33 \text{ A}$$

$$W_f = \tfrac{1}{2}LI^2 = \tfrac{1}{2} \times 4 \times 3 \cdot 33^2 = \underline{22 \cdot 18 \text{ J}}$$

3.10 Eddy currents

If a loop of conducting material is linked by a varying flux, an e.m.f. is induced in the loop and a circulating current will flow round the loop. Such

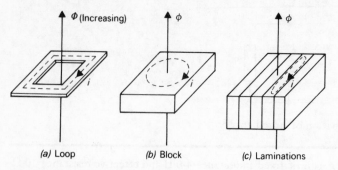

(a) Loop   *(b)* Block   *(c)* Laminations

Fig. 3.31 Eddy-current arrangements

an arrangement is shown in Fig. 3.31(*a*). The current in the loop is termed an eddy current. The eddy current flows round a path of one turn which is effectively a short-circuit.

Had the loop been replaced by a block of conducting material, a similar system of eddy currents would result in the block. In either case, eddy currents give rise to a power loss in the resistance of the eddy current path. The loss is called the eddy-current power loss.

From Lenz's law, the eddy currents flow in a direction such that their magnetic effects oppose the flux linkage changes. At high frequencies eddy currents may radically alter the flux distribution in the loop or block. However, thin sheets at low frequencies such as 50 Hz experience little alteration to the flux; generally this effect may be neglected at low frequencies.

The eddy-current power loss may be shown to be proportional to the square of the cross-sectional area normal to the direction of the field, to the square of the maximum flux density, to the square of the frequency, and inversely proportional to the resistivity of the material from which the loop or block is made. To minimise the loss only the cross-sectional area and the resistivity can be varied for any given material.

The net area of the core of a magnetic circuit cannot be reduced since this is determined by the required flux and the maximum permissible flux density, but the area can be divided into smaller sections. This is achieved by making the core from a number of thin sheets, called laminations – shown in Fig. 3.31(*c*) – which are lightly insulated from one another, e.g. by an oxide. This reduces the area of each section and hence the induced e.m.f. It also increases the resistance of the eddy-current paths since the area through which the currents can pass is smaller. Both effects combine to reduce the current and hence the power loss. The thickness of the laminations is therefore a factor in determining the eddy-current power loss. Further reductions can be obtained by using a material of higher resistivity.

Lamination is only one possible method of splitting up the eddy currents. The thickness of the ferromagnetic components can be reduced in any of the following ways:

1. by the use of laminations already discussed;
2. by making the magnetic circuit from wire (unusual);
3. by using a ferromagnetic dust core;
4. by making the core from a suitable ferrite material.

The following precautions should therefore be taken to minimise the core loss, which is the sum of the hysteresis and eddy-current power losses, in an electromagnetic system:

(a) the flux density should be kept as economically low as possible;
(b) the core should be made from a material with a relatively small hysteresis loop;
(c) the core material should have high resistivity;
(d) the magnetic circuit should be laminated or similarly broken up.

Finally it should be noted that eddy currents have many useful applications and need not be considered as imperfections of an electromagnetic system. Energy meters and eddy-current brakes depend on eddy currents for their principle of operation whilst localised heating may be induced by eddy currents.

Problems

1. A straight wire 0·1 m long carries a current 100 A and lies at right angles to a uniform magnetic field of density 1·0 T. Find the mechanical force on the conductor.
2. Two busbars (conductors made of solid bar metal) are held 100 mm apart and are supported by insulators every metre along their length. The busbars each carry a current 15 kA. What is the force acting on each insulator?
3. The plane of a square coil makes an angle of 45° with the direction of a uniform magnetic field of density 0·4 T. If the coil has sides 100 mm long and is wound with 500 turns, calculate the current that must flow to produce a torque 3·0 Nm about the neutral axis of the coil.
4. An e.m.f. of 1·5 V is induced in a straight conductor which moves with a velocity 5·0 m/s perpendicular to a magnetic field of density 0·75 T. Calculate the effective length of the conductor.
5. A magnetic flux linking 1800 turns of an electromagnet's coil changes uniformly from 0·6 mWb to 0·5 mWb in 50 ms. Find the average induced e.m.f.
6. A conductor of effective length 250 mm moves with velocity 5 m/s perpendicular to a magnetic field of uniform flux density 0·4 T. Calculate:

(*a*) the e.m.f. induced in the conductor;

(*b*) the force acting on the conductor when it carries a current 20 A;

(*c*) the power required to drive the conductor.

Give a diagram of the relative directions of the field, the motion of the conductor and the induced e.m.f.

7. A straight wire 1·0 m long carries a current 100 mA and lies at right angles to a uniform magnetic field of density 1·5 T. Find the force on the conductor and also the power to move it at a speed 10 m/s in a plane at right angles to the field.

8. A coil of 1000 turns gives rise to a flux 1·5 mWb when passing a given current. If this current is reversed in 0·2 s, what is the average e.m.f. induced in the coil?

9. An average e.m.f. 100 V is induced in a 400-turn coil when the coil is passed through a field of flux 20 μWb. Determine the time taken to pass through the field.

10. A current 4 A produces a flux 4·8 μWb in an air-cored coil of 1600 turns. What is the inductance of the coil?

11. An air-cored coil of inductance 4·5 mH has an axial length 314 mm and a cross-sectional area 500 mm^2. How many turns are there in the coil?

12. A current 2·5 A flows through a 1000-turn coil wound on a rod of Perspex. The coil inductance is 0·6 H. What magnetic flux is set up?

13. A ferromagnetic circuit has a uniform cross-sectional area 500 mm^2 and a mean diameter 200 mm. The relative permeability of the ferromagnetic material is 2000 and the flux density in it is 1·5 T. Calculate the reluctance of the magnetic circuit and the inductance of a 200-turn coil wound on it.

14. A 2000-turn coil is uniformly wound on a wooden ring of mean diameter 320 mm and cross-sectional area 400 mm^2. Calculate the inductance of the toroid so formed.

15. What is the e.m.f. induced in a 500-μH coil when the current is changing at the rate 4000 A/s?

16. An air-cored coil is 1·0 m long and 60 mm in diameter, and has 5000 turns of wire wound on it. Calculate the inductance of the coil.

A 500-turn coil of 40 mm diameter is placed axially in the centre of the previous coil, and a current of 3·0 A in the 5000-turn coil is reversed at a uniform rate in 10 ms. Calculate the e.m.f. induced in the 500-turn coil.

17. A 100-turn coil is uniformly wound on a nylon ring of mean diameter 200 mm and cross-sectional area 800 mm^2. Determine:

(*a*) the magnetic field strength at the mean circumference of the ring when the coil current is 2·0 A;

(*b*) the current required to produce a flux 1·0 μWb;

(*c*) the self inductance of the coil.

18. A coil having resistance 3 kΩ and inductance 0·3 H passes a current through it which varies as follows:

(*a*) uniform increase from 8 mA to 12 mA in 0·2 ms;

(*b*) constant at 12 mA for 0·5 ms;

 (c) uniform fall to 0 A in 0·8 ms.

  Plot graphs representing the variations of current, induced e.m.f. and applied voltage.

19. A coil of resistance 20 Ω and inductance 0·1 H is connected to a source of current which rises uniformly from 0 to 2 A in 10 ms, remains constant at 2 A for 20 ms, and falls uniformly to 0 in 5 ms. Plot to scale graphs showing the variations with time of:

 (a) the voltage drop across the resistance;

 (b) the induced e.m.f.;

 (c) the p.d. across the circuit.

20. If an e.m.f. 10 V is induced in a coil when the current in a second coil varies at the rate 200 A/s, what is the mutual inductance of the two coils?

21. Two identical coils are inductively linked together so that when they are connected in series, they may either give an effective inductance of 8 H or 4 H. Calculate the self inductance of each coil and the mutual inductance between them.

22. A mutual inductor is constructed by winding a primary coil of 723 turns uniformly on a cylindrical former over a length 840 mm and placing a second coil of 1000 turns wound on a diameter of 31·8 mm coaxially within the primary coil. Assuming the field within the primary coil to be uniform and the reluctance of the magnetic circuit outside the coil to be negligible, calculate the mutual inductance between the two coils.

23. Two coils A and B are inductively coupled. The self inductance of coil A is 380 μH and of coil B is 540 μH. When the coils are connected in series-aiding, the total inductance is 1500 μH. Calculate:

 (a) the mutual inductance between the coils;

 (b) the total inductance if the connections to coil B are reversed.

24. A 1200-turn coil passes a current 3·0 A and is consequently linked by a flux 20 mWb. Calculate:

 (a) the inductance of the coil;

 (b) the energy stored in the magnetic field;

 (c) the average induced e.m.f. if the circuit is interrupted in 0·1 s.

25. A current 15 A flows through a coil of inductance 60 mH. If the circuit is interrupted in 15 ms, calculate the energy dissipated and the average rate of dissipation.

26. Two coils have self inductances 30 mH and 14 mH and mutual inductance 6 mH. The current in the coils when connected in series is 2 A. Determine the two values of energy that may be stored in the resulting arrangements.

27. A transformer is supplied from a 240-V supply and its primary winding has 80 turns. If the secondary winding has 200 turns, what is the induced e.m.f. in the secondary winding?

28. A 240/110-V transformer has a secondary winding of 350 turns. Determine the number of turns in the primary winding.

1. 10 N
2. 450 N
3. 2·12 A
4. 0·4 m
5. 3·6 V
6. 0·5 V, 2·0 N, 10 W
7. 0·15 N, 1·5 W
8. 15 V
9. 80 μs
10. 1·92 mH
11. 1500 turns
12. 1·5 mWb
13. 500 000 /H, 0·08 H
14. 2 mH
15. 2 V
16. 88·8 mH, 2·37 V
17. 318 At/m, 6·24 A, 64 μH

18.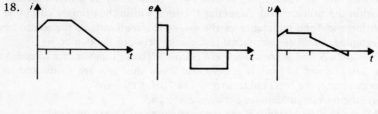

19.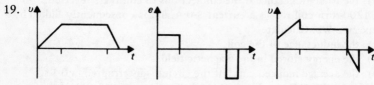

20. 0·05 H
21. 3 H, 1 H
22. 860 μH
23. 290 μH, 340 μH
24. 8 H, 36 J, 240 V
25. 6·75 J, 450 W
26. 0·112 J, 0·064 J
27. 600 V
28. 764 turns

Chapter 4

Capacitors and capacitance

Electrostatics is the study of electric fields set up by the presence of charges of electricity in systems of conductors and insulators. Its study leads to an understanding of the capacitance effects found in all circuits. Capacitance is particularly important in electronic and communication circuits, yet its more minor role in power systems is quite significant.

4.1 Properties of an electric field

When a current flows at the rate of one ampere, the charge that passes through a cross-section of the conductor during a period of one second is one coulomb. The coulomb is the unit of electrical charge.

If a current can be arranged to flow into a body during a finite period of time, the body will acquire a charge. Since conventional current is the flow of positive charge (i.e. it is the opposite of the electron flow which actually takes place from negative to positive in an electrical system), the body will acquire a positive charge. Conversely, if the current had been arranged to flow from the body, it would become deficient in positive charge and would therefore acquire a negative charge. Prior to such effects being imposed on it, the uncharged body would have had an equal number of positive and of negative charges due to the balance of its atomic structure. After this balance has been upset, the body will try to regain its original condition, and this action takes the form of positive and negative charges searching for one another.

At this point, it is worth looking at some simple experiments that you could carry out to observe these interactions between electrical charges. First there is a test that requires two glass rods, one of which is suspended by a thread tied round the middle of the rod as shown in Fig. 4.1. Both rods are rubbed with a silk cloth and then the free rod is held in the indicated position close to the suspended rod. The result is that the suspended rod turns away from the held rod.

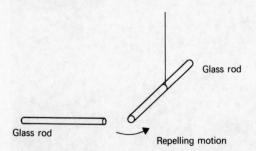

Fig. 4.1 Interaction between charged glass rods

Because each rod was treated in the same manner, it is reasonable to conclude that each has the same electrical effect. Further, since the rods have repelled one another, then similar or like effects repel one another.

This test may now be compared with another in which a rod of ebony is rubbed with a woollen cloth and the rod held in the position shown in Fig. 4.2, relative to the same glass rod still under the influence of having been rubbed with a silk cloth. In this case, the glass rod turns towards the ebony rod.

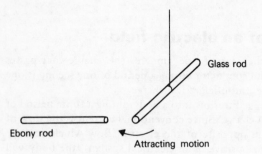

Fig. 4.2 Interaction between a charged ebony rod and a charged glass rod

Because there has been a change of material used and of the resulting action, it may be observed that there must be an alternative form of electrical effect and further, since the rods have been attracted to one another, then dissimilar or unlike effects attract one another.

These electrical effects are caused by the rods having been charged by their interactions with the cloths. Either the rods have lost charge to the cloths or the cloths have lost charge to the rods — whichever it is, the transfer of electrons from one to the other has lead in one case to there being an excess of electrons on the held rod, and a deficiency of electrons on the other held rod. From the experiments, it is not possible to say which is which but it is possible to say that the effects observed are due to the interaction of the electrical charges and therefore the rule may be formulated that:

Like charges repel, unlike charges attract.

This may be expressed diagramatically as shown in Fig. 4.3.

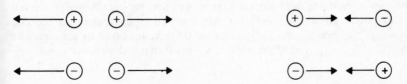

Fig. 4.3 Interaction of electrical charges

Many more such experiments need to be carried out to determine the precise nature of the interchange of charge that has been observed in the experiments described, but they would show that rubbing the glass rods with the silk cloth removes electrons from the glass rods, leaving the rods in a state of positive charge, whilst the silk has a negative charge due to the electrons it has acquired.

Conversely, the ebony has acquired electrons from the wool and therefore has become negatively charged, whilst the wool has taken on a positive charge.

However, these conventions are relatively unimportant compared with the principal observation — unlike charges attract! It is for this reason that positive and negative charges, no matter where they may be situated, search one another out. These forces of attraction may be very strong, and their effects are increased by the repulsion that like charges have for one another.

The space surrounding a charge can be investigated using a small charged body. This investigation is similar to that applied to the magnetic field surrounding a current-carrying conductor. However, in this case, the charged body is either attracted or repelled by the charge under investigation. The space in which this effect can be observed is termed the electric field of the charge. The force on the small charged body defines the strength of this field and is termed the electric force.

As in the magnetic case, the lines of force can be traced out. These lines are again given certain properties:

1.   In an electric field, each line of force will emanate from or terminate in a

charge. The conventional direction of the line is from a positive charge to a negative charge.

2. The direction of the line is that of the force experienced by a positive charge placed at a point in the electric field. (It is assumed that the search charge has no effect on the field distribution.)

3. The lines of force never intersect, since the resultant force at any point in an electric field can have only one direction.

It should be noted that whilst it is possible to observe the electric force acting on a small charged body in principle, it is extremely difficult to obtain experimental verification of the field distribution, and indirect methods generally have to be used.

The force of attraction or repulsion acts directly between two adjacent charges. The lines of force therefore always radiate out from equipotential surfaces at right angles (a surface that is equipotential has the same potential at all points on it). A conductor will have an equipotential surface and therefore all lines of force will be normal (at right angles) to its surfaces. The most simple case is that of the isolated spherical charge shown in Fig. 4.4.

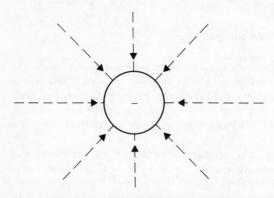

Fig. 4.4 Electric field about an isolated spherical charge

Most electric fields exist between two conductors having equal but opposite charges. Two important arrangements of conductors are parallel plates and concentric cylinders. The former appears in practical form in many capacitors whilst the latter has the cross-sectional form of a coaxial cable. The appropriate fields are shown in Fig. 4.5.

In the arrangements shown in Fig. 4.5, it is important that the charges be kept apart. They must therefore be insulated from one another although they are held in the conducting materials. The intervening space between the charges is filled with any insulating material which, in the context of electric fields, is termed a dielectric. Suitable dielectrics include air, paper, nylon, mica and ceramic.

Finally it will be noted that although equipotential surfaces occur in

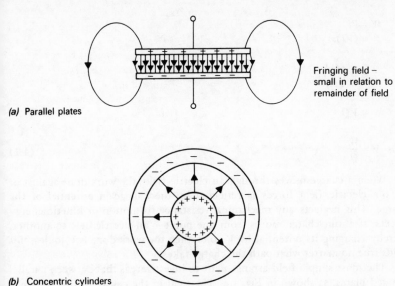

(a) Parallel plates

Fringing field –
small in relation to
remainder of field

(b) Concentric cylinders
(cable)

Fig. 4.5 Electric fields between oppositely charged surfaces

conductors, they need not occur in insulators. It is quite possible that all the excess charge remains for a long period of time on the surface of one part only of an insulator. It will be remembered that an insulator is a very poor conductor and therefore is unable to redistribute the charge about its surface in the manner of a conductor. Nevertheless, given time the charge will be dissipated, no insulator or dielectric being perfect.

4.2 Electric field strength and electric potential

An electric field is investigated by observing its effect on a charge. Suppose the charge is small enough not to disturb the configuration of the field. The magnitude of the force experienced at a point in a field by this charge is termed the electric field strength at that point. It may be measured in newtons per coulomb of charge and represented by the symbol E. It can also be termed the electric stress or electrostatic field strength.

It should be noted that a coulomb is a very large charge and it would disrupt the field being investigated. However, as the force is expressed in terms of newtons per coulomb, a much smaller quantity of charge may be used from which this ratio of newtons per coulomb may be derived.

From the definition of the volt, one joule of energy is required to raise the potential of one coulomb of charge through one volt. This may be shown as follows:

$$W = Pt$$
$$= (VI)t$$

$$= V\left(\frac{Q}{t}\right)t$$

$$= VQ$$

thus $V = \dfrac{W}{Q}$ $\qquad\qquad\qquad\qquad\qquad\qquad\qquad$ (4.1)

When a charge moves through an electric field, the work done against or by the electric field forces is reflected by the change in potential of the charge. This neglects any mechanical resistance to motion or kinetic energy effects. If a unit charge moves from one point in an electric field to another, thereby charging its potential by V volts, then the work done is V joules; this holds true no matter what path the charge takes.

The most simple field arrangement to investigate is that between parallel charged plates, as shown in Fig. 4.6. The field in the centre of this system is essentially uniform.

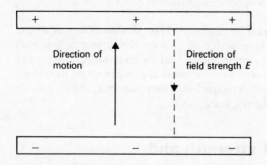

Fig. 4.6 Work done by moving a charge within the field between parallel charged plates

Let the p.d. between the plates be V volts. The work done in transferring a unit charge from one plate to the other through the electric field will be V joules. Consider part of the transfer process as indicated in Fig. 4.7. Here the unit charged is moved a short distance δl in a direction at an angle θ to the direction of the field. Since the field is uniform, the work done is

$$-E \cdot \delta l \cdot \cos \theta$$

The negative sign is included because the motion of the charge is in the opposite direction to that of the electric field strength. Conversely, it can be stated that the electric field strength has a negative direction with respect to the motion. Either way, it has to be noted that the force has a magnitude E,

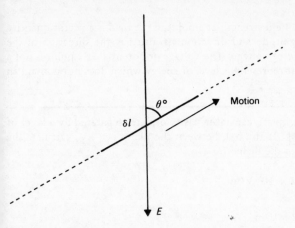

Fig. 4.7 Movement of a charge in an electric field

being the number of newtons of force acting on a unit charge, and the distance of motion in the direction of the field is $\delta l \cdot \cos \theta$.

In the parallel-plate arrangement, the usual charge motion is considered parallel to the lines of force. This action may be assumed in any electric field unless otherwise stated, thus $\theta = 0$ and $\cos \theta = 1$. The work done therefore is given by:

$$-E \cdot \delta l$$

Let δV be the increase in potential due to the movement through δl of the charge, thus

$$\delta V = -E \cdot \delta l$$

$$E = -\frac{\delta V}{\delta l} \tag{4.2}$$

In a uniform field, it is possible to consider not only short distances as above but also total distances such as the length between parallel charged plates. Thus for parallel charged plates of potential difference V separated by a distance d, then

$$E = -\frac{V}{d} \tag{4.3}$$

It can be seen that the electric field strength measured in the direction of the field is given by the rate of change of potential measured in the opposite direction at any point in the field. Although the electric field strength can be measured in newtons per coulomb, it follows from Relation 4.2 that it can also be measured in volts per metre.

Electric field strength   Symbol: E Unit: volt per metre (V/m)

Note that the electric field strength at a point in the field is a vector quantity since it has both magnitude and direction. It also has the direction of the greatest rate of change of voltage. The voltage or potential at a point is not a vector quantity since it represents a level of energy which does not contain an element of direction.

Example 4.1 A parallel-plate capacitor has two plates separated by a layer of dielectric 1·5 mm thick. If the p.d. between the plates is 3 kV, calculate the electric field strength in the dielectric.

$$E = \frac{V}{d} = \frac{3000}{1·5 \times 10^{-3}} = 2 \times 10^6 \text{ V/m}$$

$$= \underline{2 \text{ MV/m}}$$

Most dielectric layers are measured in millimetres and consequently this answer may also be expressed as 2 kV/mm.

4.3 Electric flux and electric flux density

The total electric effect of a system as described by the lines of electric force is termed the electric flux linking the system. The unit of electric flux is the coulomb, i.e. the same unit as used to measure electric charge.

Electric flux   **Symbol: Ψ**   Unit: coulomb (C)

A flux of Ψ coulombs is created by a charge of Q coulombs. The electric flux and the charge that creates it are total quantities which are important in terms of discussing the quantities relating to entire systems. However, as with magnetic systems, it can also be important to have an understanding of the effects of the distribution of the fields within a system and thus the electric flux density is a measure of the electric flux passing normally, i.e. at right angles, through a unit area.

Electric flux density   **Symbol: D**   **Unit: coulomb per square metre (C/m^2)**

In a uniform field, if a flux $\Psi = Q$ passes normally through an area A, then

$$D = \frac{Q}{A} \tag{4.4}$$

Again the electric flux density is a vector quantity having both magnitude and direction, the direction being that of the lines of force.

Example 4.2 Two parallel plates are charged to each hold an electric charge of $8 \mu C$. Given that the area of each plate is 0.04 m^2 and that all the flux is contained between the plates, calculate the electric flux density in the dielectric separating the plates.

$$D = \frac{Q}{A} = \frac{8 \times 10^{-6}}{4 \times 10^{-2}} = 200 \times 10^{-6} \text{ C/m}^2$$

$$= \underline{200 \ \mu C/m^2}$$

4.4 Permittivity

The flux density may be considered to result from the electric field strength. For any given value of electric field strength E, the value of the resulting flux density D depends on the medium in which the flux is produced. The ratio D to E is termed the absolute permittivity of the medium.

Absolute permittivity　　　Symbol: ϵ　　　Unit: farad per metre (F/m)

It follows therefore that

$$\frac{D}{E} = \epsilon$$

$$D = \epsilon E \tag{4.5}$$

This relation may be compared with its magnetic equivalent, $B = \mu H$. Again a basic value of permittivity is set by taking that value corresponding to free space. If the flux density due to an electric field strength exists in a medium other than free space, the permittivity is found to change in value. The absolute permittivity ϵ is then expressed as a multiple of that for free space ϵ_0, where ϵ_0 is the absolute permittivity of free space.

Permittivity of free space　　　Symbol: ϵ_0　　　Unit: farad per metre (F/m)

It may be shown by experiment that

$$\epsilon_0 = \frac{1}{36\pi} \times 10^{-9} \text{ F/m}$$

$$= 8.854 \times 10^{-12} \text{ F/m}$$

The ratio of the absolute permittivity of a material to the absolute permittivity of free space is termed the relative permittivity ϵ_r.

Relative permittivity   Symbol: ϵ_r Unit: none

$$\epsilon_r = \frac{\epsilon}{\epsilon_0}$$

$$\epsilon = \epsilon_0 \epsilon_r \tag{4.6}$$

It follows that the general case of Relation 4.5 is

$$D = \epsilon_0 \epsilon_r E \tag{4.7}$$

For air, ϵ_r may be taken as unity; most other materials have values between 1 and 10. Only water and titanate compounds exceed this range, the latter giving values of several hundreds. Typical values of relative permittivities are given in Table 4.1.

Table 4.1 Table of typical Relative Permittivities.

Material	ϵ_r
Air	$1{\cdot}0006 \simeq 1$
Bakelite	5
Barium titanate	6000
Glass	7
Insulating oil	3
Mica	5
Paper	2·5
Polythene	2·2
Rubber	3

Example 4.3 Two parallel plates are charged to have a potential difference of 100 V. Each has an area of 0·05 m^2 and they are separated by 1·0 mm of air. Assuming that all the electric flux is contained between the plates, calculate the electric charge on each plate.

$$E = \frac{\delta V}{\delta l} = \frac{100}{1 \times 10^{-3}} = 100 \times 10^3 \text{ V/m}$$

$$D = \epsilon_0 \epsilon_r E = 1 \times 8{\cdot}854 \times 10^{-12} \times 100 \times 10^3 = 8{\cdot}854 \times 10^{-7} \text{ C/m}^2$$
$$Q = DA = 8{\cdot}854 \times 10^{-7} \times 0{\cdot}05 = 4{\cdot}427 \times 10^{-8} \text{ C}$$
$$= \underline{44{\cdot}27 \text{ nC}}$$

It will be noted that Q represents the electric flux and also the charge on
each plate, thus the electric charge on each plate has been calculated.

4.5 Capacitance

This chapter started with the charging of a body by causing a flow of charge
to enter or leave the body. In the analysis that followed, specific arrangements
such as the pair of parallel plates were used to retain the charge. Devices
created specifically for this purpose of retaining charge are termed capacitors.

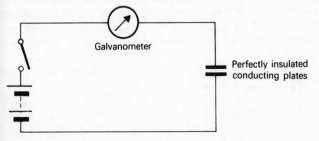

Fig. 4.8 Charging a capacitor

Consider again the charging process. A possible circuit is that shown in
Fig. 4.8. When the switch is closed, the galvanometer deflects momentarily,
showing that a current is passed for a short period of time and has then
ceased to flow. This burst of current is the flow of charge to or from the
capacitor plates.

From the circuit diagram, it can be seen that the top plate of the
capacitor now has a deficiency of electrons, these having been attracted to
the positive plate of the battery. The transfer of these electrons is equivalent
to a conventional current flowing into the top plate of the capacitor.
However, the plates are insulated from one another by the dielectric and the
circuit is therefore incomplete. The current flow can only accumulate on the
top plate, making it positively charged. An equal but opposite action takes
place at the lower plate, making it negatively charged. Thus the charge on
each plate is of the same magnitude but of opposite polarity.

The process of transferring charge cannot take place indefinitely because
the accumulated plate charges repel further charge movements within the
circuit. For instance, the first quantity of charge to arrive at a plate of the
capacitor does so unimpeded. However, the second quantity to arrive does so
against the repelling electrostatic force of the first charge. This difficulty
increases with the arrival of each subsequent quantity of charge, until it is
impossible for any further quantity of charge to be transferred.

This effect is better described in terms of the potential difference that
appears between the plates due to the charges on the plates. The magnitude
of the p.d. depends on the quantity of charge that has accumulated and is
equal to the work done in moving a unit charge from one plate to the other.

The cause of the transfer of charge is the e.m.f. of the battery. This e.m.f. acts against the p.d. between the capacitor plates and, so long as it exceeds the capacitor p.d., charge continues to move around the circuit. As the difference decreases, the rate of charge transfer decreases until it ceases altogether. The capacitor is then charged so that the p.d. between the plates is equal to the e.m.f. of the battery. If the e.m.f. of the battery is V, it follows that the p.d. between the capacitor plates is V.

The charging process takes a very short period of time unless the resistance of the circuit is high relative to the capacity of the capacitor. The quantity of charge that is transferred from one plate to the other can be measured if the galvanometer of the previous experiment is replaced by a ballistic galvanometer, which is a special form of galvanometer used to measure electric charge. A possible experimental network is shown in Fig. 4.9.

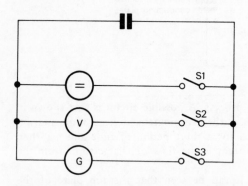

Fig. 4.9 Determination of voltage/charge characteristic of a capacitor

When switch S1 is closed, the capacitor is connected to the d.c. supply and after a short period of time the capacitor is charged to the supply voltage. Switch S1 is then opened and switch S2 closed in order that the p.d. across the capacitor may be measured by the voltmeter. Note that switch S1 has been opened in order that the potential difference measured is that of the charge on the capacitor and not that of the supply. Finally switch S2 is opened and the quantity of charge in the capacitor is measured by the ballistic galvanometer by closing switch S3.

This experiment is carried out for a range of p.d.s with the result that a voltage/charge characteristic may be obtained. A typical characteristic is shown in Fig. 4.10.

From the results of this experiment, it is seen that the p.d. V is proportional to the transferred charge Q.

$$V \propto Q$$

This relation can be expressed in the form

$$Q = CV$$

$$(4.8)$$

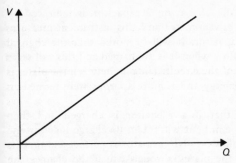

Fig. 4.10 Typical voltage/charge characteristic of a capacitor

where C is a constant termed the capacitance of the capacitor. The capacitance of a capacitor is that property whereby a capacitor accumulates charge when a potential difference is applied to it. Capacitance is measured in farads and a capacitor that accumulates a charge of one coulomb when a potential difference of one volt is applied to it has a capacitance of one farad.

Capacitance   **Symbol:** C **Unit: farad (F)**

Capacitance may be thought of as a factor of 'goodness': it describes the ability of a capacitor to hold charge. It relates the amount of charge per unit of voltage that the capacitor may contain. The farad, however, is rather an unfortunate unit because it is immense. Most capacitors are therefore rated either in microfarads or picofarads.

So long as the e.m.f. of the battery in Fig. 4.8 is maintained, the charge will remain on the capacitor. If the battery is removed and then replaced by a resistor or some other load, or even a short-circuit, the plates' charges will move round the circuit to recombine and neutralise one another. This effect can be observed from the deflection of the galvanometer in Fig. 4.11 when the switch is moved from the 'charge' position 1 to the 'discharge' position 2. When the switch is moved to position 2, the galvanometer however deflects in the opposite direction from that during charging, thus showing the change of direction of charge flow.

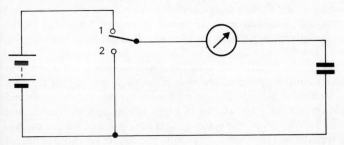

Fig. 4.11 Discharge of a capacitor

The experiment measuring the charge on a capacitor as indicated by Fig. 4.9 incorporated a ballistic galvanometer and this instrument measures the charge by discharging the capacitor. It will be noted that the charged capacitor gives rise to a current flow when it is discharged and this will serve to dissipate heat in the resistance of the circuit. The p.d. between the plates is therefore related to a source of energy and is more appropriately termed an e.m.f.

It should not be thought that if a capacitor is charged and then disconnected from its source of e.m.f., it will retain its charge indefinitely. Instead the charge will slowly leak away. No insulator is perfect and there is always a leakage path between the plates, through which the charges can move and neutralise one another. Most capacitors will retain their charges for some considerable period of time. When handling large capacitors, it is as well to check that they are discharged.

Finally it should be noted that capacitance is not a property of capacitors alone. Capacitance exists between any two parts of a circuit that are at different potentials. However, the effect of capacitance is generally so small that it need only be taken into account either in the case of the capacitance of a very long transmission line or of operation at higher frequencies of a.c. systems.

Example 4.4 Calculate the charge on an $8\text{-}\mu\text{F}$ capacitor when the applied voltage across the plates is 150 V. If the applied voltage were doubled, what would the charge on the plates become?

$$Q = CV = 8 \times 10^{-6} \times 150 = 1\cdot2 \times 10^{-3}\,\text{C}$$
$$= \underline{1\cdot2\ \text{mC}}$$

Since the charge is proportional to the applied voltage, the result of doubling the applied voltage would be to double the charge, i.e. $\underline{2\cdot4\ \text{mC}}$.

4.6 Simple parallel-plate capacitor

Although there are many forms of capacitor, the most important arrangement is the parallel-plate capacitor. Most capacitors are either formed by a stack of such plates or by a pair of such plates rolled up like a Swiss roll. These forms of construction are described in more detail in para. 4.9 but due to the thinness of the dielectric separating the plates, it is suitable to analyse their performance by considering a uniform field between parallel plates.

Consider again the experiment using the network shown in Fig. 4.9, but let the capacitor consist of two conducting plates mounted so that they are separated by a uniform air gap. The experiment is carried out as before and the results plotted on the graph shown in Fig. 4.12, giving the characteristic for experiment 1. Now adjust the plates so that the distance between them is reduced and repeat the experiment. Typically, the results are those indicated by the characteristic for experiment 2.

$$C = \frac{Q}{V}$$

However, the ratio of Q to V is the gradient of the characteristics in Fig. 4.12 and hence it may be observed that the closer the plates are positioned to one another, the greater is the capacitance C.

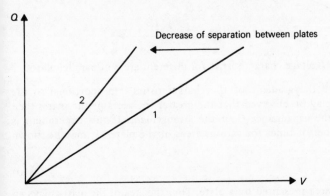

Fig. 4.12 Charge/voltage characteristics for different separations of parallel plates

If the experiment is repeated a number of times for various separations of the plates, it may be shown that

$$C \propto \frac{1}{d} \tag{4.9}$$

where d is the distance between the parallel plates. Thus the distance between the parallel plates plays an important part in determining the capacitance of the arrangement. The plates cannot be brought too close to one another otherwise the electric charges will jump the gap separating the plates. Thus the insulating dielectric would break down and the charges on the plates would no longer remain apart. For a given working voltage, the greater the maximum possible electric field strength of the dielectric, the less will be the necessary thickness of dielectric material.

Having considered the separation of the plates, it is now necessary to consider their areas. Each plate may be considered to have the same area through which the electric field acts, and these are the areas that each plate presents towards the other. Again the experiment using the network shown in Fig. 4.9 is used, there being two plates separated by a uniform air gap, and the experiment is carried out as before. The results are plotted on the graph shown in Fig. 4.13, giving the characteristic for experiment A. The plates are then replaced with plates of a bigger area but held the same distance apart as the first set of plates. Typically, the results are those indicated by the characteristic for experiment B.

120

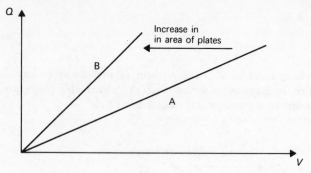

Fig. 4.13 Charge/voltage characteristics for different areas of parallel plates

Again, since the gradient of the characteristics is proportional to the capacitance, it may be observed that the greater the areas of the plates then the greater is the capacitance C of the arrangement. If this experiment is repeated a number of times for various areas of the plates, it may be shown that

$$C \propto A \qquad (4.10)$$

where A is the area presented by a plate. Thus the area of the plates plays an important part in determining the capacitance of a capacitor. It would be too cumbersome to keep on increasing the plates outwards and it is for this reason that they may be cut up and stacked upon each other or alternatively rolled up like a Swiss roll.

Finally, in each of the experiments it has been noted that there has been an air gap separating the plates. Again repeat the experiment with an air-gap separation of the plates and plot the results on the graph as shown in Fig. 4.14, giving the characteristic for experiment R. The air gap is then filled with a sheet of suitable dielectric material, for example nylon, and the experiment repeated. Typically, the results are those indicated by the characteristic for experiment S.

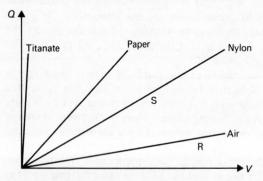

Fig. 4.14 Charge/voltage characteristics for different dielectric materials between the plates

Yet again, from the gradients of the characteristics it may be observed that the capacitance C varies with the dielectric material used to fill the gap between the conducting plates. It may be shown that this variation depends on the relative permittivities of the dielectrics as follows.

Consider two parallel plates each of area A and spaced a distance d apart. The fringing field at the edges of the plates and shown in Fig. 4.5 may be neglected provided the area of the plates is large whilst the spacing is very small. Also the field between the plates may be assumed to be uniform.

Let the plates be given a charge Q hence giving rise to an electric flux Q and to a potential difference V between the plates.

Since $\quad D = \dfrac{Q}{A}$

then $\quad Q = DA$

Also the work done in transferring a unit charge from one plate to the other through the electric field is

$$Ed = V$$

But $\quad C = \dfrac{Q}{V}$

$$= \frac{DA}{Ed}$$

$$= \frac{D}{E} \cdot \frac{A}{d}$$

But $\quad D = \epsilon_0 \epsilon_r E$

where ϵ_r is the relative permittivity of the dielectric separating the plates of the capacitor; hence

$$\frac{D}{E} = \epsilon_0 \epsilon_r$$

and $\quad C = \dfrac{\epsilon_0 \epsilon_r A}{d}$ $\qquad\qquad$ (4.11)

If this relation is rearranged, then

$$\epsilon = \frac{Cd}{A}$$

Inspection of this relation shows that the permittivity must be measured in farads per metre, as noted in para. 4.4.

Also from Relation 4.11, it follows that

$$C \propto \epsilon_r \qquad\qquad (4.12)$$

Most materials have a relative permittivity of less than 10 and only the use of titanate compounds as dielectrics permits drastic improvement in the values of capacitance.

Example 4.5 Calculate the capacitance of two metal plates each of area 30 m^2 and separated by a dielectric 2·0 mm thick and of relative permittivity 6.

If the electric field strength of the dielectric is 500 V/mm, calculate the total charge on each plate.

$$C = \frac{\epsilon_0 \epsilon_r A}{d} = \frac{8 \cdot 854 \times 10^{-12} \times 6 \times 30}{2 \cdot 0 \times 10^{-3}} = 0 \cdot 798 \times 10^{-6} \text{ F}$$

$$= 0 \cdot 798 \ \mu\text{F}$$

$$V = Ed = 500 \times 10^3 \times 2 \cdot 0 \times 10^{-3} = 1000 \text{ V}$$

$$Q = CV = 0 \cdot 798 \times 10^{-6} \times 1000 = 0 \cdot 798 \times 10^{-3} \text{ C}$$

$$= \underline{0 \cdot 798 \text{ mC}}$$

This represents the charge on each plate, the charges being equal.

4.7   Parallel- and series-connected capacitors

Networks and complex circuits can be made by connecting two or more capacitors together. Just as with resistors, the least number of capacitors that can be considered to cover the general cases is three. First then consider three capacitors connected in parallel as shown in Fig. 4.15. When the switch is closed, all three capacitors are charged till a p.d. V is maintained between their plates.

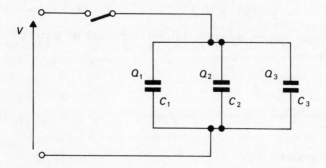

Fig. 4.15 Parallel-connected capacitors

Let the charges acquired by capacitors of capacitance C_1, C_2 and C_3 be Q_1, Q_2 and Q_3 respectively. It follows that

$$Q_1 = C_1 V$$
$$Q_2 = C_2 V$$

and $\qquad Q_3 = C_3V$

Let the total charge on the capacitors be Q and the total effective capacitance of the network be C, hence

$$Q = CV$$

The total charge of the capacitors is

$$\begin{aligned} Q &= Q_1 + Q_2 + Q_3 \\ &= C_1V + C_2V + C_3V \\ &= (C_1 + C_2 + C_3)V \end{aligned}$$

but $\qquad Q = CV$

therefore $\quad C = C_1 + C_2 + C_3$ $\hfill$ (4.13)

Although this analysis was based on three capacitors, the number of capacitors would have made no difference to the form of result. Thus, for instance, for two capacitors

$$C = C_1 + C_2$$

Example 4.6 A network consists of an 8-μF capacitor connected in parallel with a 4-μF capacitor to a 15-V d.c. supply. Calculate the charge taken from the source.

$C = C_1 + C_2 = (8 \times 10^{-6}) + (4 \times 10^{-6}) = 12 \times 10^{-6} \text{ F}$
$Q = CV = 12 \times 10^{-6} \times 15 = 180 \times 10^{-6} \text{ C}$
$$= \underline{180 \ \mu C}$$

Example 4.7 A network comprises three capacitors connected in parallel to give a total effective capacitance of 86 μF. If two of the capacitors have capacitances of 10 μF and 20 μF, what is the capacitance of the third capacitor?

$C = C_1 + C_2 + C_3$
$(86 \times 10^{-6}) = (10 \times 10^{-6}) + (20 \times 10^{-6}) + C_3$
$C_3 = 56 \times 10^{-6} \text{ F}$
$$= \underline{56 \ \mu F}$$

Example 4.8 A 16-μF capacitor is charged to 100 V and is then disconnected from the source of e.m.f. It is then connected across a 4-μF capacitor which is initially uncharged. Determine:

(a) the original charge on the 16-μF capacitor;
(b) the voltage across the combined circuit.

$Q = C_1V = 16 \times 10^{-6} \times 100 = 1{\cdot}6 \times 10^{-3} \text{ C}$
$$= \underline{1{\cdot}6 \text{ mC}}$$

This charge is now distributed between the two capacitors, of which the total capacitance is

$$C = C_1 + C_2 = (16 + 4) \times 10^{-6} = 20 \times 10^{-6} \, F$$
$$V = \frac{Q}{C} = \frac{1 \cdot 6 \times 10^{-3}}{20 \times 10^{-6}} = \underline{80 \, V}$$

Before progressing to consider the effect of connecting capacitors in series, it is necessary to give some consideration to induced charges. If an uncharged conductor is brought towards a charged body, a movement of charge will take place within the conductor. The unlike charges within the conductor will be attracted towards the charged body and equivalent like charges will be repelled in the opposite direction. These separated charges within the conductor are induced charges and are indicated in Fig. 4.16.

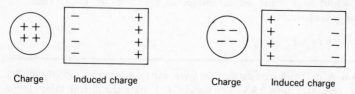

Charge   Induced charge   Charge   Induced charge

Fig. 4.16 Induced charges

The most simple method of arranging the introduction of a conductor into the influence of charged bodies is to place a slab of conductor between the plates of a parallel-plate capacitor. It may be assumed that the entire electric field passes through the conductor slab. The charges on the capacitor plates attract the unlike charges of the slab. This movement within the slab continues until the induced charges on each surface of the slab are equal to the charges on the corresponding capacitor plates. This corresponds with the force per unit charge within the conductor being zero. The arrangement is shown in Fig. 4.17.

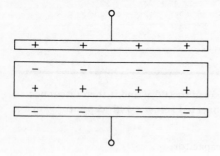

Fig. 4.17 Effect of a conductor slab in between the plates of a parallel-plate capacitor

It should be noted that the number of charges which move is only a small part of the total charges available in the conductor.

When two capacitors are connected in series, the applied e.m.f. causes
charge to accumulate on the plates connected to the external supply. The
intermediate plates are charged due to induced charge moving within that
part of the system, so that balance of charge is maintained on each plate. This
compares with the movement within the slab described above except that the
surfaces of the slab have been separated, leaving only a connecting wire
between them. It should be noted that in the series connection, again the
charge on each plate is numerically the same.

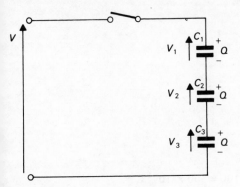

Fig. 4.18 Capacitors in series

Consider three capacitors connected in series as shown in Fig. 4.18. When
the switch is closed, a charge Q moves round the circuit and thus each
capacitor acquires a charge Q as shown.

Let the capacitors of capacitance C_1, C_2 and C_3 acquire p.d.s V_1, V_2 and
V_3 respectively; then

$$Q = C_1V_1 = C_2V_2 = C_3V_3$$

Let the total applied voltage be V and the effective capacitance of the
series capacitors be C, hence

$$Q = CV$$

By Kirchhoff's second law,

$$V = V_1 + V_2 + V_3$$

$$= \frac{Q}{C_1} + \frac{Q}{C_2} + \frac{Q}{C_3}$$

$$= Q\left(\frac{1}{C_1} + \frac{1}{C_2} + \frac{1}{C_3}\right)$$

$$= Q \cdot \frac{1}{C}$$

$$\frac{1}{C} = \frac{1}{C_1} + \frac{1}{C_2} + \frac{1}{C_3} \qquad (4.14)$$

Example 4.9 Three capacitors of capacitance C_1 (20 μF), C_2 (20 μF) and C_3 (10 μF) are connected in series to a 100-V d.c. supply. Calculate:

(a) the effective capacitance of the circuit;
(b) the charge on each capacitor;
(c) the p.d. across each capacitor.

$$\frac{1}{C} = \frac{1}{C_1} + \frac{1}{C_2} + \frac{1}{C_3}$$

$$= \frac{10^6}{20} + \frac{10^6}{20} + \frac{10^6}{10}$$

$$= \frac{10^6}{5}$$

$$C = 5 \times 10^{-6} \text{ F} = \underline{5 \ \mu\text{F}}$$

$$Q = CV = 5 \times 10^{-6} \times 100 = 500 \times 10^{-6} \text{ C}$$
$$= \underline{500 \ \mu\text{C}}$$

$$V_1 = \frac{Q}{C_1} = \frac{500 \times 10^{-6}}{20 \times 10^{-6}} = \underline{25 \text{ V}}$$

Similarly $V_2 = \underline{25 \text{ V}}$

$$V_3 = \frac{Q}{C_3} = \frac{500 \times 10^{-6}}{10 \times 10^{-6}} = \underline{50 \text{ V}}$$

It is interesting to note in this example that it is the smallest capacitance that sustains the greatest p.d. across it.

The analysis of the series-capacitor circuit was based on three capacitors connected in series, but the form of Relation 4.14 holds true for any number of series-connected capacitors. In particular, note the case of two series-connected capacitors.

$$\frac{1}{C} = \frac{1}{C_1} + \frac{1}{C_2}$$

$$C = \frac{C_1 \cdot C_2}{C_1 + C_2} \qquad (4.15)$$

As before, the charge Q is the same on each capacitor, hence

$$Q = CV = C_1V_1 = C_2V_2$$

$$\frac{C_1 \cdot C_2}{C_1 + C_2} \cdot V = C_1 V_1 = C_2 V_2$$

hence $\qquad V_1 = \frac{C_2}{C_1 + C_2} \cdot V \qquad\qquad\qquad\qquad$ (4.16)

also $\qquad V_2 = \frac{C_1}{C_1 + C_2} \cdot V$

The similarity between these relations and the relations for the division of a current between two parallel-connected resistors is immediately apparent.

Example 4.10 Two ideal capacitors of 4 μF and 1 μF are connected in series across a 100-V d.c. supply. Find the p.d. across each capacitor.

Letting 4 μF be C_1 and 1 μF be C_2,

$$V_1 = \frac{C_2}{C_1 + C_2} \cdot V = \frac{1 \times 10^{-6}}{(4 \times 10^{-6}) + (1 \times 10^{-6})} \times 100$$

$$= \underline{20 \text{ V}}$$

and $\qquad V_2 = \frac{C_1}{C_1 + C_2} \cdot V = \frac{4 \times 10^{-6}}{(4 \times 10^{-6}) + (1 \times 10^{-6})} \times 100$

$$= \underline{80 \text{ V}}$$

Alternatively $\quad V_2 = V - V_1 = 100 - 20 = \underline{80 \text{ V}}$

Finally, it is possible to have series-parallel connected arrangements of capacitors. Whilst these may be analysed, such an exercise is of relatively little value and the process of dealing with such arrangements is better considered by means of an example.

Example 4.11 Find the equivalent capacitance of the circuit shown in Fig. 4.19.

$C_{BC} = 4 + 8 = 12 \ \mu$F

The network now reduces to that shown in Fig. 4.20.

$$C_{AC} = \frac{12 \times 16}{12 + 16} = \underline{6 \cdot 86 \ \mu\text{F}}$$

128

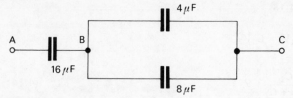

Fig. 4.19

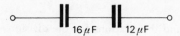

Fig. 4.20

4.8 Charging current and energy storage

During the charging process of a capacitor, let δQ be the small charge accumulated during a period δt. The average current during this period is given by the rate of arrival of charge, i.e.

$$I_{av} = \frac{\delta Q}{\delta t}$$

However, at any instant

$$Q = CV$$

hence $I_{av} = \dfrac{\delta(CV)}{\delta t}$

It is usual to find that the capacitance is a constant unless there is movement between the plates. Assuming C constant,

$$I_{av} = C \cdot \frac{\delta V}{\delta t}$$

If the period of time considered is very short, then the period can be considered to be an instant and the current during that instant will be given by

$$i = C \cdot \frac{\delta V}{\delta t} \qquad (4.17)$$

If you are familiar with the notation of calculus, Relation 4.17 may be expressed as

$$i = C \cdot \frac{dv}{dt}$$

where v is the instantaneous value of the p.d.

Although Relation 4.17 was derived on the basis of an accumulation of
charge taking place in a particular time, it should be remembered that this can
either be an increase or a decrease. In the latter case, $\frac{\delta V}{\delta t}$ has a negative value as
the p.d. decreases with the passing of time.

Example 4.12 A direct potential difference of 200 V is suddenly applied to a
circuit comprising an uncharged capacitor of 100 μF in series with a 1000-Ω
resistor. Calculate the rate of rise of voltage across the capacitor.

Once the capacitor is completely charged, the source of e.m.f. is replaced
by a short circuit. Calculate the initial rate of decrease of voltage across the
capacitor. Because the capacitor is initially uncharged, there will be no initial
p.d. between the plates. When the supply e.m.f. is applied, the corresponding
voltage drop must appear across the 1000-Ω resistor. Let the initial instantaneous current be i_0

$$i_0 = \frac{V}{R} = \frac{200}{1000} = 0.2 \text{ A}$$

$$= C \cdot \frac{\delta V}{\delta t} = 100 \times 10^{-6} \times \frac{\delta V}{\delta t}$$

$$\frac{\delta V}{\delta t} = \frac{0.2}{100 \times 10^{-6}} = 2000 \text{ V/s}$$

$$= \underline{2 \text{ kV/s}}$$

When the capacitor is discharged, the full p.d. is applied to the resistor.
This gives the same current as the initial current during charging and it
follows that the initial rate of voltage decrease is -2 kV/s.

Returning to the charging process, consider a capacitor of capacitance C
being charged at a constant rate I for a period of time t. Given that the
capacitor was initially discharged, the charge at the end of time t is

$$Q = It$$

The p.d. between the capacitor plates will have steadily increased during
this time from zero to a final value V. The average p.d. between the plates
during charging is therefore $\frac{1}{2}V$. The average power to the capacitor during
charging is $\frac{1}{2}VI$ and therefore the total energy stored in the capacitor is

$$W_f = \frac{1}{2}VIt$$
$$= \frac{1}{2}VQ$$
$$= \frac{1}{2}CV^2 \tag{4.18}$$

This energy stored in the field should not be confused with the work of
transferring charge as defined in Relation 4.1.

Again if you are familiar with the notation of calculus, a more general proof takes the following form. Let the p.d. between the plates at any instant be v and the corresponding charging current be i. During the period dt, the energy supplied to the capacitor is vi. But

$$i = C \cdot \frac{dv}{dt}$$

$$i \cdot dt = C \cdot dv$$

The energy supplied therefore is $Cv \cdot dv$. If the capacitor is charged to a p.d. V, then the energy stored is given by

$$W_f = \int_0^V Cv \cdot dv = \tfrac{1}{2}CV^2 \text{ as before.}$$

It should be noted that the energy is stored in the electric field within the dielectric. Given a simple parallel-plate capacitor in which the plates are separated by a slab of dielectric material of cross-sectional area A and thickness d, the dielectric completely filling the gap between the plates, then the energy density w_f in the gap is given by

$$w_f = \frac{W_f}{Ad}$$

$$= \tfrac{1}{2}CV^2 \cdot \frac{1}{Ad}$$

$$= \frac{1}{2} \cdot \frac{\epsilon A}{d} \cdot \frac{V^2}{Ad}$$

$$= \tfrac{1}{2}\epsilon \left(\frac{V}{d}\right)^2$$

$$= \tfrac{1}{2}\epsilon E^2 \tag{4.19}$$

$$= \tfrac{1}{2}DE$$

$$= \tfrac{1}{2} \cdot \frac{D^2}{\epsilon} \tag{4.20}$$

This stored energy can be returned to the source provided there is no resistance in the circuit. However, any circuit will have some resistance and the passage of the charging or discharging current through it will dissipate some energy in the form of heat.

The total energy acquired by the capacitor is $\tfrac{1}{2}CV^2$ ($= \tfrac{1}{2}VIt$) whilst the total energy delivered from the source is VIt during the charging process. The difference between the supply voltage and the voltage across the capacitor is due to the voltage drop across the limiting resistor in the circuit. From these expressions, it can be observed that the energy dissipated by the resistor is equal to the energy stored in the capacitor. This relation holds true no matter what the circuit resistance may be.

Apart from the energy dissipated in the circuit resistance, it is not possible to return all the stored energy to the supply. Apart from the loss due to leakage, there is a further loss termed the dielectric loss. This loss compares somewhat with the hysteresis loss in ferromagnetic materials. In most capacitors, this loss is so small that it may be neglected.

Example 4.13 In the circuit shown in Fig. 4.21, the battery e.m.f. is 100 V and the capacitor has a capacitance of 1 μF. The switch is operated 100 times every second. Calculate the average current through the switch between switching operations and also calculate the average power dissipation in the resistor. It may be assumed that the capacitor is ideal and that the capacitor is fully charged or discharged before the subsequent switching.

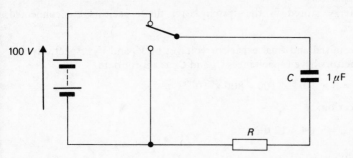

Fig. 4.21

The maximum charge accumulated by the capacitor is

$$Q = CV = 1 \times 10^{-6} \times 100 = 100 \times 10^{-6} \text{ C}$$

The time taken to acquire this charge (or to lose it) is

$$T = \frac{1}{f} = \frac{1}{100} = 0 \cdot 01 \text{ s}$$

hence $$I_{av} = \frac{\delta Q}{\delta t} = \frac{100 \times 10^{-6}}{0 \cdot 01} = 0 \cdot 01 \text{ A}$$

$$= \underline{10 \text{ mA}}$$

The maximum energy stored during charging is

$$W_f = \tfrac{1}{2}CV^2 = \tfrac{1}{2} \times 1 \cdot 0 \times 10^{-6} \times 100^2 = 0 \cdot 005 \text{ J}$$

During the charging period, a similar quantity of energy must be dissipated in the resistor. In the subsequent discharging period, the stored energy in the capacitor is dissipated in the resistor. Hence every switching action results in 0·005 J being dissipated by the resistor. For 100 switching operations, the energy dissipated is

$$W = 100 \times 0.005 = 0.5 \text{ J}$$

Hence the average power is given by

$$P_{av} = \frac{\delta W}{\delta t} = \frac{0.5}{1} = \underline{0.5 \text{ W}}$$

Example 4.14 An 8-μF capacitor is charged from a 100-V d.c. supply, from which it is then disconnected. It is immediately connected in parallel with a 4-μF capacitor which was previously uncharged. Calculate:

(a) the p.d. across the combination;
(b) the energy stored in the 8-μF capacitor before being connected to the 4-μF capacitor;
(c) the energy stored in the system after the capacitors are connected together.

Let the initial and final capacitor voltages be V_1 and V_2 respectively and let the capacitors have capacitances C_8 and C_4 as appropriate.

$$Q = C_8 V_1 = 8 \times 10^{-6} \times 100 = 800 \times 10^{-6} \text{ C}$$

After connection,

$$C = C_8 + C_4 = 8 + 4 = 12 \text{ } \mu\text{F}$$

$$V_2 = \frac{Q}{C} = \frac{800 \times 10^{-6}}{12 \times 10^{-6}} = \underline{66.7 \text{ V}}$$

Before connection,

$$W_{f1} = \tfrac{1}{2} C_8 V_1^{2} = \tfrac{1}{2} \times 8 \times 10^{-6} \times 100^2 = 4 \times 10^{-2} \text{ J}$$
$$= \underline{40 \text{ mJ}}$$

After connection,

$$W_{f2} = \tfrac{1}{2} C V_2^{2} = \tfrac{1}{2} \times 12 \times 10^{-6} \times 66.7^2 = 2.67 \times 10^{-2} \text{ J}$$
$$= \underline{26.7 \text{ mJ}}$$

It is interesting to note that there is a loss of energy, some of which appears as a heat loss in the circuit resistance due to the passage of current, and also in a small amount of electromagnetic energy radiation during the energy transfer period.

4.9 Practical capacitors

There are a considerable number of ways in which a capacitor may be made.

The method of manufacture depends on the application envisaged, but the
principal groups are as follows:

(*a*) *Air capacitors.* In this form of capacitor, the dielectric is air which is a relatively poor choice because of the low value of relative permittivity. However, this type usually consists of one set of fixed plates and one set of movable plates. The movable plates may be rotated between the fixed plates thereby varying the area of the field, as indicated in Fig. 4.22. The plates are normally made of aluminium sheet. The application for this device lies in electronic devices that require to be tuned, e.g. radios.

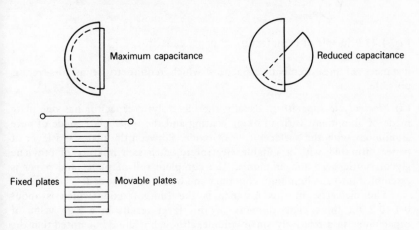

Fig. 4.22 Variable air capacitor

(*b*) *Paper capacitors.* In this case, the electrodes consist of thin metal foil interleaved with sheets of paper which is impregnated with either wax or oil. The thin foil is about 6 μm thick whilst the paper is about 15 μm thick. As has been noted previously, these layers are rolled together like a Swiss roll. This is achieved by rolling the layers on to a spindle as indicated by Fig. 4.24. The greater the capacitance required, the larger the roll is made although if one roll is not sufficient then a number of rolls may be connected in parallel. The layers of foil have copper tags connected to them in order that the plates may be connected to the external terminals.

Paper capacitors have a wide range of applications including power-factor correction capacitors, smoothing capacitors, energy storage and fluorescent lighting capacitors. High-voltage d.c. capacitors are made from two or more paper capacitors permanently connected in series and these may be used for radio and television applications.

(*c*) *Mica capacitors.* There are various forms of construction of mica capacitors but all have the common dielectric of mica. All forms of construction are expensive but the advantage of this dielectric is the very low dielectric loss. This may be important in high-frequency operations or in

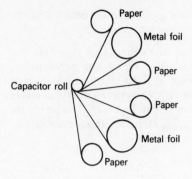

Fig. 4.23 Principle of manufacture of paper capacitor

instances of measurements capacitors which require to be as loss-free as possible.

(*d*) *Electrolytic capacitors.* Usually the electrolytic capacitor has one plate made of aluminium with an oxide coating and the other plate made of pure aluminium with the surfaces free of oxide. Between the plates is a layer of paper saturated with a suitable electrolyte, such as a mixture of ethylene glycol, boric acid and ammonia. The complete roll of plates and paper is assembled into an aluminium container and hermetically sealed.

The dielectric in this instance is the film of oxide which is about $0.1-0.2\ \mu m$ thick. The thinness of this layer results in a high value of capacitance in a relatively small volume, although it should be noted that the layer thicknesses are about three times those of the paper-capacitor materials.

For the range of oxide thickness indiated, a working voltage of about 100 V would be possible. Electrolytic capacitors therefore find their applications where high values of capacitance are required in small bulk but working voltages are relatively low. If too high a voltage is applied, the dielectric breaks down and the expansion of gas explodes the sealed container, which is a possible source of danger.

More usual disadvantages are that the insulation resistance of the electrolytic capacitor is low because a small current will flow during use to maintain the oxide layer. Also it is only suitable for applications where the terminal voltage never reverses its direction. Thus the electrolytic capacitor is polarised, and if the terminal voltage acts in the wrong direction, the oxide layer is damaged and the dielectric is destroyed.

It should be noted that it is possible to make electrolytic capacitors to operate with alternating voltages provided that the application of the alternating voltage is intermittent. A typical use would be in the starting of capacitor-start motors in which case the capacitor is only connected into the circuit while the motor is running up to operating speed.

(*e*) *Tantalum electrolytic capacitors.* These capacitors are much smaller than the corresponding aluminium electrolytic capacitors. The construction may take the form indicated in Fig. 4.24, in which one plate consists of pressed,

sintered tantalum powder coated with an oxide layer which is the dielectric.
The case of brass, copper or even silver forms the other plate. Layers of manganese dioxide and graphite form the electrolyte.

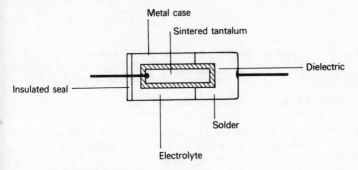

Fig. 4.24 Sintered tantalum capacitor

(f) *Other capacitors.* There are further ranges of capacitors which include the metallised-paper capacitor, which is similar to the paper capacitor except that the paper is coated with a thin layer of metal on one side. Two such layers are rolled together to form a capacitor, being mounted in a sealed container. The advantage of this form is that it is self-healing, i.e. should a localised breakdown of the dielectric occur, the heat vaporises the metallic coating and the conductor around the problem area is thereby removed. Such a capacitor may be used for spark suppression in a car ignition system.

Ceramic capacitors are formed from metallic coatings on the opposite faces of a thin slab of ceramic material. The capacitances values available are small but are useful in high-frequency applications, especially in cases where high temperatures may be experienced.

Various titanates have very high values of relative permittivities and lend themselves to the manufacture of extremely small capacitors. At a time of extreme miniaturisation, titanate capacitors have a wide range of applications.

Reference has been made to the breakdown of the dielectric material in capacitors. This occurs when the electric field between the plates can no longer maintain the required electric field strength and the material breaks down, resulting usually in a small hole through the dielectric rendering it useless as an insulator.

The electric field strength required to cause such a breakdown of the insulating material is termed the dielectric strength, usually measured in megavolts per metre. This varies with the thickness of the dielectric material as is typically instanced by the characteristic for air shown in Fig. 4.25.

Other materials can sustain much higher dielectric strengths as indicated by Table 4.2. For the purposes of comparison, all the values given apply to 1·0-mm thick specimen of the material. The dielectric strength determines the working voltage of the capacitor and its construction is therefore a compro-

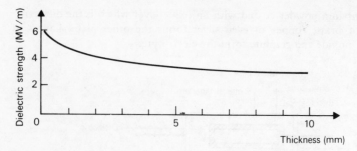

Fig. 4.25 Dielectric strength/thickness characteristic for air

m̄ẹe between the relative permittivity of the dielectric helping to determine the capacitance, and the thickness of the dielectric determining, in conjunction with the dielectric stress, the working voltage.

Table 4.2 Typical Dielectric Strengths of Capacitor Dielectric Materials.

Material	Dielectric Strength MV/m
Air	3
Glass	22
Insulating oil	70
Mica	140
Paper	4
Polythene	60
Titanate	6
Waxed paper	28

Finally, the effect of rolling a parallel-plate capacitor's plates should be considered. As in the case of the paper capacitor, two layers of paper have been interspersed with two sheets of aluminium foil as indicated in Fig. 4.26.

Fig. 4.26 Rolled, parallel-plate capacitor

Examination of this diagram shows that, the outside layer apart, both sides of each sheet of foil are effective. It follows that the capacitance of such

an arrangement is almost twice that of the simple parallel-plate capacitor
because the area on both sides of each plate must now be taken into account.

Example 4.15 A capacitor is made from two thin sheets of aluminium foil, which are flat and measure 50 mm by 30 m. The sheets are separated by a sheet of polythene 0·2 mm thick and of relative permittivity 2·3. Calculate the capacitance of the capacitor.

If a second identical layer of polythene is laid on top of the previous arrangement and the complete assembly is rolled up, estimate the capacitance of the new arrangement.

If the electric field strength in the dielectric under normal working conditions is 14 MV/m, calculate the terminal p.d. of the capacitor.

$$C = \frac{\epsilon_0 \epsilon_r A}{d} = \frac{8\cdot854 \times 10^{-12} \times 2\cdot3 \times 50 \times 10^{-3} \times 30}{0\cdot2 \times 10^{-3}}$$

$$= 1\cdot527 \times 10^{-7} \text{ F}$$
$$= \underline{0\cdot1527 \,\mu F}$$

When the assembly is rolled up, the capacitance will be approximately double, i.e. $\underline{0\cdot3054 \,\mu F}$

$$V = Ed = 14 \times 10^6 \times 0\cdot2 \times 10^{-3} = 2800 \text{ V}$$
$$= \underline{2\cdot8 \text{ kV}}$$

Problems

1. An 8-μF capacitor is charged by a current of 2 μA for a period 500 s. Calculate the final p.d. across the capacitor, assuming that it was initially discharged.

   Had the capacitor initially held a charge of 0·5 mC, to what p.d. would the charging have raised the capacitor?

2. A capacitor of plate area 400 cm^2 holds a charge of 2 μC. Determine the electric flux density of the electric field.

3. A direct potential 200 V is applied across the plates of a two-plate capacitor of capacitance 0·05 μF. The effective area of each plate is 0·05 m^2 and the absolute permittivity of the dielectric is **20 pF/m**. Calculate:
   (a) the electric flux density;
   (b) the electric field strength.

4. A capacitor has a dielectric that is 0·15 mm thick. If the maximum electric field strength that the dielectric can maintain is 6 MV/m, determine the maximum voltage that may be applied to the capacitor.

5. A parallel-plate capacitor of **500 pF** capacitance has an effective plate area 0·025 m^2. The relative permittivity of the dielectric is 2·5. If a constant voltage 500 V is maintained across the plates, calculate:

(*a*) the electric flux;
   (*b*) the electric flux density;
   (*c*) the electric field strength.

6. A fully charged capacitor is discharged through a resistor. The voltage across the capacitor falls from 250 V to 50 V in 5 s and during this time the average current is 2·0 mA. Calculate the capacitance of the capacitor.

7. The p.d. 10 kV is applied to the terminals of a capacitor consisting of two circular plates each having an area 0·01 m² separated by a dielectric 1·0 mm thick. The resulting capacitance of the arrangement is 300 pF. Calculate:
   (*a*) the total electric flux;
   (*b*) the electric flux density;
   (*c*) the relative permittivity of the dielectric.

8. A parallel-plate capacitor is built up from two metal plates, each of area 0·02 m², separated 0·5 mm by a sheet of mica of relative permittivity 6. Calculate the capacitance of the capacitor.

   The capacitor is charged to a p.d. 100 V between the plates and is then isolated from the supply. The sheet of mica is removed without altering the distance between the plates and without allowing any charge to leak away. What is the new p.d. between the plates?

9. A capacitor is to be made with capacitance 0·1 μF and operating p.d. 400 V. The dielectric may safely be stressed to a maximum electric field strength 20 MV/m. Determine:
   (*a*) the thickness of the dielectric;
   (*b*) the plate area, given that the relative permittivity of the dielectric is 2·5.

10. Three capacitors have capacitances 4 μF, 8 μF and 12 μF respectively. Calculate the total capacitance when:
    (*a*) they are covered in parallel;
    (*b*) they are connected in series.

11. A capacitor of capacitance 12 μF is connected in series with two parallel-connected capacitors of capacitances 4 μF and 8 μF respectively. Determine the capacitance of the arrangement.

    If a p.d. 10 V is applied to the circuit, what is the charge on each capacitor?

12. A circuit ABCD is made up as follows. AB consists of a 5-μF capacitor in parallel with a 7-μF capacitor. BC consists of a 2-μF capacitor and CD consists of an 8-μF capacitor. Also a 2-μF capacitor is connected between A and D. If a direct potential difference of 100 V is applied across AD, determine:
    (*a*) the effective capacitance between A and D;
    (*b*) the energy stored in the network.

13. Three capacitors of 4 μF, 6 μF and 12 μF capacitance respectively are connected in series to a 200-V d.c. supply. Calculate:
    (*a*) the charge on each capacitor;
    (*b*) the p.d. across each capacitor;
    (*c*) the energy stored in each capacitor.

14. A capacitor is formed by two flat metal plates each of area 5000 mm^2 and separated by a dielectric 1·0 mm thick. The capacitance of this arrangement is 200 pF and a p.d. of 10 kV is applied to the terminals. Calculate:
    (*a*) the charge on the plates;
    (*b*) the relative permittivity of the dielectric;
    (*c*) the electric flux density;
    (*d*) the energy stored.

15. A 20-pF capacitor is to be made using two parallel metal plates, the width of which is fixed at 50 mm. The maximum potential gradient in the air dielectric is not to exceed 60 kV/m when a p.d. of 100 V is applied across the plates. Determine the length of the plates.

    If the capacitor is connected in series with a second capacitor of 50 pF and a p.d. of 100 V is applied across the circuit, find the voltage across each capacitor.

    Calculate the energy stored in the electric fields, assuming that the capacitors are perfect.

16. A 5-μF capacitor with a dielectric of paper has to operate on a peak voltage 500 V. This capacitor is to be charged from a d.c. source. Determine:
    (*a*) the plate area and spacing if the maximum permissible strength in the paper is 250 kV/m and the relative permittivity is 6;
    (*b*) the p.d. across the capacitor after 7·5 s if the charging current is maintained constant at 0·1 mA.

17. Two parallel-plate capacitors A and B are connected in series. A has a plate area 5000 m^2, an air dielectric, and the distance between the plates is 1·0 mm. B has a plate area 2000 m^2, a solid dielectric of relative permittivity 4 and of thickness 0·5 mm. Find:
    (*a*) the voltage across the combination if the field strength in capacitor A is 100 kV/m;
    (*b*) the charge on each capacitor;
    (*c*) the energy stored in the electric fields.

18. A parallel-plate capacitor is made from two plates 254 mm in diameter and mounted 2·0 mm apart in air. A 1·0-mm thick sheet of nylon is placed between the plates and the resulting capacitance becomes 360 pF. Find the relative permittivity of the nylon; you may assume that the nylon gives two series-connected capacitors, one with 1·0 mm of air and the other with 1·0 mm of nylon.

19. A direct p.d. of 100 V is applied to two series-connected capacitors A and B and the p.d.s across them are found to be 60 V and 40 V respectively. A 2-μF capacitor is connected in parallel with A and the p.d. across B rises to 90 V. Calculate the capacitance of A and of B.

1. 125 V, 187·5 V
2. 50 $\mu C/m^2$
3. 0·2 mC/m^2, 10 MV/m
4. 900 V
5. **0·25 μC, 0·01 mC/m^2, 453 MV/m**
6. 50 μF
7. 3 μC, 0·3 mC/m^2, 3·39
8. 2120 pF, 600 V
9. 0·02 mm, 904 cm^2
10. 24 μF, 2·18 μF
11. 6 μF, 60 μC, 20 μC, 40 μC
12. 3·41 μF, 17·05 mJ
13. 400 μC, 100 V, 66·7 V, 33·3 V, 20 mJ, 13·3 mJ, 6·6 mJ
14. 2 μC, 4·52, 400 $\mu C/m^2$, 10 mJ
15. **7·53 cm, 71·5 V, 28·5 V, 7 × 10^{-8} J**
16. 188·5 m^2, 2·0 mm, 150 V
17. **131 V, 4400 μC, 0·221 J, 0·070 J**
18. 4·1
19. 0·16 μF, 0·24 μF

Chapter 5

Alternating voltages and currents

Of all the electrical energy consumed, over 90 per cent is generated, distributed and utilised as alternating current. Perhaps the most important reason for this widespread application of alternating current is the ease with which the voltage may be changed by means of the transformer. Also, the higher the voltage with which electrical energy is distributed, the higher the efficiency of energy distribution — although other factors dictate the highest economic working alternating voltage to be about 400 kV.

The quantity of energy consumed, however, is not necessarily a guide to the importance of the means of its utilisation. Thus a computer may produce many important results for the expenditure of very little energy. All communications electronic equipment and many other light-current devices operate on alternating current superimposed on direct current; thus in almost every field of electrical and electronic interest, alternating current plays a leading role.

Before proceeding to describe the action of alternating current in circuits and networks, it is necessary to consider the principles of alternating voltages and currents. It is therefore the objective of this chapter to provide the basic understanding of these quantities.

5.1   Production of an alternating e.m.f.

A simple device that will generate an alternating e.m.f. is shown in Fig. 5.1. The loop made of a conducting material is able to rotate at uniform angular velocity about an axis symmetrically placed with respect to the magnetic field, which may be assumed to be uniform. The rotation of the coil causes an e.m.f. to be generated in the coil, as would be expected from Faraday's law.

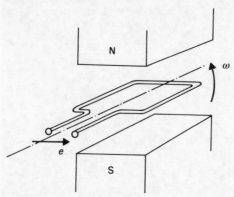

Fig. 5.1 Simple a.c. generator

It will be shown that the e.m.f. induced in the coil continually varies in magnitude and reverses its direction at regular intervals. Such an e.m.f. is termed an alternating e.m.f. and the value of this varying e.m.f. at any given instant is called the instantaneous e.m.f. It is usual to indicate instantaneous values by using lower-case letters: thus the instantaneous e.m.f. is given the symbol e.

Consider the rotation of the coil at positions indicated in Fig. 5.2 and taken for convenience at 30° intervals. These are the positions through which a given conductor passes as its coil makes a complete revolution. Using position 0 as the starting point, at position 1 the conductor and the coil will have rotated through 30°, at position 2 they will have rotated through 60°, and so on.

The e.m.f./angular displacement characteristic shown in Fig. 5.2 indicates the instantaneous values of e.m.f. induced in the conductor at the various positions noted.

The e.m.f. induced in the conductor at position 0 is zero because the motion of the conductor is parallel to the lines of force in the field and therefore, no lines being cut, there is no induced e.m.f. As the conductor passes positions 1 and 2, it cuts through the field lines with increasing velocity and, by the time it passes position 3, the conductor is cutting the field at right angles, thereby inducing the maximum value of e.m.f. E_m.

Having passed the position 3, the conductor continues to cut the field but with decreasing velocity: thus the e.m.f. reduces in value until by position 6 the e.m.f. is again zero.

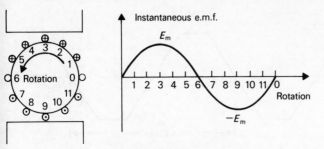

Fig. 5.2 Effect of coil rotation on induced e.m.f.

Throughout the motion from position 0 up to position 6, the induced e.m.f. has acted out from the plane of the paper in the sense that it would try to cause a current flow in that direction. Having passed position 6, the conductor starts to cut the field in the opposite direction, thus reversing the direction of the induced e.m.f. On the instantaneous e.m.f. characteristic, these reversed e.m.f.s are shown as being of negative values.

As the velocity of the conductor cutting across the field increases, the e.m.f. also increases, reaching a maximum value at position 9, and decreases thereafter until again becoming zero at position 0, which brings the conductor back to its starting point. For every successive revolution, this cycle of events will be repeated.

The characteristic obtained from these observations represents the variation of the induced e.m.f. in a conductor for a complete revolution of the coil in a two-pole generator. Conventionally, the e.m.f. values shown above the horizontal axis are said to be positive whilst those below are negative. Most modern sources of alternating e.m.f. generate an e.m.f. which has a characteristic whose positive values are exactly like the negative values as indicated.

Having generated an alternating e.m.f., there remains the problem of its measurement. A battery may produce a steady 2 V which is always there, but how are you to describe a voltage that continually changes its value? To answer this question, it is necessary to embark on what may appear to be a mathematics lesson with electrical terms thrown in for good measure, but it is important that the terms now introduced be clearly understood since much of the ensuing theory of electrical and electronic engineering is based on them.

5.2 Frequency and period

If the instantaneous values of an alternating quantity are plotted to a base of time, the resulting graph is termed a waveform graph. A possible wave diagram is shown in Fig. 5.3.

The wave diagram shows that after some time the wave starts to repeat.

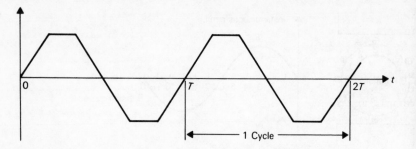

Fig. 5.3 Frequency and period of an alternating quantity

The sequence of events during this time is termed a cycle; one cycle is indicated in Fig. 5.3. The time taken for one cycle is called a period, or more specifically the period of the waveform.

Period   **Symbol:** T **Unit: second (s)**

Of generally greater interest is the number of cycles occurring per second; this rate of repetition is termed the frequency. It will become apparent that the frequency is fundamental to all a.c. circuit analysis.

Frequency   **Symbol:** f **Unit: hertz (Hz)**

The unit of frequency used to be the cycle per second (c/s) and this is still to be found in use, e.g. on the dials of old instruments. It follows from the definitions of period and frequency that

$$T = \frac{1}{f} \tag{5.1}$$

Of all possible alternating quantities in electrical engineering, that which is most important is the sinusoidal wave. It is important because most alternating voltages vary either sinusoidally or almost sinusoidally. Even in cases that are non-sinusoidal, it should still be noted that any alternating quantity approximates to a sinusoidal quantity. The practical implications of non-sinusoidal waveforms are discussed in Chapter 6.

5.3   Sinusoidal waves

A sinusoidal quantity is one that can be expressed instantaneously by a sinusoidal function of time, e.g. a sinusoidally varying voltage may be expressed as

$$v = V_m \sin \omega t$$

where V_m and ω are appropriate constants that may be interpreted as follows.

The maximum value of a sine is 1; thus V_m is the maximum or peak value of the alternating voltage. That it is a maximum is indicated by the subscript m. The peak value of a given sinusoidal quantity is a constant, and therefore a capital V is used to indicate the voltage in the symbol V_m. This compares with the lower-case v which indicates a varying quantity.

The other constant ω determines the rate of alternation of the voltage. The time taken for one cycle is T seconds producing a corresponding change from 0 to 2π radians, hence

$$\omega T = 2\pi$$

$$\omega = \frac{2\pi}{T}$$

From this expression, it will be seen that the constant ω is measured in radians per second. It is termed the angular frequency.

Angular frequency   **Symbol: ω**   **Unit: radian per second (rad/s)**

However, from Relation 5.1

$$f = \frac{1}{T}$$

Substituting this in the previous expression,

$$\omega = \frac{2\pi}{T}$$

then $\omega = 2\pi f$ \hfill (5.2)

It follows that the sinusoidal voltage may be expressed as

$$v = V_m \sin 2\pi ft$$

The appropriate waveform diagram is shown in Fig. 5.4.

In a similar manner, an alternating current can be expressed as

$$i = I_m \sin \omega t$$
$$= I_m \sin 2\pi ft$$

Finally, there is the common situation whereby a sinusoidally varying quantity is superimposed on a steady value, e.g. an alternating voltage is superimposed on a direct voltage. In such circumstances the maximum value of the total voltage and the minimum value of the total voltage differ in magnitude. This is illustrated in Fig. 5.5 and the effect should be compared with that of a voltage which has a simple sine waveform in which the minimum value is taken to be the negative maximum and the positive and

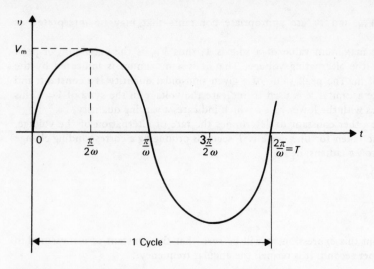

Fig. 5.4 Waveform of a sinusoidally alternating voltage

negative maxima are equal in magnitude but opposite in polarity. In the case of superimposed voltages, the difference between the maximum and minimum values is described as the peak-to peak voltage as illustrated.

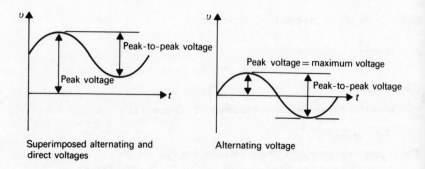

Fig. 5.5 Superimposed alternating and direct voltages

Again in the case of the superimposed voltages, the peak voltage is the greatest voltage experienced. Only in the case of a pure alternating quantity with no direct component does the peak voltage equal half the peak-to-peak voltage and therefore corresponds to the maximum voltage. In pure sinusoidal alternating voltages, the peak voltage is equivalent to the amplitude of the sinusoidal variation.

5.4 Peak, average and r.m.s. values

Generally, the electrical effect of a current depends on the value of that current. For instance, the deflection of a moving-coil instrument is proportional to the average or mean value of current in the moving coil. However, if a pure sinusoidal alternating current is passed through the coil, the positive half of the waveform is cancelled out by the subsequent negative half with the result that the average current is zero and therefore the instrument experiences no deflection.

Nevertheless, it is possible to modify the instrument circuit in order to either prevent one half on the current waveform from acting through the coil, or even to reverse its direction, in which case both halves of the waveform result in current passing through the coil in the same direction. Such arrangements will be considered at the end of this chapter but for the moment, it is sufficient to consider the average or mean value of a half cycle of current.

The waveform of a half cycle of current is shown in Fig. 5.6. For convenience, the peak value of the current has been taken as 1·0 A; thus $I_m = 1·0$ A. It follows that the waveform being taken as basically sinusoidal may be defined by

$i = I_m \sin \omega t$
$= \sin \omega t$

In order that the graph might be drawn, the numbers in Table 5.1 were extracted from sine tables — only two decimal places are given since it would not be possible to draw to a greater accuracy unless a very large diagram were produced.

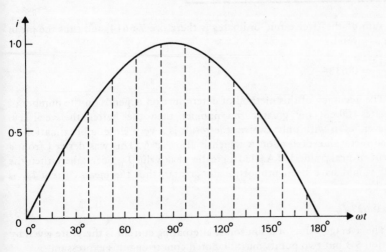

Fig. 5.6 Sinusoidal waveform — analysis of mean value of half cycle

ωt (°)	0	15	30	45	60	75	90
i (A)	0	0·26	0·50	0·71	0·87	0·97	1·00
ωt (°)	180	165	150	135	120	105	90

This average value of the current may be found by applying the mid-ordinate rule, which may be expressed as

$$\text{mean value} = \frac{\text{sum of mid-ordinates}}{\text{number of mid-ordinates}}$$

The mid-ordinates are taken at the middle of each 15° ordinate as indicated by the dotted lines. These may either be measured from the scale diagram or can quite easily be taken from sine tables as in Table 5.2.

Table 5.2

Mid-ordinate angle	$i = \sin \omega t$	Mid-ordinate angle
7·5°	0·1305	172·5°
22·5°	0·3827	157·5°
37·5°	0·6088	142·5°
52·5°	0·7934	127·5°
67·5°	0·9239	112·5°
82·5°	0·9914	97·5°

The sum of the twelve mid-ordinates is therefore 7·6614, and thus the mean value is given by

$$\frac{7·6614}{12} = 0·6384 \text{ A}$$

The accuracy of this method of determination depends on the number of ordinates taken; the greater the number then the better the accuracy. However, even with only twelve, the result is a very close approximation to the correct value of 0·6366 A which is also $2/\pi$ A. This was derived from a current of peak value 1·0 A. Had a greater peak value I_m been taken, then the result would have been proportionally greater; thus the mean current I_{av} is given by

$$I_{av} = 0·637 \, I_m \tag{5.3}$$

The average value of a sinusoidal alternating current is therefore given by Relation 5.3 but two points must be noted concerning this expression:

1. It only applies to sine waveforms.

2. It is based on the average of a half cycle.

Finally, the relation was derived from the consideration of a current, but it would have been equally applicable to consider a sinusoidally varying voltage, whence

$$V_{av} = 0.637\ V_m \tag{5.4}$$

However, the reason for creating an electric current is the transmission of energy and because current is a rate of flow of charge, it follows that the effective value of the current should be related to the rate of energy transfer. Thus an alternating current is usually defined in terms of the average power which it may cause.

Consider again the current $i = I_m \sin \omega t$ flowing through a resistor of resistance R. At any instant, the power p is given by

$$p = i^2 R$$

The average power P can be calculated over the period of one cycle.

$$P = R \times (\text{mean value of } i^2)$$

If the effective value of the current is I then

$$P = I^2 R$$

where I^2 = (mean value of i^2)

= (mean value of $I_m^2 \sin^2 \omega t$)

= $I_m^2 \times$ (mean value of $\sin^2 \omega t$), since I_m is constant.

Figure 5.7 indicates the waveforms of $\sin \omega t$ and $\sin^2 \omega t$. It may be observed that the $\sin^2 \omega t$ waveform is of twice the frequency of the basic $\sin \omega t$ and varies about a mid value of $\frac{1}{2}$ Taken in this way, it may be considered to be a double-frequency cosine wave alternating about a mid value of $\frac{1}{2}$ and therefore

$$\sin^2 \omega t = \tfrac{1}{2} - \tfrac{1}{2} \cos 2\omega t.$$

The mean value of a cosine wave taken over a complete cycle is zero because, as with the sine wave, the positive and negative loops are equal in area but opposite in sign, thereby cancelling each other out. Thus the mean value of $\sin^2 \omega t$ is $\frac{1}{2}$ taken over a complete cycle, and

$$I^2 = \tfrac{1}{2} I_m^2$$

So $\qquad I = \dfrac{I_m}{\sqrt{2}} = 0.707\ I_m \tag{5.5}$

This is the effective value of the current and is termed the root mean square (r.m.s.) current. Similarly, for a sinusoidal voltage given by $v = V_m \sin \omega t$,

$$V = \dfrac{V_m}{\sqrt{2}} = 0.707\ V_m \tag{5.6}$$

It will also be noted that a capital symbol is used to denote the r.m.s. value. The r.m.s. value is equivalent to the corresponding d.c. value; for instance, a direct current I will produce the same heating effect in a resistance as will an alternating current of r.m.s. value I.

In an a.c. circuit, voltages and currents are normally given in r.m.s. values unless otherwise stated. Further, it may be assumed that an alternating quantity varies sinusoidally unless otherwise stated. Thus a.c. measuring devices generally are calibrated to read the r.m.s. values of the appropriate sinusoidal a.c. quantities.

The derivation of the r.m.s. Relation 5.5 has been abbreviated in order to minimise the time spent on repetitive arithmetic, but for those readers who require a fuller explanation, the derivation of the r.m.s. value may be obtained as follows.

Again the waveforms for the initial analysis are based on the current $i = I_m \sin \omega t$, where $I_m = 1 \cdot 0$ A. It follows that $i^2 = \sin^2 \omega t$ and the waveform in Fig. 5.7 is drawn from the numbers in Table 5.3, extracted from sine tables.

Table 5.3

$\omega t \ (^\circ)$	0	15	30	45	60	75	90
i (A)	0	0·26	0·50	0·71	0·87	0·97	1·00
i^2	0	0·07	0·25	0·50	0·76	0·94	1·00
$\omega t \ (^\circ)$	180	165	150	135	120	105	90

The mid-ordinates of i^2 may be obtained from the diagram but as before, it is better to extract them from sine tables and squaring the appropriate values as in Table 5.4.

Table 5.4

Mid-ordinate angle	i	i^2	Mid-ordinate angle
7·5°	0·1305	0·0170	172·5°
22·5°	0·3827	0·1465	157·5°
37·5°	0·6088	0·3706	142·5°
52·5°	0·7934	0·6295	127·5°
67·5°	0·9239	0·8536	112·5°
82·5°	0·9914	0·9829	97·5°

The sum of the twelve mid-ordinates is therefore 6·0002, thus the mean value of i^2 is given by

$$\frac{6 \cdot 0002}{12} = 0 \cdot 5$$

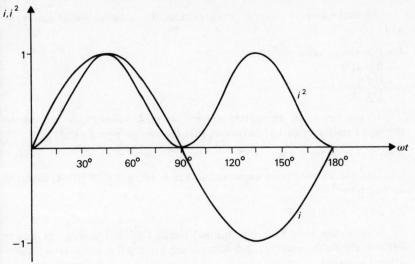

Fig. 5.7 Derivation of r.m.s. value

Had a greater number of ordinates been taken, the result of the mean square determination would have been exactly 0·5 and not fractionally above it as would appear from the above calculation.

It is inconvenient to deal with the mean square value of a current, and therefore the square root of the mean square value is taken, i.e. the root mean square or r.m.s. value.

Thus for the given waveform, the r.m.s. value is

$$\sqrt{0{\cdot}5} = \sqrt{\tfrac{1}{2}}$$

$$= \frac{1}{\sqrt{2}}$$

$$= 0{\cdot}707$$

For the given example, it follows that the r.m.s. current I is 0·707 A. Had a greater peak value I_m been taken, the result would have been proportionally greater; thus the r.m.s. current is given by

$$I = 0{\cdot}707\,I_m \tag{5.7}$$

The r.m.s. value of a sinusoidally alternating current is therefore given by Relation 5.7 but again it must be remembered that this expression only applies to sinusoidal waveforms. Examples will be given later to indicate the effect of waveforms not being sinusoidal. Relation 5.7 is also quite often given in the form

$$I = \frac{1}{\sqrt{2}}\,I_m \tag{5.8}$$

Again the average power P can be calculated over the period of one cycle, and

$P = R \times$ (mean value of i^2)
$\quad = R \times (I^2)$
$\quad = I^2R$
$\quad = \frac{1}{2}I_m{}^2R$

If the sinusoidal alternating current of peak value 1·0 A had passed through a resistance of 1 Ω, it follows that the average power would be

$P = \frac{1}{2} \times 1·0^2 \times 1 = 0·5$ W

Had the current been expressed in r.m.s. terms, i.e. 0·707 A, then the average power is

$P = 0·707^2 \times 1 = 0·5$ W

This would have been the normal method of determining the power because alternating currents and voltages are expressed in r.m.s. values unless otherwise stated.

This fuller determination of r.m.s. values has been derived from consideration of a current, but equally a voltage could have been considered, giving

$$V = \frac{1}{\sqrt{2}} V_m = 0·707 \, V_m \tag{5.9}$$

The r.m.s. value can be related to the average value by a factor termed the form factor, k_f.

$$k_f = \frac{\text{r.m.s. value}}{\text{average value}} \tag{5.10}$$

Typically $k_f = \dfrac{0·707 \, I_m}{0·637 \, I_m}$

$\qquad k_f = 1·11$

This gives the form factor for sine waves as 1·11. A square wave can be shown to have a form factor of 1·0 whilst a triangular wave has a form factor of 1·15. Many modern control devices produce waveforms with form factors of very high values, say 4 or 5. In this respect, the form factors give an indication of the 'peakiness' of the waveform. However, this is better expressed by the peak (or crest) factor given by

$$\text{peak factor} = \frac{\text{peak value}}{\text{r.m.s. value}} \tag{5.12}$$

For a sine wave, this factor is

$$\frac{1}{0·707} = 1·414$$

Example 5.1 An alternating current of sinusoidal waveform has an r.m.s. value of 10·0 A. What are the peak values of this current over one cycle?

$$I_m = \frac{I}{0·707} = \frac{10}{0·707} = 14·14 \text{ A}$$

The peak values therefore are 14·14 A and −14·14 A

Example 5.2 An alternating voltage has the equation $v = 141·4 \sin 377t$; what are the values of

(a) r.m.s. voltage;
(b) frequency;
(c) the instantaneous voltage when $t = 3$ ms?

The relation is of the form $v = V_m \sin \omega t$ and by comparison,

$$V_m = 141·4 \text{ V}$$
$$= \sqrt{2}\, V$$

hence
$$V = \frac{141·4}{\sqrt{2}} = 100 \text{ V}$$

Also by comparison, $\omega = 377$ rad/s
$$= 2\pi f$$

hence
$$f = \frac{377}{2\pi} = 60 \text{ Hz}$$

Finally $v = 141·4 \sin 377t$

When $t = 3 \times 10^{-3}$ s
$$v = 141·4 \sin (377 \times 3 \times 10^{-3}) = 141·4 \sin 1·131$$
$$= 141·4 \times 0·904 = 127·8 \text{ V}$$

Note that in this example, it was necessary to determine the sine of 1·131 radians, which could either be obtained from suitable tables, or from a calculator. Alternatively, 1·131 radians may be converted into degree measurement, i.e. $1·131 \text{ rad} \equiv 1·131 \times \frac{180}{\pi} = 64·8°$.

Example 5.3 A current has the following steady values in amperes for equal intervals of time changing instantaneously from one value to the next:

0, 10, 20, 10, 0, −10, −20, −10, etc.

Calculate the r.m.s. value of the current and its form factor.

154

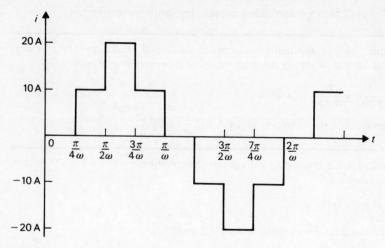

Fig. 5.8

Because of the symmetry of the waveform it is only necessary to calculate the values over first half cycle.

$$I_{av} = \frac{\text{area under characteristic}}{\text{length of base}}$$

$$= \frac{0\left(\frac{\pi}{4\omega} - 0\right) + 10\left(\frac{\pi}{2\omega} - \frac{\pi}{4\omega}\right) + 20\left(\frac{3\pi}{4\omega} - \frac{\pi}{2\omega}\right) + 10\left(\frac{\pi}{\omega} - \frac{3\pi}{4\omega}\right)}{\frac{\pi}{\omega} - 0}$$

$$= 10 \text{ A}$$

The mean square value is

$$I^2 = \frac{0\left(\frac{\pi}{4\omega} - 0\right) + 10^2\left(\frac{\pi}{2\omega} - \frac{\pi}{4\omega}\right) + 20^2\left(\frac{3\pi}{4\omega} - \frac{\pi}{2\omega}\right) + 10^2\left(\frac{\pi}{\omega} - \frac{3\pi}{4\omega}\right)}{\frac{\pi}{\omega} - 0}$$

$$= 150$$

$$I = \sqrt{150} = \underline{12 \cdot 25 \text{ A}}$$

$$k_f = \frac{I}{I_{av}} = \frac{12 \cdot 25}{10} = \underline{1 \cdot 225}$$

Example 5.4 Calculate the form factor for each of the following waveforms shown in Fig. 5.9.

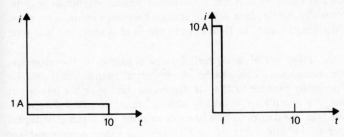

Fig. 5.9

$$I_{av} = \frac{1(10 - 0)}{10 - 0} = 1{\cdot}0 \text{ A} \qquad I_{av} = \frac{10(1 - 0) + 0(10 - 1)}{10 - 0} = 1{\cdot}0 \text{ A}$$

$$I = \left(\frac{1^2(10 - 0)}{10 - 0} \right)^{\frac{1}{2}} = 1{\cdot}0 \text{ A} \qquad I = \left(\frac{10^2(1 - 0) + 0(10 - 1)}{10 - 0} \right)^{\frac{1}{2}}$$

$$= 3{\cdot}16 \text{ A}$$

$$k_f = \frac{I}{I_{av}} = \frac{1{\cdot}0}{1{\cdot}0} \qquad\qquad k_f = \frac{I}{I_{av}} = \frac{3{\cdot}16}{1{\cdot}0}$$

$$= \underline{1{\cdot}0} \qquad\qquad = \underline{3{\cdot}16}$$

It will be noted that the first waveform is essentially that of a direct current in which the mean current and the r.m.s. current have the same value. It is for this reason that the r.m.s. value of an alternating current may be equated to the mean value of a direct current.

It will also be noted how the second waveform gives the same mean current but the short bursts of high current result in a much higher heating effect, which is a problem to be taken into account in many control circuits.

5.5 Vector, complexor and phasor diagrams

A vector quantity is one that has magnitude and direction at a point in space. For instance, a force may be represented by a vector, the length of the vector indicating the magnitude of the force and the direction of the vector indicating the direction of the line of action of the force. More generally, a vector quantity can be represented in a diagram by a line drawn in the appropriate direction and of a length appropriate to the magnitude of the quantity. Vectors are introduced in most elementary mathematics courses

156 and it is therefore assumed that you are familiar with vectors. Those who have not been introduced to them in mathematics will have used vectors to solve mechanical force problems.

Any electrical quantity that has direction as well as magnitude may be expressed vectorially. So far, four such quantities have been introduced, these being the field strengths and the field densities of both electric and magnetic fields.

One of the most useful analytical devices available to the electrical engineer is the complexor. This can be a non-vector quantity that may be illustrated in a similar manner to that of the vector, but with the important difference that the complexor is drawn with reference to some datum. In most cases, we take the datum to be a line drawn along the x-axis (horizontal axis) of a graph, the line being of unit length. All other complexors are relatively bigger or smaller and may be drawn at some angle relative to the given line.

In particular, we are interested in one form of complexor which is made to rotate about one end in the plane of the diagram. The rotation has constant angular velocity. From this process, we make an important observation — the geometric projection upon a datum varies sinusoidally. This sounds rather grand so consider an instance of this operation.

Complexor OA is rotating with constant angular velocity ω about end O as shown in Fig. 5.10. Time is measured from the instant when OA is horizontal and about to rotate into the first quadrant and some $\dfrac{\theta_1}{\omega}$ seconds later, OA reaches some random position OA_1. It follows that OA_1 makes an angle θ_1 with the horizontal axis and from Fig. 5.10,

$$\frac{A_1P_1}{OA_1} = \sin \theta_1$$

where P_1 is the projection of A_1 on the horizontal axis as shown.

If this process is repeated at regular intervals and the corresponding values of AP are plotted to a base of time, the resulting graph is a sine wave.

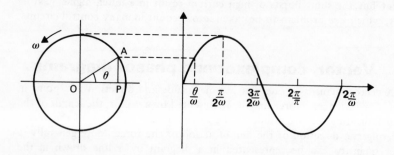

Fig. 5.10 Production of a sine wave from a rotating complexor

$$\theta = \omega t$$

When $\theta = 2\pi$, one complete sine wave will have been produced on the graph. Also it will be seen that the length OA represents the maximum value of the sinusoidal quantity.

The rotation of the complexor in this case is time dependent: thus in that grand phrase already mentioned, its projection upon a datum has been seen to vary sinusoidally. But if a rotating complexor can give rise to a sine wave, then equally a rotating complexor may represent a sinusoidally varying quantity. A complexor that represents or is derived from a time-varying sinusoidal quantity (such as a voltage or a current) is termed a phasor, thus, in the instance considered, OA is a phasor.

A phasor has the advantage of being much more concise than the corresponding sinusoidal waveform and it is much easier to draw and to manipulate. An a.c. circuit is chiefly analysed in terms of the relationship between phasors denoting the various physical quantities such as voltage and current. However, in a circuit these have the same angular frequency and there is no relative motion between the phasors, i.e. they would rotate at the same speed. It follows that they can be displayed in a stationary instantaneous diagram, the common angular rotation being disregarded. Such diagrams are referred to as phasor diagrams.

A phasor is denoted in print by italic bold-faced or Clarendon type, e.g. I. In handwriting, an over-dotted symbol is used, e.g. $\dot{I}$. Note that I represents a current phasor whilst I represents only the magnitude of the current.

For the routine interests of the reader, the differences between vector and phasor diagrams will not be too important, but it is helpful to remember that a vector has space coordinates whilst the phasor is derived from time-varying sinusoids. However, both may be operated in diagram form in the same manner. The above statements of the principles concerned sound rather complicated, so let us proceed to use these principles, when it will be seen that they really are quite easy to apply.

5.6 Relationships between alternating quantities

In previous sections, it has been assumed that any alternating quantity can be expressed in the form $i = I_m \sin \omega t$. This infers that $i = 0$ when $t = 0$. However, it is quite possible that the quantity will have some other value when $t = 0$. Suppose that $i = I_m \sin \phi$ when $t = 0$. The general expression for i must therefore be modified to

$$i = I_m \sin (\omega t + \phi) \tag{5.13}$$

ϕ is termed the phase angle and represents the rotation of the phasor from the horizontal axis when $t = 0$. The effect of ϕ is illustrated in Fig. 5.11.

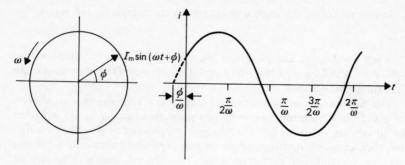

Fig. 5.11 Effect of phase angle

It has already been noted that a diagram may involve more than one phasor. In such a case, let us illustrate the relation between Relation 5.13 and the corresponding waveforms by considering the following currents:

$i_1 = I_{1m} \sin \omega t$

$i_2 = I_{2m} \sin (\omega t + \dfrac{\pi}{6}) = I_{2m} \sin (\omega t + 30°)$

$i_3 = I_{3m} \sin (\omega t - \dfrac{\pi}{4}) = I_{3m} \sin (\omega t - 45°)$

Degrees and radians are commonly used together in this context, as will be seen in the rest of this chapter.

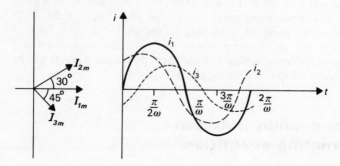

Fig. 5.12 Sinusoidal currents of the same frequency

The instantaneous phasor diagram for these currents and the corresponding waveforms are shown in Fig. 5.12. The diagram is drawn for the instant $t = 0$. It is admissible to draw the three phasors on one diagram since each has the same angular frequency.

Instead of drawing the phasor diagram to a scale appropriate to the maximum values, it could have been drawn to a scale appropriate to the r.m.s.

$$\frac{I_m}{I} = \sqrt{2} = 1 \cdot 41$$

The diagram showing r.m.s. values is usually drawn in the same position as the instantaneous phasor diagram corresponding to $t = 0$. The r.m.s. phasor and the instantaneous phasor diagrams are compared in Fig. 5.13.

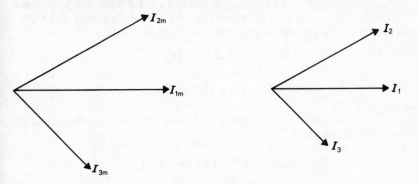

Fig. 5.13 Instantaneous phasor and r.m.s. phasor diagrams

Because most phasor diagrams show r.m.s. values, the terms r.m.s. may be dropped for convenience; thus it may be assumed that any further reference to phasor diagrams infers the use of r.m.s. values. Instantaneous phasor diagrams retain their former interpretation.

In the phasor diagram shown in Fig. 5.13, the phasors are denoted I_1, I_2 and I_3. This corresponds to the previous remarks on notation.

It should be noted that only the instantaneous phasor diagrams can be made to rotate and produce corresponding waveform diagrams. The r.m.s. diagrams must not be made to rotate with this object in mind, since they merely denote the effective values of alternating quantities. The use for such phasor diagrams is to illustrate the phase relationships between alternating quantities. For example, with reference to Fig. 5.12, which is a simple diagram derived from Fig. 5.11:

1. The phase angles between the phasors in the phasor diagram denote the order in which the various quantities reach their maximum values. In Fig. 5.12, this order is I_2, I_1, I_3.
2. Since I_2 reaches its peak before I_1 and I_3, it is said to lead each of the others. Similarly I_1 leads I_3. Note that I_2 leads I_1 by $30°$ and I_2 leads I_3 by $75°$. Also I_1 leads I_3 by $45°$.
3. Since I_3 reaches its peak after I_1 and I_2, it is said to lag each of the others. Similarly I_1 lags I_2. Note that I_3 lags I_2 by $75°$ and I_3 lags I_1 by $45°$. Also I_1 lags I_2 by $30°$.

4. The phase angles permit the time intervals between the instants of peak value to be determined. Thus I_2 leads I_3 by

$$\frac{\frac{\pi}{6} + \frac{\pi}{4}}{\omega} = \frac{5\pi}{12\omega} \text{ seconds}$$

Example 5.5 The currents in two branches of a network may be defined by $i_1 = I_{1m} \sin(\omega t + 36°)$ and $i_2 = I_{2m} \sin(\omega t - 24°)$. Calculate the phase angle of I_2 with respect to I_1 and, given that the supply frequency is 15 kHz, calculate the time interval between the instants of peak value.

Phase angle = 36 + 24 = 60°, i.e. I_2 lags I_1 by $\underline{60°}$.

$$T = \frac{1}{f} = \frac{1}{15 \times 10^3} = 66 \cdot 67 \times 10^{-6} \text{ s}$$

This is the time for a complete cycle but the time appropriate to the phase angle is given by

$$t = \frac{60}{360} \times 66 \cdot 67 \times 10^{-6} = 11 \cdot 11 \times 10^{-6} \text{ s}$$

$$= \underline{11 \cdot 11 \ \mu s}$$

It will be noted that although the current expressions were given in terms of the angular frequency ω, it was not necessary to involve its use and the frequency f was sufficient.

It is strictly considered essential that all quantities represented in a phasor diagram should be of a like nature and relating to the same frequency of variation. However, engineers find it convenient to ignore such considerations in part and therefore they draw phasor diagrams with both voltages and currents represented in them. Provided that both voltages and currents relate to the same frequency, this gives a convenient method of illustrating their phase relationships. However, it is essential that that is all that is taken from such diagrams and that no attempt is made to, say, add a voltage to a current, which would give a meaningless result.

A typical voltage and current phasor diagram is shown in Fig. 5.14 along with the corresponding waveform diagrams. It compares with the previous diagrams which only dealt with currents, but in this instance the voltage has been given the form $v = V_m \sin \omega t$ and the current is $i = I_m \sin(\omega t + \phi)$. The phase angle between them is generally given the symbol ϕ.

Because almost all supplies are specified in terms of their voltages, the voltage in Fig. 5.14 is taken as reference and therefore is specified so that it lies along the horizontal axis. Supplies are specified in terms of voltage because it is the general practice to maintain the supply voltage constant and to vary the current according to the power required. It is possible to maintain a constant current and to vary the voltage according to the power required, but this is only practised in a few restricted applications.

In Fig. 5.14, the current I reaches its peak before the voltage V and it is said that I leads V. In this case, I leads V by the phase angle ϕ. It could also be said that the voltage lags the current but this changes the emphasis away from the voltage as reference and therefore this form of expression is less useful.

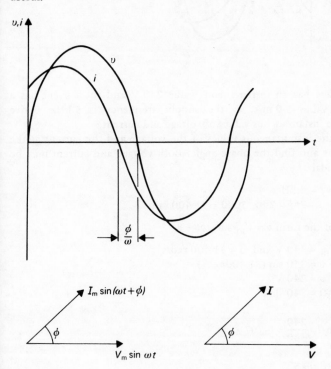

Fig. 5.14 Voltage and current phasor and waveform diagrams

Example 5.6 A sinusoidally alternating voltage of peak value 24 V gives rise to a current of maximum value 16 A. This current is also sinusoidal and lags the voltage by $45°$. Represent the voltage and current waveforms in proper phase relationship over one complete cycle.

Taking the voltage as reference, $v = V_m \sin \omega t = 24 \sin \omega t$
Similarly $i = I_m \sin (\omega t + \phi) = 16 \sin (\omega t - 45°)$

From these expressions, the instantaneous phasor diagram and hence the waveform diagram can be drawn as shown in Fig. 5.15.

Example 5.7 In an a.c. circuit, the voltage is found to have a peak value 340 V whilst the current has a peak value 14·1 mA. At some instant, taken as

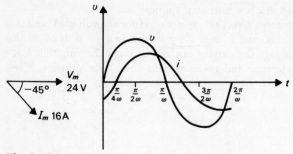

Fig. 5.15

$t = 0$, the voltage has an instantaneous value 240 V and the current has a corresponding value 5·0 mA. If the supply frequency is 5 kHz, derive relations for the instantaneous values of voltage and current.

Calculate the instantaneous values of the voltage and the current at the instant $t = 50\ \mu s$ and find the phase angle. Both voltage and current may be assumed sinusoidal.

$$f = 5 \text{ kHz}$$
$$\omega = 2\pi f = 2\pi \times 5000 = 31\ 400 \text{ rad/s}$$

The voltage is of the form $v = V_m \sin (\omega t + \theta)$

but $\qquad V_m = 340$ V and $\omega = 31\ 400$ rad/s
hence $\qquad v = 340 \sin (31\ 400t + \theta)$
At $t = 0$, $\qquad v = 240$ V
thus $\qquad 240 = 340 \sin \theta$

$$\sin \theta = \frac{240}{340} = 0.707$$

$$\theta = 45°$$

Only the first available solution for θ need be taken, thus

$$\underline{v = 340 \sin (31\ 400t + 45°)}$$

Again it will be seen that this solution provides a trigonometrical solution in which radian measurement is mixed with measurement in degrees.

The current is of the form $i = I_m \sin (\omega t + \beta) = 14·1 \times 10^{-3} \sin (\omega t + \beta)$

When $t = 0$, $\quad i = 5·0 \times 10^{-3}$ A thus

$$5·0 \times 10^{-3} = 14·1 \times 10^{-3} \sin \beta$$

$$\sin \beta = \frac{5·0 \times 10^{-3}}{14·1 \times 10^{-3}}$$

$$\beta = 20·6°$$
$$\underline{i = 14·1 \times 10^{-3} \sin (31\ 400t + 20·6°)}$$

At $t = 50 \, \mu s$,

$$v = 340 \sin (31\,400 \times 50 \times 10^{-6} + 45°)$$
$$= 340 \sin (1·57 + 45°)$$

But $1·57$ rad $= 1·57 \times \dfrac{180}{\pi} = 90°$

hence $\quad v = 340 \sin (90° + 45°) = \underline{240 \text{ V}}$

Also $\quad i = 14·1 \times 10^{-3} \sin (90° + 20·6°)$
$$= 13·3 \times 10^{-3} \text{ A} = \underline{13·3 \text{ mA}}$$

The phase angle between the voltage and the current is given by

$$\phi = \theta - \beta = 45° - 20·6° = 24·4°$$

It can also be seen that the voltage leads the current, but in the normal method of expression, the current lags the voltage and the phase angle is defined as

$$\phi = \underline{24·4° \text{ lag}}$$

5.7 Polar notation

It is awkward to define alternating quantities in such forms as $v = V_m \sin (\omega t + \phi)$, especially bearing in mind the importance of r.m.s. values. A useful form of notation defining a phasor is polar notation, taking the form $A\angle\theta.1$, where 1 is a unit reference step. A unit reference step is one of unit scale length in some fixed axis, usually taken as the positive direction along the x-axis. The value A serves to change the magnitude whilst the angle θ is the angle through which the phasor has been rotated. Provided the unit reference step is taken as stated, it may be omitted but its existence must not be forgotten.

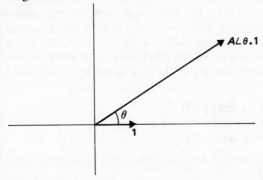

Fig. 5.16 Polar diagram

Any diagram using coordinate axes of the form shown in Fig. 5.16 is termed an Argand diagram or a complexor diagram. Thus any quantity

164 expressed on such a diagram is in general a complexor. However, if its position represents time with respect to the datum, then the complexors become phasors. In the given case, the unit reference step would represent some instant in time, normally that corresponding to $t = 0$. In the case of the r.m.s. phasor diagram, this condition is not fulfilled but the phase relationship remains illustrated.

5.8   Addition and subtraction of sinusoidally alternating quantities

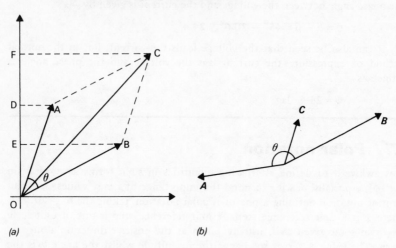

Fig. 5.17 Addition of phasors

Let A and B in Fig. 5.17(b) be two instantaneous phasors representing, at some given instant, two sinusoidally alternating quantities which have the same frequency but differ in phase angle by θ. The phasors may be added together by completing the parallelogram OACB as shown in Fig. 5.17(a), and drawing the diagonal OC which may be taken as a phasor C. OA, OB and OC are projected on to the vertical axis to give the corresponding instantaneous values of the phasors thus:

the instantaneous value of A is given by OD
the instantaneous value of B is given by OE
the instantaneous value of C is given by OF

The opposite sides of a parallelogram are equal; thus OA = BC and the projections on to the vertical axis OD = EF.

But OE + EF = OF

thus the instantaneous value of C is equal to the sum of the instantaneous values of A and B.

It follows that OC represents the maximum value of the resultant phasor
and C is the phasor sum of A and B. OC is less in magnitude than the
arithmetic sum of OA and OB except in the case where A and B are in phase.
Figure 5.17(b) indicates that as θ tends toward $180°$, then OC can become
much less than either of the component phasors. The general instance
considered indicates that it is seldom correct in a.c. analysis to add currents
or to add voltages together arithmetically. This is a common mistake arising
from our earlier consideration of d.c. analysis in which there was no problem
of variation with time. Great care must be taken to bear in mind the
additional factor of time that has now been introduced.

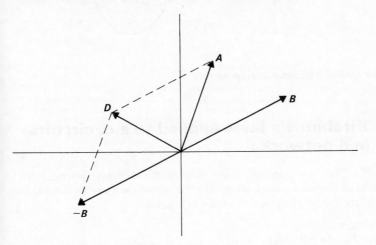

Fig. 5.18 Subtraction of phasors

If B is to be subtracted from A then B is rotated through $180°$ to give
$-B$. This new phasor is then added to A as before and the resultant phasor D
shown in Fig. 5.18 is given by the phasor difference between A and B.

Both the addition and the subtraction processes considered above have
been dealt with on the basis of considering a particular instant. However, you
could draw out the corresponding sinusoidal waveforms shown in Fig. 5.19
and observe that no matter which instant is chosen, the general relations
always hold true; but it must be emphasised that:

1. the frequency of each component is the same;
2. the period of each component is the same.

Adding and subtracting waveforms is a time-consuming affair; addition
and subtraction of phasors is achieved much more rapidly, either by means of
scale diagrams or algebraic manipulation. For this reason, our future studies
shall concentrate on these means of processing the stated operations. Let us
consider further then the addition and subtraction of phasors by their
application to a.c. systems.

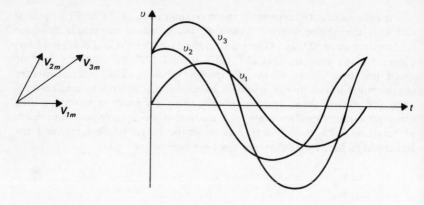

Fig. 5.19 Addition of sinusoidal quantities

5.9 Kirchhoff's laws applied to a.c. circuits and networks

Kirchhoff's first law states that the sum of the currents flowing into a junction in an electric network is equal to the sum of the currents flowing out from the junction. In the junction shown in Fig. 5.20,

$$i_1 = i_2 + i_3$$

Let $\quad i_2 = I_{2m} \sin (\omega t + \phi_2)$

and $\quad i_3 = I_{3m} \sin (\omega t + \phi_3)$

These are two sinusoidal currents of the same frequency; this is a reasonable assumption since the majority of a.c. circuits and networks involve only one frequency.

$$i_1 = I_{2m} \sin (\omega t + \phi_2) + I_{3m} \sin (\omega t + \phi_3)$$

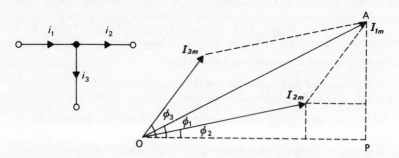

Fig. 5.20 Kirchhoff's first law applied to an a.c. network

Taking the vertical components as before, but at the instant $t = 0$, as
shown in the phasor diagram of Fig. 5.20,

$$PA = I_{2m} \sin \phi_2 + I_{3m} \sin \phi_3$$
$$= I_{1m} \sin \phi_1$$

Similarly, taking the horizontal components,

$$OP = I_{2m} \cos \phi_2 + I_{3m} \cos \phi_3$$
$$= I_{1m} \cos \phi_1$$

But
$$OA^2 = OP^2 + PA^2$$
$$I_{1m}^2 = I_{1m}^2 \cos^2\phi_1 + I_{1m}^2 \sin^2\phi_1$$
$$= (I_{2m} \cos \phi_2 + I_{3m} \cos \phi_3)^2 + (I_{2m} \sin \phi_2 + I_{3m} \cos \phi_3)^2$$

From this expression, it is therefore possible to derive the magnitude of
the resultant sinusoidal current, which takes the form

$$i = I_{1m} \sin (\omega t + \phi_1)$$

ϕ_1 may be evaluated from:

$$\cos \phi_1 = \frac{OP}{OA} = \frac{I_{2m} \cos \phi_2 + I_{3m} \cos \phi_3}{I_{1m}}$$

or
$$\sin \phi_1 = \frac{PA}{OA}$$

or
$$\tan \phi_1 = \frac{PA}{OP}$$

To summarise, OA is the phasor sum of I_{2m} and I_{3m} at the given instant
$t = 0$, which may be expressed as

$$I_{1m} = I_{2m} + I_{3m}$$

This form of result applies to any number of branches at a junction. Also
the result can be extended to cover r.m.s. phasors, which is the more usual
application. Thus

$$I_1 = I_2 + I_3$$

All of the above material is rather difficult to take in, so do not worry if
you find that it does not seem to mean too much to you. The practice in this
case is much easier than the theory as instanced by the following examples.

Example 5.8 By means of a graphical addition of the appropriate phasors,
determine the current I_1 in Fig. 5.21 given that $I_2 = 2 \angle 30°$ A and
$I_3 = 3 \angle 0°$ A. Give the answer both in polar rotation and also in the form
$i = I_m \sin (\omega t + \phi)$.

In order to produce the graphical solution required, it is first necessary to
determine a suitable scale. We know that the resultant current cannot be

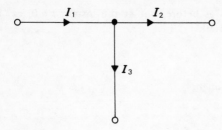

Fig. 5.21

greater than the arithmetic sum and is likely to be less: however, taking the arithmetic sum of the currents, i.e. 5 A, a suitable scale might be 0·5 A/cm since this would involve a maximum line length of 10 cm which can be drawn within the page area available.

I_2 is drawn at $30°$ to the horizontal as shown in Fig. 5.22 and to a length 4 cm. Notice that the angle is positive and therefore the phasor lies in the first quadrant. I_3 is drawn along the horizontal axis since its angle is $0°$; its length is 6 cm being that appropriate to 3 A.

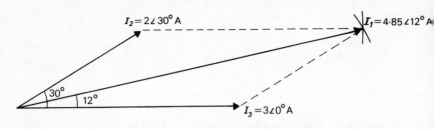

Fig. 5.22

By completing the parallelogram as shown, the resultant current I_1 is given by the diagonal of the construction. By measurement of the diagonal, its length is 9·7 cm and therefore the resultant current is 4·85 A. The angle ϕ_1 may be measured by a protractor and is found to be $12°$. Thus the resultant current is

$I_1 = 4.85 \angle 12° \text{ A}$

If you do not have a protractor available for measuring the phasor angles, a useful alternative is indicated in Fig. 5.23.

Draw a circle of radius 10 cm. To obtain an angle of $30°$ as required by phasor I_2, look up the value of cos $30°$, which is found to be 0·87. Measure 8·7 cm along the horizontal axis and project a line vertically upwards; where this line meets the circle indicates a point lying on a line at $30°$ to the horizontal. Note that you have created a right-angled triangle of adjacent side 8·7 cm and hypotenuse 10 cm, giving a cosine ratio of $\frac{8·7}{10} = 0.87$, which corresponds to an angle of $30°$.

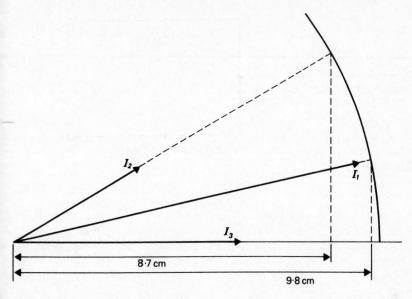

8·7 cm

9·8 cm

Fig. 5.23

In order to obtain ϕ_1, project I_1 to meet the circle and drop a line vertically from the point of intersection. Measure the distance from the origin along the horizontal axis to the point of intersection with the vertical line, which in this case gives a distance of 9·8 cm. Thus $\cos \phi_1 = \dfrac{9·8}{10} = 0·98$, thus giving ϕ_1 approximately equal to $12°$.

With a little practice, this alternative technique can be very useful.

Finally the current is to be expressed in the form $i = I_m \sin (\omega t + \phi)$. The currents I_2 and I_3 are given in r.m.s. form — lower-case letters would have been used had instantaneous values been intended. It follows that $I_{1m} = \sqrt{2} \times 4·85 = 6·86$ A and hence

$$i_1 = \underline{6·86 \sin (\omega t + 12°) \text{ A}}$$

The above example has been explained in considerable detail because it is an extremely important form of calculation. However, in normal circumstances the form of solution would be much more brief as indicated by Example 5.9. If you have fully understood the previous example, you should now be able to follow the procedure as laid out in this further example.

Example 5.9 For the network indicated in Fig. 5.24, calculate graphically the current I_2, giving your answer in polar form.

A suitable scale would be 1 mA/cm. Draw the phasor diagram shown in Fig. 5.25 and determine $I_2 = I_1 - I_3$.

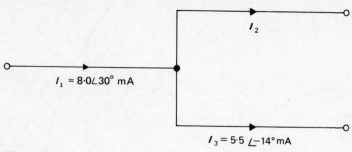

Fig. 5.24

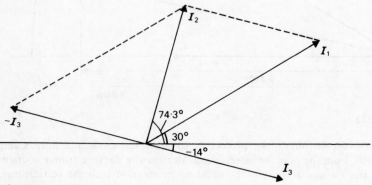

Fig. 5.25

From the phasor diagram,

$I_2 = \underline{5\cdot54 \angle 74\cdot3^\circ \text{ mA}}$

Example 5.10 The instantaneous values of two alternating currents may be represented by $i_1 = 6 \sin \omega t$ amperes and $i_2 = 4 \sin \left(\omega t - \frac{\pi}{3}\right)$ amperes. Derive a similar expression for the total current.

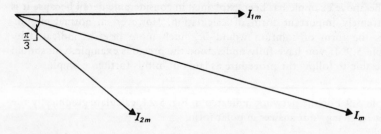

Fig. 5.26

For the instant $t = 0$, the phasor diagram is shown in Fig. 5.26.

$I_m \cos \phi = I_{1m} \cos \phi_1 + I_{2m} \cos \phi_2$

$$= 6 \cos 0 + 4 \cos \frac{-\pi}{3}$$

$$= 6 + 2 = 8 \text{ A}$$

$I_m \sin \phi = I_{1m} \sin \phi_1 + I_{2m} \sin \phi_2$

$$= 6 \sin 0 + 4 \sin \frac{-\pi}{3}$$

$$= 0 - 3 \cdot 46 = -3 \cdot 46 \text{ A}$$

$$I_m{}^2 = 8^2 + (-3 \cdot 46)^2$$

$$I_m = 8 \cdot 72 \text{ A}$$

also $\sin \phi = \dfrac{-3 \cdot 46}{8 \cdot 72} = -0 \cdot 397$

$$\phi = -23 \cdot 4° = -0 \cdot 41 \text{ rad}$$

Hence total current is given by

$$i = 8 \cdot 72 \sin (\omega t - 0 \cdot 41) \text{ amperes}$$

Kirchhoff's second law states that at any instant, the sum of the e.m.f.s round any closed loop is equal to the sum of the voltage drops. In the circuit shown in Fig. 5.27, it follows that

$$e = v_1 + v_2$$

By the same methods already described, the instantaneous phasor diagram can be constructed as shown in Fig. 5.27, the diagram interpreting the relation.

$$E_{1m} = V_{1m} + V_{2m}$$

Finally, instead of using instantaneous phasor values, r.m.s. values could have been used and a diagram drawn to illustrate

$$E_1 = V_1 + V_2$$

It should be noted that phasors can only be added in this way provided they represent quantities which are both sinusoidal and of the same frequency.

Example 5.11 A circuit comprising four loads connected in series has the following volt drops across each of the loads:

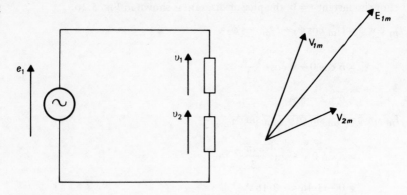

Fig. 5.27 Kirchhoff's second law applied to an a.c. circuit

$v_1 = 50 \sin \omega t$
$v_2 = 25 \sin (\omega t + 60°)$
$v_3 = 40 \cos \omega t$
$v_4 = 30 \sin (\omega t - 45°)$

If the voltage drops are measured in volts, calculate the supply voltage, giving your answer in similar form.

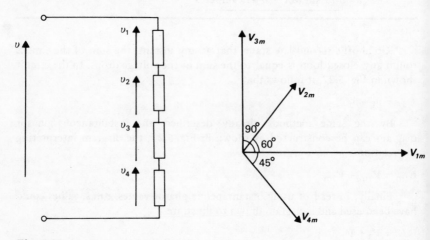

Fig. 5.28

The instantaneous phasor diagram is shown in Fig. 5.28. The sum of the voltages may be carried out as shown in Fig. 5.29. Note that $v_3 = 40 \cos \omega t = 40 \sin (\omega t + 90°)$ volts.

From the phasor summation diagram,

$v = \underline{93 \sin (\omega t + 26°)}$ volts

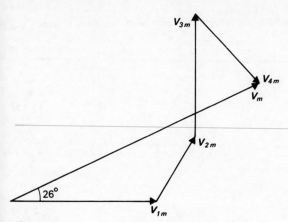

Fig. 5.29

The solution can also be obtained by analysis, the phasors being resolved into their horizontal and vertical components, thus

$$V_m \cos \phi = V_{1m} \cos \phi_1 + V_{2m} \cos \phi_2 + V_{3m} \cos \phi_3 + V_{4m} \cos \phi_4$$
$$= 50 \cos 0° + 25 \cos 60° + 40 \cos 90° + 30 \cos -45°$$
$$= 83 \cdot 7 \text{ V}$$
$$V_m \sin \phi = V_{1m} \sin \phi_1 + V_{2m} \sin \phi_2 + V_{3m} \sin \phi_3 + V_{4m} \sin \phi_4$$
$$= 50 \sin 0° + 25 \sin 60° + 40 \sin 90° + 30 \sin -45°$$
$$= 40 \cdot 4 \text{ V}$$
$$V_m = (V_m{}^2 \cos^2\phi + V_m{}^2 \sin^2\phi)^{\frac{1}{2}}$$
$$= (83 \cdot 7^2 + 40 \cdot 4^2)^{\frac{1}{2}}$$
$$= \underline{93 \cdot 0 \text{ V}}$$
$$\sin \phi = \frac{V_m \sin \phi}{V_m} = \frac{40 \cdot 4}{93 \cdot 0} = 0 \cdot 435$$
$$\phi = 25 \cdot 6°$$
$$v = \underline{93 \sin (\omega t + 25 \cdot 6°) \text{ volts}}$$

5.10 Resistance in an a.c. circuit

All circuits incorporate resistance to some degree. However, just as in the d.c. circuit, only the relatively large values of resistance in a circuit need be considered. In the purely resistive circuit shown in Fig. 5.30, suppose that the source voltage may be represented by $v = V_m \sin \omega t$ and that the circuit resistance may be represented by R. At any instant, the resulting current is given by

$$i = \frac{v}{R} = \frac{V_m}{R} \sin \omega t \qquad (5.14)$$

The maximum value of this expression occurs when $\sin \omega t = 1$, hence

$$I_m = \frac{V_m}{R}$$

Substituting in Relation 5.14

$$i = I_m \sin \omega t \qquad (5.15)$$

Also $V_m = I_m R$

$$\frac{V_m}{\sqrt{2}} = \frac{I_m}{\sqrt{2}} \cdot R$$

Hence in r.m.s. values

$$V = IR \qquad (5.16)$$

The voltage and the current waveforms for such an arrangement are shown in Fig. 5.30. Both waveforms are sinusoidal and they rise and fall together. When two sine waves behave in this manner, they are said to be in phase with one another. They pass through zero at the same instants, i.e. when $t = 0, \dfrac{\pi}{\omega}, \dfrac{2\pi}{\omega}$, etc. pass through their positive maximum values at the same instants, i.e. when $t = \dfrac{\pi}{2\omega}$, etc. and pass through their negative maximum values at the same instants, i.e. when $t = \dfrac{3\pi}{2\omega}$, etc. Thus the voltage and the current in a purely resistive circuit are in phase.

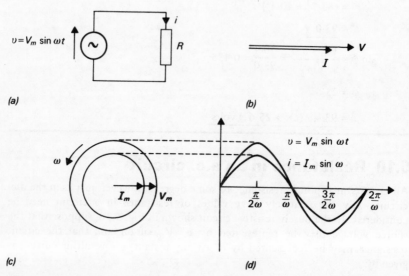

Fig. 5.30 Purely resistive circuit (*a*) circuit diagram (*b*) phasor diagram (*c*) instantaneous phasor diagram (*d*) waveform diagram

The instantaneous phasor diagram has been drawn for the instant $t = 0$.
When the instantaneous values of the phasors are plotted against the vertical axis, the instantaneous voltages and currents are obtained as before. The phasor diagram, on the other hand, represents the r.m.s. values and the relative directions of the phasors have time significance only. It is generally convenient to take the voltage as reference, and its phasor is drawn horizontally.

The passage of a current through a resistor causes energy to be dissipated in the form of heat. By definition, r.m.s. current is the effective value of an alternating current in terms of the average rate of energy dissipation; thus

$$P = I^2 R = VI = \frac{V^2}{R} \tag{5.17}$$

Example 5.12 What is the current flowing in a 30-Ω resistor when a 240-V, 50-Hz voltage is applied across the resistor? Draw the corresponding phasor diagram and calculate the rate of energy dissipation by the resistor.

$$I = \frac{V}{R} = \frac{240}{30} = 8 \text{ A}$$

The phasor diagram is shown in Fig. 5.31.

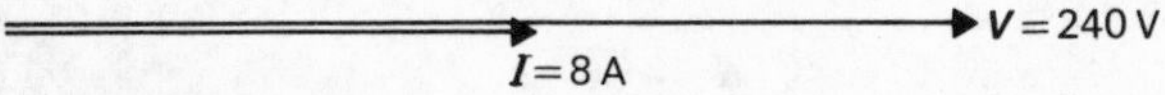

$I = 8$ A $V = 240$ V

Fig. 5.31

$$P = I^2 R = 8^2 \times 30 = \underline{1920 \text{ W}}$$

5.11 Simple rectification systems

Whilst alternating currents and voltages play the leading roles in most electrical and electronic equipment, nevertheless many devices can either only operate on unidirectional currents and voltages, or at least they require such a supply as part of their mode of operation. The process of obtaining unidirectional currents and voltages from alternating currents and voltages is termed rectification.

The device that makes such a process possible is a diode, the ideal operating characteristic of which is given in Fig. 5.32. When the applied voltage acts in the forward direction, there is no voltage drop across the diode and a current flows unimpeded. However, when the applied voltage acts in the reverse direction, a voltage drop appears across the diode and no current flows.

It is possible to obtain rectification by means of a single diode as indicated in Fig. 5.33. The current can only flow through the diode in one direction and thus the load current can only flow during alternate half cycles.

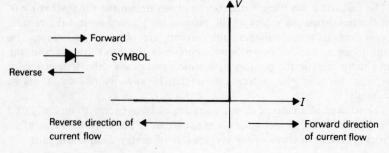

Fig. 5.32 Diode characteristics

For this reason, the system is known as half-wave rectification. The load current, and hence the voltage drop across the load, is unidirectional and could be described as direct, although this term is more usually reserved for steady unidirectional quantities.

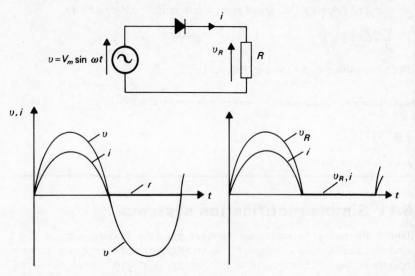

Fig. 5.33 Half-wave rectification

Because the load current and voltage fluctuate so much, a second system is preferred whereby a more continuous unidirectional supply is obtained, and at the same time use is made of both halves of the alternating supply waveform.

The second system is shown in Fig. 5.34 and is described as full-wave rectification. Diagrams (b) and (c) indicate the current paths during the appropriate half cycles, and the diodes not carrying current due to reverse connection are omitted. The resulting current and voltage waveforms for the load are now more even in their effect and tend toward being those of 'direct' quantities.

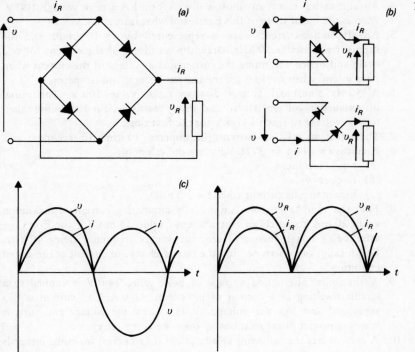

Fig. 5.34 Full-wave bridge rectification

The form of connection of diodes shown in Fig. 5.34 is termed a bridge and hence the device is known as a bridge rectifier. The diodes are most commonly semiconductor diodes although metal rectifier arrangements are also used. An application of a bridge rectifier will be considered in greater detail in Chapter 7.

Problems

1. An alternating current of sinusoidal waveform has an r.m.s. value of 10·0 A. What are the maximum values of this current during the period of one waveform?
2. An alternating voltage wave is represented by $v = 353·5 \sin \omega t$. What are the maximum and r.m.s. values of this voltage?
3. Is the value of an alternating e.m.f. at any given instant:
    (a) the r.m.s. value;
    (b) the peak value;
    (c) the minimum value;
    (d) the instantaneous value?

4. An alternating e.m.f. of sinusoidal waveform has a peak voltage 100 V. What is the mean value of this e.m.f. and what is its r.m.s. value?

5. An alternating-current wave is represented by $i = 10 \sin \omega t$ and the supply frequency is 50 kHz. Draw the waveform of the current for one cycle and hence determine the instantaneous values of the current when $t = 5$ μs and when $t = 13 \cdot 3$ μs, the current being in milliamperes.

6. A 50-Hz sinusoidal voltage has an r.m.s. value 200 V. The initial instantaneous voltage is zero and rising positively. Find the time taken for the voltage to reach 141·4 V for the first time.

7. The equation relating current (in amperes) to time (in seconds) in a circuit is $i = 141 \cdot 4 \sin 377t$. What are the values of:
   (a) r.m.s. current;
   (b) frequency;
   (c) instantaneous current when $t = 3 \cdot 0$ ms?

8. Find the time taken for a sinusoidally alternating current of maximum value 20 mA to reach an instantaneous value 15 mA for the first time after being instantaneously zero, the supply frequency being 40 kHz. Graphically, or otherwise, find the rate of change of current at the stated condition.

9. A sinusoidal alternating voltage of peak value 24·0 V is applied to a circuit resulting in a current of peak value 16·0 A. This current is also sinusoidal and lags the voltage by 45°. Draw the voltage and current waves in proper phase relationship over one complete cycle.

10. A current has the following steady values (in amperes) for equal intervals of time, changing instantaneously from one value to the next:
    0, 5, 10, 15, 10, 5, 0, −5, −10, −15, −10, −5, etc.
    Calculate the r.m.s. value of the current and the form factor.

11. Plot the half wave of current corresponding to the values in the table below. Draw a smooth curve through the points and use the mid-ordinate method to determine:
    (a) the average current;
    (b) the r.m.s. current.

Time base (in degrees)	0	20	40	60	80	100	120	140	160	180
Current (in amperes)	0	15	24	35	68	70	64	35	12	0

12. The positive half cycle of a symmetrical alternating current waveform varies as follows:

Time (ms)	0–2	2–6	6–8
Current	uniform increase from zero to 1 A	constant at 1 A	uniform decrease from 1 A to zero

   Plot to convenient scales the current waveform over one cycle and determine the r.m.s. value of the current.

13. Two sinusoidal e.m.f.s, one of r.m.s. value 10 V and the other of r.m.s. value 20 V, alternate at the same frequency 100 Hz. The 10-V e.m.f. lags

the 20-V e.m.f. by 45°. Draw the two waveforms on the same graph and
determine the period of the waves.

14. A current 20 A lags another current 40 A by 90°. By means of a scale phasor diagram, determine the magnitude of the sum of the two currents.

15. Two currents, each 10 A, come together at a junction and they are out of phase with one another by 60°. By means of a phasor diagram, determine the magnitude of the total current.

16. Two voltages, each 240 V, are in phase with one another. What is the magnitude of their sum? Also what would have been the magnitude of their sum had they been out of phase by 120°?

17. Subtract a current of 10·0 A from a current of 14·14 A given that the 14·14-A current leads the 10·0-A current by 45°.

18. For the network shown in Fig. 5.35, ammeter A1 indicates the mean current in the load as 10 A. Ammeter A2 indicates the r.m.s. supply current. Determine the indication of A2.

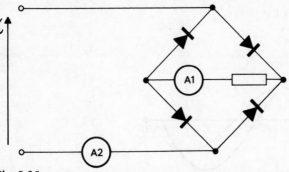

Fig. 5.35

19. Two voltage drops in a series circuit are represented by $v_1 = 100 \sin \omega t$ and $v_2 = 100 \cos \omega t$. Add these voltages by means of a phasor diagram and express the resultant voltage in the form $v = V_m \sin (\omega t \pm \phi)$.

20. The instantaneous voltages across each of four series loads are given by:

$v_1 = 100 \sin 471t$

$v_2 = 250 \cos 471t$

$v_3 = 150 \sin \left(471t + \dfrac{\pi}{6}\right)$

$v_4 = 200 \sin \left(471t - \dfrac{\pi}{4}\right)$

Determine the total potential difference, expressing the value in similar form. What will be the resultant p.d. if the polarity of v_2 is reversed?

21. Add, by means of a phasor diagram, the following currents which are given in milliamperes:

180 $i_a = 100 \sin (\omega t - 45°)$
$i_b = 50 \sin (\omega t + 30°)$
$i_c = 60 \cos \omega t$

22. Three currents may be described as $10 \angle 0°$ A, $15 \angle 30°$ A and $20 \angle -90°$ A. Find the total current that would result from their sum and express the total current in similar form.

Answers

1. 14·14 A, −14·14 A
2. **353·5 V, 250 V**
3. (*d*)
4. 63·6 V, 70·7 V
5. 10·0 mA, −8·66 mA
6. 1·67 ms
7. 100 A, 60 Hz, 127·8 A
8. 3·375 µs, 3324 A/s

9.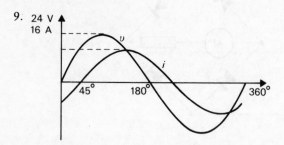

10. 8·9 A, 1·18
11. 36·9 A, 43·9 A
12. 0·81 A
13. 10 ms

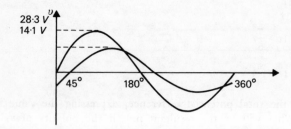

14. 44·8 A
15. 17·3 A

16. 480 V, 240 V
17. 10 A
18. 11·1 A
19. 141·4 sin $(\omega t + 45°)$
20. 414 sin $(471t + 26·5°)$, 486 sin $(471t - 40·0°)$
21. 115 sin $(\omega t + 7°)$
22. 26·17 $\angle -28·5°$ A

Chapter 6

Single-phase a.c. circuits

In previous chapters, only the effect of resistance had to be taken into account. Alternating-current circuits have other factors that must be considered; these factors are inductance and capacitance. In order to limit this introductory study, only those circuits in which both the voltage and the current waveforms are sinusoidal will be considered. This is not an unreasonable assumption since it applies to the majority of a.c. circuits; its validity will be further discussed at the end of the chapter.

6.1 Inductance

Any circuit must complete at least one turn — otherwise it would not be a circuit. However, even a circuit of one turn has inductance. Under the steady conditions of a d.c. circuit, the inductance has no effect and therefore does not require to be included in the d.c. circuit analysis of, say, Chapter 1. In an a.c. circuit, the fluctuating current gives rise to a fluctuating flux which induces an e.m.f. in the circuit; this appears as an effective voltage drop.

A pure inductor is a device that has inductance but neither resistance nor capacitance. It is represented by the symbol shown in Fig. 6.1(a). For the purpose of introducing its action, it is convenient to remember that it is a current-operated device. Let that current be of the form

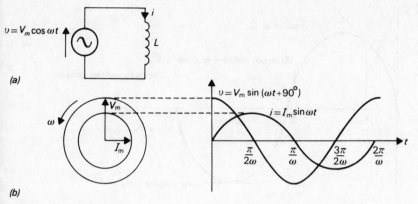

Fig. 6.1 Purely inductive circuit

$$i = I_m \sin \omega t$$

The induced e.m.f. in an inductive arrangement is given by

$$E = L \cdot \frac{I}{t}$$

Because the current is given in instantaneous values, the induced e.m.f. e must also be given in instantaneous values, thus

$$e = L \cdot \frac{\delta i}{\delta t} \qquad (6.1)$$

$\frac{\delta i}{\delta t}$ represents the rate of change of current with time and the resulting e.m.f.

waveform relating to the sinusoidal current waveform is shown in Fig. 6.7(*b*).

That this should be the case may be shown by means of Fig. 6.2. A is any point on the sinusoidal curve and the tangent to the curve drawn through point A gives the rate of change of current at that point. To obtain the gradient, take any two points on the curve closely adjacent to A, one on either side. Let the points be i_1, t_1 and i_2, t_2. Provided these are close enough to point A, then the gradient of the tangent will be approximately given by

$$\frac{\delta i}{\delta t} = \frac{i_2 - i_1}{t_2 - t_1}$$

The smaller $i_2 - i_1$ and $t_2 - t_1$ become, the more accurate is the expression.

There are certain points of outstanding interest in the current waveform shown in Fig. 6.2. At the instant $t = 0$, the current $i = 0$ but the gradient of the tangent is greatest, i.e. the maximum value of $\frac{\delta i}{\delta t}$ is obtained. Also the value of $\frac{\delta i}{\delta t}$ is positive; thus it may be observed that the corresponding value

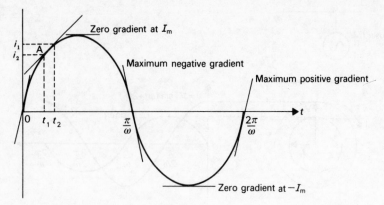

Fig. 6.2 Rate of change of current

of induced e.m.f. from Relation 6.1 is the positive maximum value. This also arises at the instant $t = \dfrac{2\pi}{\omega}$, but at $t = \dfrac{\pi}{\omega}$, even though again the gradient has the same value in magnitude, this time it is negative.

When $i = I_m$ and $i = -I_m$, the gradient is zero since δi is zero. The corresponding value of induced e.m.f. in each case is consequently zero.

By drawing a scale diagram of the sinusoidal current waveform, the gradients at all intermediate points may be determined with the result shown in Fig. 6.3. This diagram shows that the curve of $\dfrac{\delta i}{\delta t}$ to the same base of time results in a 'cosinusoidal' waveform, i.e. that corresponding to a cosine. Effectively to another scale, this is therefore the waveform of the induced e.m.f. e. By the convention already discussed in para. 3.6, this is equal to the applied voltage. We may therefore make the important observation that the applied voltage across a pure inductor leads the current by $90°$, but this is more usually stated in terms of the voltage as the reference, i.e. the current lags the applied voltage by $90°$.

Before leaving Fig. 6.3, it should be noted that the greater the frequency of the sinusoidal current, the greater is the rate of change associated with it. This may be more readily appreciated if you remember that with increase of frequency, the period of a cycle is reduced and therefore the less time there is in which the changes have to take place, i.e. the faster they have to be done.

There are therefore three factors affecting the induced e.m.f.:

(i)   the magnetic factor of goodness represented by the inductance L;
(ii) the magnitude of the current;
(iii) the frequency represented by ω.

Increase in any of these factors will increase the induced e.m.f. and therefore in r.m.s. terms

$$V = E \propto \omega L I$$

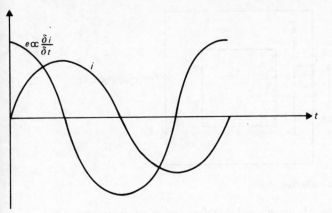

Fig. 6.3 Rate of change of current

This is generally expressed in the form

$$V = E = IX_L \tag{6.2}$$

where X_L is a constant of the system representing the product of the frequency and the inductance. X_L is said to be the inductive reactance of the circuit, the subscript L being there to remind us that it is due to the presence of inductance in the system.

Inductive reactance   **Symbol:** X_L **Unit: ohm (Ω)**

It may be shown (see Appendix A) that

$$X_L = \omega L = 2\pi f L \tag{6.3}$$

Relation 6.2 may be rewritten in the form

$$X_L = \frac{V}{I}$$

Thus it may be observed that the inductive reactance is the ratio of the voltage to the current associated with an inductor. Also the reactance indicates the ability of an inductor to restrict the current in a circuit at a given frequency.

This may well leave the thought in your mind — why does an inductor limit current especially when we have only considered resistance to do so previously? Consider a simple inductor as shown in Fig. 6.4. This version has been specially made to give a strong inductive effect, and hence it uses a coil with many turns. When an alternating voltage is applied to the coil, it causes a current to flow in the coil which in turn creates a flux in the core of the inductor. Because the applied voltage and the current are alternating, the flux must alternate, thus inducing an e.m.f. in the coil which, by Lenz's law,

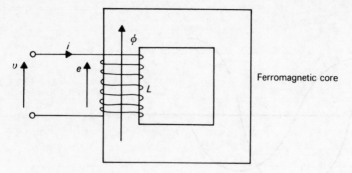

Fig. 6.4 Simple inductor

opposes the flow of current, and therefore acts as a voltage drop.

If insufficient current were to flow in the circuit, there would not be sufficient flux to induce a sufficient e.m.f. to be equal to the applied voltage, and hence the voltage would cause more current to flow until there were just enough current to produce just enough flux to produce just enough induced e.m.f. to be equal to the applied voltage. In this way, the action of the inductor is to limit the current but, unlike the resistor which depends only on its construction for its value of resistance, the inductor depends both on its construction for the value of its inductance and also on the operating frequency for the reactance that results.

Example 6.1 A 20-mH inductor of negligible resistance is connected to a source of 55-V, 50-Hz sinusoidal e.m.f. Calculate the current in the inductor.

If the inductor were connected to another source of sinusoidal e.m.f. rated at 10 V, 5 kHz, what current would flow in the inductor?

At 50 Hz, $X_L = 2\pi f L = 2\pi \times 50 \times 20 \times 10^{-3} = 6 \cdot 28 \ \Omega$

$$I = \frac{V}{X_L} = \frac{55}{6 \cdot 28} = \underline{8 \cdot 76 \ A}$$

At 5 kHz, $X_L = 2\pi f L = 2\pi \times 5000 \times 20 \times 10^{-3} = 628 \ \Omega$

$$I = \frac{V}{X_L} = \frac{10}{628} = 0 \cdot 0159 \ A = \underline{15 \cdot 9 \ mA}$$

It will be observed from this example that the change of frequency played an important part in reducing the current in the inductor. 50 Hz is the frequency associated with electricity supply to both industrial and commercial consumers with the object of transmitting large amounts of energy to them. It is thus fitting that this frequency has given rise to a large current. By comparison, the higher frequency of 5 kHz is that which might be associated

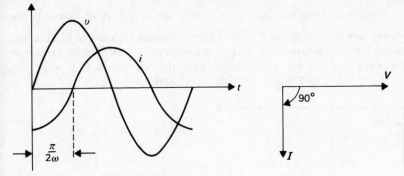

Fig. 6.5 Inductive circuit relationships

with communications systems which involve the transmission of small amounts of energy. It is again fitting that this frequency has given rise to a small current, and operations at this and higher frequencies are sometimes described as light current electrical engineering as a result.

Finally the waveform diagram of Fig. 6.5 shows the phase relationship between the voltage and the current. Here they are shown to be $\frac{\pi}{2\omega}$ seconds apart, i.e. they are one-quarter of a cycle apart, the current lagging the voltage. Such waveforms are said to be in quadrature.

In the phasor diagram, the voltage has been shown in its more usual situation, being taken as reference. It is characteristic of inductive circuits that the current lags the voltage, and in the case of a pure inductor, the angle of lag is $90°$.

It should be noted that since both the voltage and the current have the same angular frequency, they can be shown in the same phasor diagram which only indicates their relative phase displacement. The instantaneous phasor diagram is drawn at the instant $t = 0$.

Example 6.2 An alternating voltage, $v = 100 \sin 400\,t$ volts, is applied to a 2-H inductor. Derive an expression for the current in the inductor and draw the phasor diagram appropriate to the circuit.

From the voltage expression, $\omega = 400$ rad/s

$$X_L = \omega L = 400 \times 2 = 800 \ \Omega$$

$$= \frac{V}{I} = \frac{\sqrt{2} \times V}{\sqrt{2} \times I} = \frac{V_m}{I_m}$$

$$I_m = \frac{V_m}{X_L} = \frac{100}{800} = 0 \cdot 125 \ \text{A}$$

$$i = 0 \cdot 125 \sin \left(400t - \frac{\pi}{2}\right) \ \text{amperes}$$

Note that the phase angle must be retarded by $\frac{\pi}{2}$ since we know that the current lags the voltage by $90°$. The phasor diagram is shown in Fig. 6.6; this should not be confused with the instantaneous phasor diagram, and therefore the r.m.s. values for the voltage and the current are required, i.e. $V = 0·707\ V_m = 70·7$ V and $I = 0·707\ I_m = 0·088$ A.

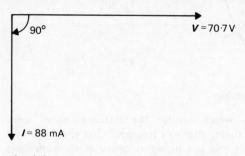

Fig. 6.6

6.2 Capacitance

Just as the physical layout of a circuit incorporates inductance into the circuit, so there must also be capacitance due to the proximity of conductors at different potentials. Every circuit has conductors at different potentials and therefore every circuit must have capacitance, although unless the areas presented by the conductors are large, the capacitance is likely to be very small. Under the steady conditions of a d.c. circuit, the capacitance has no effect and therefore does not require to be included in the d.c. circuit analysis of, say, Chapter 1. In an a.c. circuit, the fluctuating voltage gives rise to a fluctuating electric field which causes a flow of charge into and out of the conductors, giving the effect of an alternating current.

A pure capacitor is a device that has capacitance but neither resistance nor inductance. For the purpose of introducing its action in a.c. circuits, it is convenient to remember that it is a voltage-operated device. Let that voltage be of the form

$$v = V_m \sin \omega t$$

At any corresponding instant, the rate of charge flow into (or out of) the capacitor is given by

$$i = C\frac{\delta v}{\delta t} \tag{6.4}$$

$\frac{\delta v}{\delta t}$ represents the rate of change of voltage with time, and the resulting current waveform relating to the sinusoidal voltage waveform is shown in Fig. 6.7.

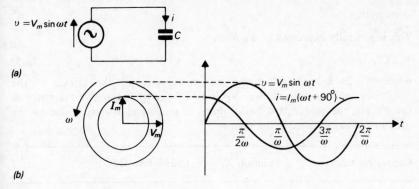

Fig. 6.7 Purely capacitive circuit

It has already been shown that the rate of change associated with a sinusoidal quantity takes the form of a 'cosinusoidal' quantity. By applying this principle to Relation 6.4, we may make the waveform diagrams shown in Fig. 6.8 and make the important observation that the applied voltage across a capacitor lags the current by $90°$, but again this is more usually stated in terms of the voltage being the reference, i.e. the current leads the applied voltage by $90°$.

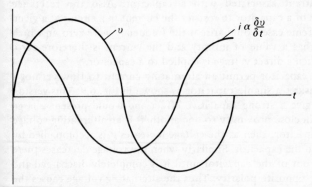

Fig. 6.8 Rate of change of voltage

Again, the greater the frequency of the voltage, the greater is the rate of change associated with it. There are therefore three factors affecting the current:

(i)   the electric factor of goodness represented by the capacitance C;
(ii) the magnitude of the voltage;
(iii) the frequency represented by ω.

Increase in any of these factors will increase the charging current, and therefore in r.m.s. terms

This is generally expressed in the form

$$V = IX_C \qquad (6.5)$$

where X_C is a constant of the system representing the effects of the frequency and the capacitance. X_C is said to be the capacitive reactance of the circuit, the subscript C being there to remind us that it is due to the presence of capacitance in the system.

Capacitive reactance   Symbol: X_C Unit: ohm (Ω)

It may be shown (see Appendix B) that

$$X_C = \frac{1}{\omega C} = \frac{1}{2\pi fC} \qquad (6.6)$$

Relation 6.5 may be rewritten in the form

$$X_C = \frac{V}{I}$$

Thus it may be observed that the capacitive reactance is the ratio of the voltage to the current associated with a capacitor. Also the reactance indicates the ability of a capacitor to restrict the current in a circuit at a given frequency. The extreme case would arise if the frequency were zero, in which case the reactance has a value of infinity and the current is therefore zero, which is the case when a direct voltage is applied to a capacitor.

So why does a capacitor permit an alternating current to flow yet not a direct current? Consider a simple capacitor as shown in Fig. 6.9. This version has been made to give a strong capacitive effect and would present a large area of conductors in close proximity to one another. If an alternating voltage is applied to the capacitor, then as the voltage increases it is accompanied by a flow of charge into the capacitor. Similarly when the voltage decreases there is a flow of charge out of the capacitor until it is completely discharged and then charged in the opposite polarity. Thus the alternating voltage causes the flow of charge into and out of the capacitor first in one direction and then in the other, and this appears as an alternating current. By comparison, a direct voltage causes the capacitor to be charged and thereafter, there being no change of voltage, there is no consequent flow of charge.

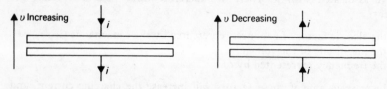

Fig. 6.9 Simple capacitor

In the alternating case, if insufficient current were to flow in the circuit, there would not be sufficient charge in the capacitor to support a p.d. between the plates equal to the applied voltage, and the applied voltage would cause more charge to flow into the capacitor until there were just enough charge to produce just enough p.d. between the plates to be equal to the applied voltage. In this way, the action of the capacitor is to limit the current and like the inductor, the capacitor depends both on its construction for the value of its capacitance and also on its operating freqeuncy for the reactance that results.

Example 6.3 A 20-μF capacitor of negligible resistance is connected to a source of 55-V, 50-Hz sinusoidal e.m.f. Calculate the current in the capacitor.

If the capacitor were connected to another source of sinusoidal e.m.f. rated at 10 V, 5 kHz, what current would flow in the capacitor?

At 50 Hz, $X_C = \dfrac{1}{2\pi fC} = \dfrac{1}{2\pi \times 50 \times 20 \times 10^{-6}} = 159 \ \Omega$

$$I = \frac{V}{X_C} = \frac{55}{159} = \underline{0 \cdot 346 \text{ A}}$$

At 5 kHz, $X_C = \dfrac{1}{2\pi fC} = \dfrac{1}{2\pi \times 5000 \times 20 \times 10^{-6}} = 1 \cdot 59 \ \Omega$

$$I = \frac{V}{X_C} = \frac{10}{1 \cdot 59} = \underline{6 \cdot 29 \text{ A}}$$

It will be observed from this example that the change of frequency played an important part in increasing the current in the capacitor. At 50 Hz, the capacitor passed quite a small current but, by comparison, the current at 5 kHz has increased to what would be a very large current at such a frequency. Certainly it could not be described as light current! And thus even at 5 kHz, 20 μF is a very large capacitance. For this reason, capacitances associated with higher frequencies are often measured in picofarads rather than microfarads.

Finally, the waveform diagram of Fig. 6.10 shows the phase relationship between the voltage and the current. Here they are shown to be $\dfrac{\pi}{2\omega}$ seconds apart, i.e. they are one-quarter of a cycle apart, the current leading the voltage. As stated already, such waveforms are said to be in quadrature.

In the phasor diagram, the voltage is taken as reference. It is characteristic of capacitive circuits that the current leads the voltage, and in the case of a pure capacitor, the angle of lead is $90°$. The phase angle of a capacitive circuit is positive or is said to lead whereas the phase angle of an inductive circuit is negative or is said to lag.

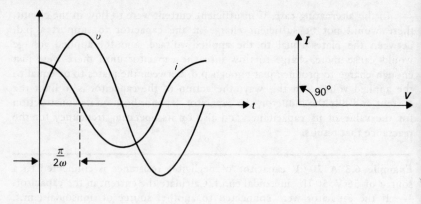

Fig. 6.10 Capacitive circuit relationships

Example 6.4 An alternating voltage, $v = 10 \sin 4000t$ volts, is applied to a 25-μF capacitor. Derive an expression for the current in the capacitor and draw the phasor diagram appropriate to the circuit.

From the voltage expression, $\omega = 4000$ rad/s

$$X_C = \frac{1}{\omega C} = \frac{1}{4000 \times 25 \times 10^{-6}} = 10 \ \Omega$$

$$= \frac{V}{I} = \frac{V_m}{I_m}$$

$$I_m = \frac{V_m}{X_C} = \frac{10}{10} = 1 \text{ A}$$

$$i = 1 \sin \left(4000t + \frac{\pi}{2}\right) \text{ amperes}$$

Note that the phase angle must be advanced by $\frac{\pi}{2}$ since we know that the

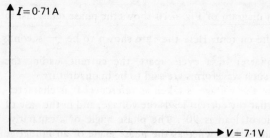

Fig. 6.11

current leads the voltage by 90°. The phasor diagram is shown in Fig. 6.11; the r.m.s. values of the voltage and the current are required for this diagram and are obtained from

$V = 0.707\ V_m = 7.1\ \text{V}$
$I = 0.707\ I_m = 0.71\ \text{A}$

6.3   Power in circuit components

We have noted that the three circuit components, resistance, inductance and capacitance, have distinctly different effects on a circuit. These effects may be summarised by Fig. 6.12.

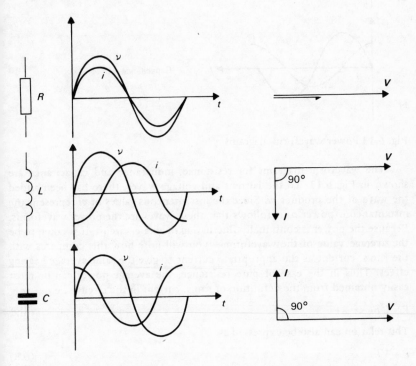

Fig. 6.12 Circuit components

However, the object of passing an electric current round any circuit is to transfer energy from one point to another. Consequently the ultimate conclusion of any circuit analysis is to determine either the energy transfer or more usually the rate of energy transfer. The rate of energy transfer is the power developed or dissipated in the circuit. With this object in mind, consider each of the circuit components in turn.

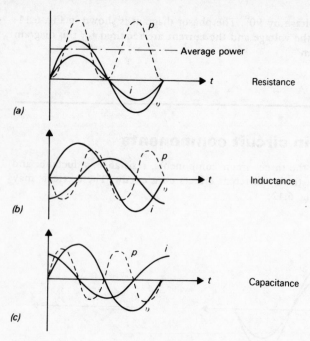

Fig. 6.13 Power waveform diagrams

The waveform diagrams for resistance, inductance and capacitance are shown in Fig. 6.13. To the current and voltage waves, there has been added the wave of the product vi. Since the instantaneous values of vi represent the instantaneous power p, it follows that these waves are the power waveforms. Because the power is continually fluctuating in an a.c. circuit, it is taken to be the average value of the waveform — you will note how this compares with the r.m.s. current as the appropriate current to give the same average heating effect. Thus in the case of pure resistance, the average power can be most easily obtained from the definition of r.m.s. current in the circuit, i.e.

$$P = I^2 R \tag{6.7}$$

This relation can also be expressed as

$$P = VI \tag{6.8}$$

which may be derived from Fig. 6.13(a). It will be observed from this diagram that the product vi results in a sinusoidal wave which is of twice the frequency of that of the current and the voltage. The average value of a sine wave over its complete period is zero, being that value which lies midway between the peak values, i.e. it is the mean of the peak-to-peak variation. In the case shown in Fig. 6.13(a), the sinusoidal wave is biased so that it only has positive values ranging from zero to $p = V_m I_m$. The peak-to-peak variation is therefore $V_m I_m - 0$ which is equal to $V_m I_m$ and the mean value of this variation is therefore $\frac{1}{2}V_m I_m$. Thus

$$P = \frac{1}{2}V_m I_m$$

But $\quad V_m = V\sqrt{2}$ and $I_m = I\sqrt{2}$

Thus $\quad P = \dfrac{(V\sqrt{2}) \cdot (I\sqrt{2})}{2}$

$\qquad\quad = VI$ as noted above.

To summarise the effect of resistance, it should be recalled that a resistor dissipates energy, i.e. it takes electrical energy from the system and converts it to heat energy which is released to the surrounding media. The process is not reversible and therefore resistance represents the means whereby electrical energy may be removed from a system. The rate at which the energy is dissipated is given by $P = VI = I^2 R$, which represents the average rate, and the power at any instant has a positive value, as seen from Fig. 6.13(a), indicating the flow of energy out from the electrical system.

In the cases of inductance and capacitance, consideration of the power waveforms, shown in Figs. 6.13(b) and (c), indicates that as with resistance, their frequencies are twice that of the supply frequency, but in each case the power wave is symmetrical about the horizontal axis. Thus the mean of the peak-to-peak variation is zero and it may be concluded that inductors and capacitors do not dissipate electrical energy. Rather they merely store energy for a short period and then release it back into the circuit.

This may be better appreciated by considering the power waveform associated with the capacitor. During the first quarter wave of the voltage, both voltage and current are positive and the power is also positive, indicating a flow of energy into the capacitor. During the next quarter cycle, the voltage remains positive but the current is negative; thus the power is negative indicating a reversal of the energy flow, i.e. out from the capacitor back toward the source. Over a complete cycle, there are two periods during which energy flows into the capacitor and two equal periods during which energy flows back out from the capacitor, the total energy transfer being zero, and therefore none has been released from the electrical system. Thus the capacitor, and similarly the inductor, serve as a short-term energy stores in the system.

Although neither an inductor nor a capacitor dissipates energy and neither experiences a net transfer of energy whereby the average power is zero, there remains a voltage and a current, the product of which does give a number. However, we have seen that this product is not the power (which is zero); it only appears to be the power and for this reason, the product of the voltage and the current in any a.c. circuit is termed the apparent power.

Apparent power　　　Symbol: S　　　**Unit: volt ampere (VA)**

$S = VI$ $\hfill$ (6.9)

A pure resistor dissipates energy and therefore is said to be *active*. The rate of energy dissipation is termed the active power.

Active power   Symbol: P Unit: watt (W)

A pure inductor or a pure capacitor does not dissipate energy and is therefore said to be *reactive*. The product of the voltage and the current associated with either an inductor or a capacitor is termed the reactive power.

Reactive power   Symbol: Q Unit: var (var)

Thus a watt is a measure of the rate of energy dissipation whilst a var is a measure of the rate of energy storage. The watt is associated with resistance whilst the var is associated with inductance and capacitance. Thus

$$P = I^2 R$$

and $$Q = I^2 X$$ (6.10)

In the case of a pure resistance, the apparent power is the active power and $S = P$. In the case of a pure inductor or a pure capacitor, the apparent power is the reactive power and $S = Q$.

Example 6.5 A 100-μF capacitor of negligible resistance is connected to a 50-V, 750-Hz sinusoidal supply. Calculate the active power and the reactive power of the circuit.

A capacitor of negligible resistance dissipates no energy, thus

$$P = \underline{0 \text{ W}}$$

$$X_C = \frac{1}{2\pi fC} = \frac{1}{2\pi \times 750 \times 100 \times 10^{-6}} = 2.12 \ \Omega$$

$$I = \frac{V}{X_C} = \frac{50}{2.12} = 23.6 \text{ A}$$

$$Q = VI = 50 \times 23.6 = \underline{1180 \text{ var}}$$

Example 6.6 An inductor of negligible resistance is connected to a 100-V, 60-Hz supply and the reactive power of the circuit is 150 var. Calculate the inductance of the inductor.

$$I = \frac{Q}{V} = \frac{150}{100} = 1.5 \text{ A}$$

$$X_L = \frac{V}{I} = \frac{100}{1.5} = 66.7 \ \Omega$$

$$= 2\pi fL = 2\pi \times 60 \times L$$

$$L = \frac{66.7}{2\pi \times 60} = 0.177 \ \text{H} = \underline{177 \ \text{mH}}$$

In each of these examples, it was acceptable to let $Q = VI$ since, for a capacitor or an inductor of negligible resistance, $Q = S = VI$. The expression holds provided that the voltage used is that across the component and the current is that in the component. When we look at circuits with more than one component in them, it is absolutely necessary to keep this point in mind, as we shall see.

However, before leaving our study of individual circuit components, or elements as they are also known, let us observe the power waveforms once more. That of the resistor is always positive and the active power obtained is the average or mean rate of energy dissipation.

In the inductive and capacitive cases, the mean value of the power waveform is zero, yet $Q = VI$. In complete contrast to the active power P, the reactive power Q represents the peak rate of energy storage and this may be observed from Fig. 6.14, which indicates the voltage, current and power appropriate to a capacitor. The r.m.s. voltage V corresponds to $0.707 \ V_m$ whilst the r.m.s. current I corresponds to $0.707 \ I_m$. From the diagram, it may be seen that these values correspond with the peak of the reactive power waveform, thus the product of r.m.s. voltage and r.m.s. current give the peak rate of energy storage.

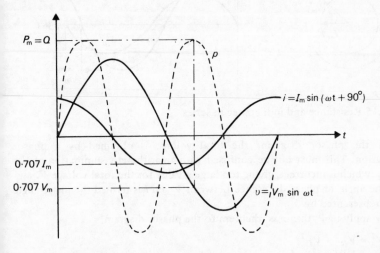

Fig. 6.14 Wave diagram of reactive power

6.4   Resistance and inductance in series

Having considered the effects of resistance and of **inductance** separately in a circuit, it is now necessary to consider their combined effects in a circuit. This can be most simply achieved by connecting resistance and inductance in series as shown in Fig. 6.15.

The common factor of any series circuit is the current. Let the current be I; then

$V_R = IR$ where V_R is in phase with I
and $V_L = IX_L$ where V_L leads I by $90°$

The phasor diagram results from an application of Kirchhoff's second law. For convenience, the current is taken as reference and the total voltage V is given by

$$V = V_R + V_L \qquad (6.11)$$

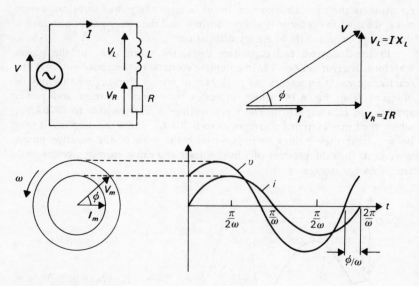

Fig. 6.15 Resistance and inductance in series

In the phasor diagram, the total voltage is obtained by a phasor summation. This must not be confused with an arithmetic summation of V_R and V_L which is incorrect, giving too large a value for the total voltage V.

The angle of phase difference between V and I is termed the phase angle and is represented by ϕ.

By applying Pythagoras' theorem to the phasor diagram,

$$V^2 = V_R{}^2 + V_L{}^2$$
$$= I^2 R^2 + I^2 X_L{}^2$$
$$= I^2(R^2 + X_L{}^2)$$

Thus $V = I(R^2 + X_L{}^2)^{\frac{1}{2}}$

and $\dfrac{V}{I} = (R^2 + X_L{}^2)^{\frac{1}{2}}$

The ratio of voltage to current is one that has been determined as being either resistance or reactance. However, the expression now obtained contains both resistance and inductance. This is termed the impedance Z; thus for a series circuit:

$$\frac{V}{I} = Z \tag{6.12}$$

where
$$\begin{aligned} Z &= (R^2 + X_L{}^2)^{\frac{1}{2}} \\ &= (R^2 + \omega^2 L^2)^{\frac{1}{2}} \\ &= (R^2 + (2\pi fL)^2)^{\frac{1}{2}} \end{aligned} \tag{6.13}$$

Relation 6.12 may also be expresed as $V = IZ$ which may be taken as a development of the relation $V = IR$ used in d.c. circuit analysis. However, for any given frequency, the impedance is constant and hence Ohm's law also applies to a.c. circuit analysis.

Impedance   **Symbol:** Z **Unit: ohm (Ω)**

Although impedance has been introduced in the context of a series circuit, its application is more general, since in any a.c. circuit or network the impedance represents the ratio of voltage to current across any component or combination of components.

The instantaneous phasor diagram and the resulting wave diagram show that the current lags the voltage by a phase angle greater than $0°$ but less than $90°$. The phase angle between voltage and current is determined by the ratio of resistance to inductive reactance in the circuit. The greater the value of this ratio, the less will be the angle ϕ.

This statement can be developed by again considering the phasor diagram. Each side of the summation triangle has the same factor I. Consequently the triangle can be drawn to some other scale using only the values of resistance, reactance and impedance, as shown in Fig. 6.16. Such a triangle is termed an impedance triangle.

Just as in Fig. 6.15, the triangle is again right-angled. This compares with Relation 6.13 and by the geometry of the diagram

$$\tan \phi = \frac{V_L}{V_R} = \frac{IX_L}{IR}$$

$$= \frac{X_L}{R} \tag{6.14}$$

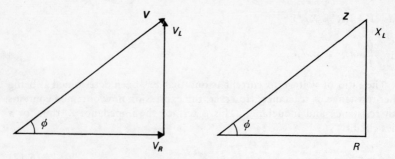

Fig. 6.16 Voltage and impedance triangles

To emphasise that the current lags the voltage it is usual to give either the resulting angle as a negative value or else to use the word 'lag' after the angle. This is illustrated in Example 6.7.

The phase angle may also be derived from:

$$\cos \phi = \frac{V_R}{V} = \frac{R}{Z} = \frac{R}{(R^2 + \omega^2 L^2)^{\frac{1}{2}}} \tag{6.15}$$

$$\text{and } \sin \phi = \frac{V_L}{V} = \frac{X_L}{Z} = \frac{V_{XL}}{(R^2 + X_L^2)^{\frac{1}{2}}} \tag{6.16}$$

Example 6.7 A resistance of $7.0\,\Omega$ is connected in series with a pure inductance of 31.8 mH and the circuit is connected to a 100-V, 50-Hz sinusoidal supply, as shown in Fig. 6.17. Calculate:

(a) the circuit current;
(b) the phase angle.

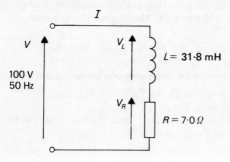

Fig. 6.17

$$X_L = 2\pi fL = 2\pi \times 50 \times 31.8 \times 10^{-3} = 10.0\,\Omega$$
$$Z = (R^2 + X_L^2)^{\frac{1}{2}} = (7.0^2 + 10.0^2)^{\frac{1}{2}} = 12.2\,\Omega$$

$$I = \frac{V}{Z} = \frac{100}{12 \cdot 2} = \underline{8 \cdot 2 \text{ A}}$$

$$\tan \phi = \frac{X_L}{R} = \frac{10 \cdot 0}{7 \cdot 0} = 1 \cdot 429$$

$$\phi = \underline{55 \cdot 1}^{\circ} \text{ lag or } \underline{-55 \cdot 1}^{\circ}$$

Example 6.8 A pure inductance of 636 mH is connected in series with a pure resistance of 75 Ω, as shown in Fig. 6.18. The circuit is supplied from a 50-Hz sinusoidal source and the voltage across the 75-Ω resistor is found to be 150 V. Calculate the supply voltage.

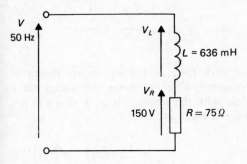

Fig. 6.18

$$V_R = 150 \text{ V}$$

$$I = \frac{V_R}{R} = \frac{150}{75} = 2 \text{ A}$$

$$X_L = 2\pi f L = 2\pi \times 50 \times 636 \times 10^{-3} = 100 \ \Omega$$
$$V_L = I X_L = 2 \times 100 = 200 \text{ V}$$
$$V = (V_R^2 + V_L^2)^{\frac{1}{2}} = (150^2 + 200^2)^{\frac{1}{2}} = \underline{250 \text{ V}}$$

Alternatively $\quad Z = (R^2 + X_L^2)^{\frac{1}{2}} = (75^2 + 100^2)^{\frac{1}{2}} = 125 \ \Omega$
$$V = IZ = 2 \times 125 = \underline{250 \text{ V}}$$

Inductors used to be referred to as chokes, and this old term is still used by many engineers. The description 'choke' refers to the action of an inductor in choking or restricting the applied voltage so that a circuit component might experience a lesser voltage. The inductor or choke had the advantage over a series resistor that it did not dissipate energy and the principle of this action is still widely used as a cheap method of reducing voltage. Example 6.9 illustrates this action.

Example 6.9 A 140-V, 60-W lamp is to be operated from a 220-V, 50-Hz supply. Calculate the values of: (a) non-inductive resistance; (b) pure inductance, that would be required in order that the lamp operates at its correct working voltage. Which would be preferable?

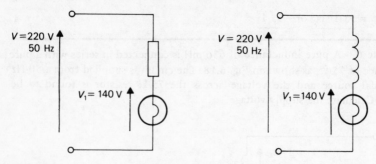

Fig. 6.19

The circuit arrangements for each form of connection are shown in Fig. 6.19. Because the lamp is resistive as is the resistance, the voltage drops across each component are in phase with the supply voltage as shown in the corresponding phasor diagrams given in Fig. 6.20.

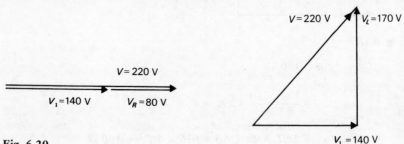

Fig. 6.20

To calculate the resistance of the resistor, from the phasor diagram,

$$V_R = V - V_1 = 220 - 140 = 80 \text{ V}$$

But the lamp power is 60 W, hence

$$P_1 = V_1 I = 140I = 60$$
$$I = 0.43 \text{ A}$$

This current flows through all the circuit components, hence

$$R = \frac{V_R}{I} = \frac{80}{0.43} = \underline{186 \ \Omega}$$

To calculate the reactance of the inductor, from the phasor diagram,

$$V_L{}^2 = V^2 - V_1{}^2 = 220^2 - 140^2 = 28\ 800$$
$$V_L = 170 \text{ V}$$

But $\qquad I = 0{\cdot}43$ A as before, since the lamp requires the same current

Thus $\quad X_L = \dfrac{V_L}{I} = \dfrac{170}{0{\cdot}43} = 395\ \Omega$

$$= 2\pi f L = 2\pi \times 50 \times L$$

$$L = \frac{395}{2\pi \times 50} = \underline{1{\cdot}26\ \text{H}}$$

The inductor would be preferable to the resistor since the former does not dissipate energy, whilst the resistor would give rise to a continuous waste of energy.

So far, it has been considered that all components have been pure. Thus a resistor had resistance only and an inductor had inductance only. In practice, it is difficult to make components that are essentially pure and impossible to make components that are pure. However, in most cases the inductance of a resistor can be neglected.

An inductor is another matter because it requires many turns of conductor whereby the magnetic system may be energised. This involves a conductor which is sufficiently long that its resistance may not be negligible. In such a case, the inductor may effectively be represented by resistance in series with inductance as illustrated by Example 6.10. It should be noted that some inductors have ferromagnetic cores, in which case the effective resistance of the inductor is due in part to the resistance of the winding and in part to the heating effect caused by hysteresis and eddy currents associated with the core; in such cases, the coil resistance measured by direct current only indicates the resistance of the coil conductor, yet if the resistance is derived from an a.c. test, the effective resistance is higher because the alternating current gives rise to hysteresis and eddy currents.

Example 6.10 A coil, having both inductance and resistance, has an impedance of 50 Ω and the phase angle of the current through it with respect to the voltage across it is 45° lag. The coil is connected in series with a 40-Ω resistor across a sinusoidal supply. The circuit current is 3·0 A; by constructing a phasor diagram, estimate the supply voltage and the circuit phase angle.

$$V_R = IR = 3 \times 40 = 120 \text{ V}$$
$$V_{Lr} = IZ_{Lr} = 3 \times 50 = 150 \text{ V}$$

The use of subscript notation should be noted in the previous line. It would have been incorrect to write $V_{Lr} = IZ$ since Z is used to represent the

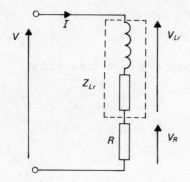

Fig. 6.21

total circuit impedance. In more complex problems, numbers can be used, e.g. Z_1, Z_2, Z_3, etc.

The phasor diagram is constructed by drawing the phasor V_R to some appropriate scale. The direction of this phasor will coincide with that of the current I. Since the voltage across the coil will lead the current by 45°, phasor V_{Lr} can also be drawn. Phasor summation of the two voltages gives the total voltage, thus from the diagram,

$$V = 250 \text{ V}$$
and $\phi = 26°$ lag

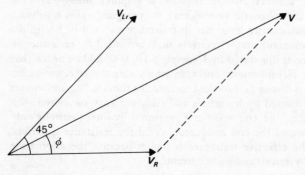

Fig. 6.22

6.5   Resistance and capacitance in series

The effect of connecting resistance and capacitance in series is shown in Fig. 6.23. Again the current is initially taken as reference.

The circuit voltage is derived from the following relations.

$V_R = IR$, where V_R is in phase with I
$V_C = IX_C$, where V_C lags I by 90°.
$V = V_R + V_C$

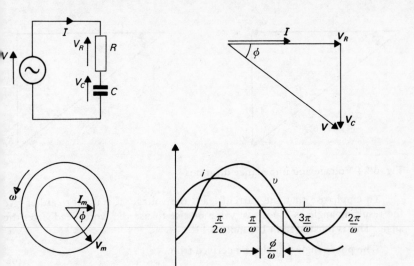

Fig. 6.23 Resistance and capacitance in series

Also $\quad V = (V_R{}^2 + V_C{}^2)^{\frac{1}{2}}$

$\qquad\qquad = (I^2R^2 + I^2X_C{}^2)^{\frac{1}{2}}$

$\qquad\qquad = I(R^2 + X_C{}^2)^{\frac{1}{2}}$

Let $\qquad V = IZ$ $\hfill (6.17)$

where $\quad Z = (R^2 + X_C{}^2)^{\frac{1}{2}}$ $\hfill (6.18)$

$\qquad\qquad = \left(R^2 + \dfrac{1}{\omega^2 C^2} \right)^{\frac{1}{2}}$ $\hfill (6.19)$

Again Z is the impedance of the circuit. For any given frequency, the impedance remains constant and is thus the constant used in Ohm's law, i.e. the impedance is the ratio of the voltage across the circuit to the current flowing through it, other conditions remaining unchanged.

The instantaneous phasor diagram, and the resulting wave diagram, show that the current leads the applied voltage by a phase angle greater than $0°$ but less than $90°$. The phase angle ϕ between voltage and current is determined by the ratio of resistance to capacitive reactance in the circuit. The greater the value of this ratio, the less will be the angle ϕ. This can be illustrated by drawing the impedance triangle for the circuit as shown in Fig. 6.24.

By the geometry of the diagrams,

$\tan \phi = \dfrac{V_C}{V_R} = \dfrac{IX_C}{IR}$

$\qquad = \dfrac{X_C}{R}$ $\hfill (6.20)$

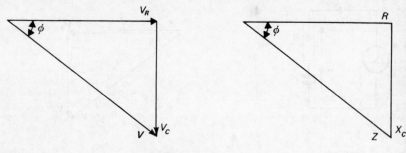

Fig. 6.24 Voltage and impedance diagrams

To emphasise that the current leads the voltage, it is usual to either give the resulting angle as a positive value or else to use the word 'lead' after the angle. This is illustrated in Example 6.11.

The phase angle can also be derived from

$$\cos \phi = \frac{V_R}{V} = \frac{IR}{IZ}$$

$$= \frac{R}{Z} \tag{6.21}$$

$$= \frac{R}{\left(R^2 + \dfrac{1}{\omega^2 C^2} \right)^{\frac{1}{2}}}$$

Also $\sin \phi = \dfrac{V_C}{V} = \dfrac{IX_C}{IZ}$

$$= \frac{X_C}{Z} \tag{6.22}$$

Example 6.11 A capacitor of capacitance 800 pF takes a current of 1·0 mA when connected to a 25-V, a.c. supply. Calculate:

(a) the frequency of the applied voltage;
(b) the resistance to be connected in series with the capacitor to reduce the current in the circuit to 0·5 mA at the same frequency;
(c) the phase angle of the resulting circuit.

$$X_C = \frac{V}{I} = \frac{25}{1 \times 10^{-3}} = 25\ 000\ \Omega$$

$$= \frac{1}{2\pi f C}$$

$$f = \frac{1}{2\pi C X_C} = \frac{1}{2\pi \times 800 \times 10^{-12} \times 25 \times 10^3} = \underline{7950 \text{ Hz}}$$

When the resistance is connected in series with the capacitor, the circuit is now as shown in Fig. 6.25.

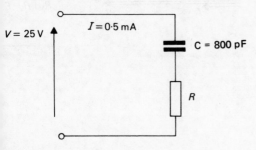

Fig. 6.25

$$Z = \frac{V}{I} = \frac{25}{0 \cdot 5 \times 10^{-3}} = 50\,000 \; \Omega$$

$$= (R^2 + X_C{}^2)^{\frac{1}{2}}$$

But $X_C = 25\,000 \; \Omega$

hence $R = 43\,300 \; \Omega = \underline{43 \cdot 3 \text{ k}\Omega}$

$$\cos \phi = \frac{R}{Z} = \frac{43\,300}{50\,000} = 0 \cdot 866$$

$$\phi = \underline{+30^\circ} \text{ or } \underline{30^\circ \text{ lead}}$$

Unlike inductors, capacitors are reasonably pure and the effect of the resistance of the conductors within a capacitor may generally be neglected. Thus it is usual to assume that the current in a capacitor leads the voltage by 90°, an assumption that could not readily be made in the case of the inductor.

6.6   Like components in series

Having considered the various possible circuit components separately, as well as combinations of resistance with inductance and with capacitance, it is worth noting the effects of combining like components in series.

Because the derivations of the results are similar to those given in the sections dealing with the series connection of unlike components, it is only necessary to tabulate them as given in Fig. 6.26.

Like components are associated with voltages that are separately in phase with one another, provided that we are dealing with a series circuit. It follows

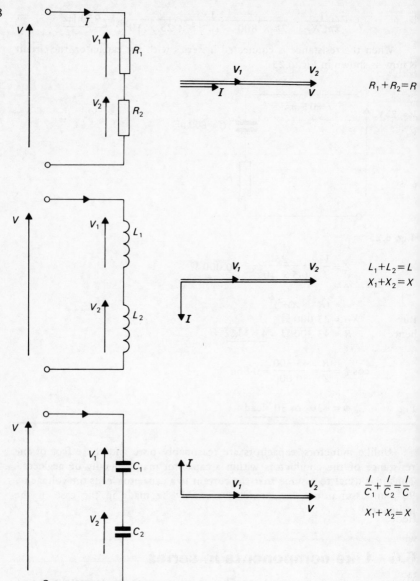

Fig. 6.26 Series connection of like components

that the voltages associated with like, series-connected components may be added arithmetically. A particular instance of this was illustrated in Example 6.9.

6.7 General a.c. series circuit

The general a.c. series circuit is one that contains resistance, inductance and capacitance. As before, the phasor diagram, shown in Fig. 6.27, is drawn by taking the current as reference. However when the voltage phasors are added together, it is seen that the voltage across the inductance V_L and the voltage across the capacitance V_C are in phase opposition. It follows that the circuit can either be effectively inductive or capacitive depending on whether V_L or V_C is predominant.

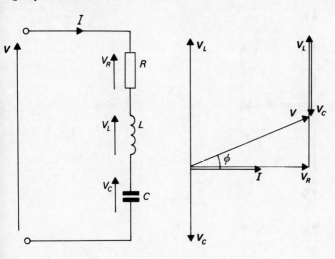

Fig. 6.27 General a.c. series circuit

$$V = (V_R{}^2 + (V_L - V_C)^2)^{\frac{1}{2}}$$
$$= (I^2R^2 + (IX_L - IX_C)^2)^{\frac{1}{2}}$$
$$= I(R^2 + (X_L - X_C)^2)^{\frac{1}{2}}$$

Hence $\quad V = IZ$

where $\quad Z = (R^2 + (X_L - X_C)^2)^{\frac{1}{2}}$ \hfill (6.23)

There are three possible forms of solution to Relation 6.23 and these are tabulated in Fig. 6.28.

It will be noted that if:

(a) $X_L - X_C$ is positive ($X_L > X_C$), the circuit is effectively inductive and the current lags the voltage;

(b) $X_L - X_C$ is negative ($X_L < X_C$), the circuit is effectively capacitive and the current leads the voltage;

(c) $X_L - X_C$ is zero ($X_L = X_C$), the circuit is effectively resistive.

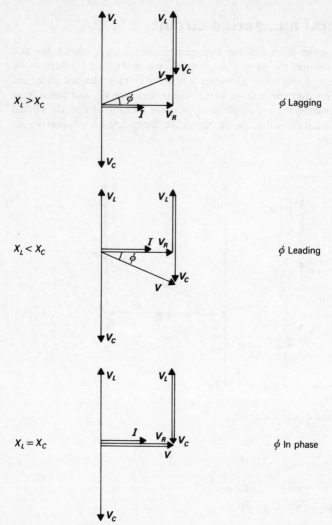

Fig. 6.28 Various conditions of general a.c. series circuit

The impedance triangle corresponding to the inductive case is shown in Fig. 6.29. It should be noted that the negative sign used in conjunction with the value of the capacitive reactance X_C does not effect the value of the derived impedance, since it is squared values which are being used, and so the negative sign disappears. The negative sign arises from the convention of phasor notation on diagrams.

The phase angle is obtained in the usual manner:

$$\tan \phi = \frac{V_L - V_C}{V_R}$$

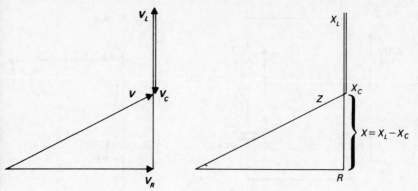

Fig. 6.29 Voltage and impedance diagrams for series circuits

$$= \frac{X_L - X_C}{R} \tag{6.24}$$

Also $\cos \phi = \dfrac{V_R}{V}$

$$= \frac{R}{Z} \tag{6.25}$$

and $\sin \phi = \dfrac{V_L - V_C}{V}$

$$= \frac{X_L - X_C}{Z} \tag{6.26}$$

In these cases, negative values indicate that the phase angle lies in the fourth quadrant, appropriate to the voltage lagging the current. However, it will be recalled that the voltage is usually taken as reference and the results of most calculations would be expressed graphically with the voltage as reference as in the following examples.

Example 6.12 A 240-V, 50-Hz a.c. supply is applied to a coil of 60 mH inductance and 2·5 Ω effective resistance connected in series with a 68-μF capacitor. Calculate the current and phase angle of the circuit. Also calculate the voltage across each of the circuit components.

$$X_L = 2\pi f L = 2\pi \times 50 \times 60 \times 10^{-3} = 18\!\cdot\!85 \ \Omega$$

$$X_C = \frac{1}{2\pi f C} = \frac{1}{2\pi \times 50 \times 68 \times 10^{-6}} = 46\!\cdot\!8 \ \Omega$$

212

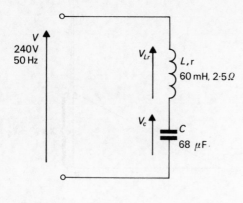

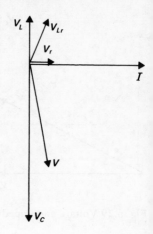

Fig. 6.30

$$X = X_L - X_C = 18 \cdot 85 - 46 \cdot 8 = -27 \cdot 95 \ \Omega$$
$$Z = (R^2 + X^2)^{\frac{1}{2}} = (2 \cdot 5^2 + 27 \cdot 95^2)^{\frac{1}{2}} = 28 \cdot 06 \ \Omega$$

$$I = \frac{V}{Z} = \frac{240}{28 \cdot 06} = \underline{8 \cdot 55 \text{ A}}$$

$$\cos \phi = \frac{R}{Z} = \frac{2 \cdot 5}{28 \cdot 06} = 0 \cdot 0891$$

$$\phi = \underline{85^\circ \text{ lead}}$$
$$Z_{LR} = (R^2 + X_L^2)^{\frac{1}{2}} = (2 \cdot 5^2 + 18 \cdot 85^2)^{\frac{1}{2}} = 19 \cdot 1 \ \Omega$$
$$V_{LR} = I Z_{LR} = 8 \cdot 55 \times 19 \cdot 1 = \underline{163 \cdot 3 \text{ V}}$$
$$V_C = I X_C = 8 \cdot 55 \times 46 \cdot 8 = \underline{400 \cdot 1 \text{ V}}$$

This example illustrates an interesting point about series circuits — the voltage across one of the components may exceed the supply voltage. In this case, the voltage across the capacitor is much larger than that across the coil and is larger than the supply voltage. This effect is especially apparent in circuits with low resistance.

Series circuits become more complicated when they comprise two or more impedances. Consider two impedances connected in series as shown in Fig. 6.31. As usual in series-circuit analysis, the phasor diagram is drawn with the current I as reference, and is completed by applying the following relations:

$$V_1 = I Z_1$$
$$V_2 = I Z_2$$
$$V = V_1 + V_2$$

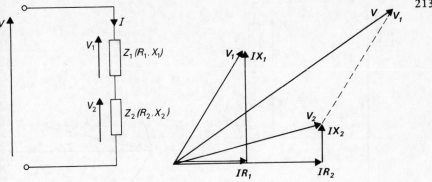

Fig. 6.31 Circuit comprising impedances in series

By the geometry of the diagram,

$$V = [(IR_1 + IR_2)^2 + (IX_1 + IX_2)^2]^{\frac{1}{2}}$$
$$= I[(R_1 + R_2)^2 + (X_1 + X_2)^2]^{\frac{1}{2}}$$
$$= IZ$$

where
$$Z = [(R_1 + R_2)^2 + (X_1 + X_2)^2]^{\frac{1}{2}} \tag{6.27}$$

Thus the circuit impedance is found by collecting the separate resistances and reactances into like groups; this was anticipated by our observations in para. 6.6. The complicated series circuit is now simplified into one effective impedance equivalent in every way when observed from the circuit terminals.

Example 6.13 Three impedances are connected in series across a 20-V, 50-kHz a.c. supply. The first impedance is a 10-Ω resistor, the second a coil of 15-Ω inductive reactance and 5-Ω resistance, and the third consists of a 15-Ω resistor in series with a 25-Ω capacitor. Calculate:

(a) the circuit current;
(b) the circuit phase angle;
(c) the impedance voltage drops.

$$R = R_1 + R_2 + R_3 = 10 + 5 + 15 = 30 \ \Omega$$
$$X = X_2 + X_3 = 15 - 25 = -10 \ \Omega$$
$$Z = (R^2 + X^2)^{\frac{1}{2}} = (30^2 + 10^2)^{\frac{1}{2}} = 31 \cdot 6 \ \Omega$$

$$I = \frac{V}{Z} = \frac{20}{31 \cdot 6} = \underline{0 \cdot 632 \ \text{A}}$$

$$\cos \phi = \frac{R}{Z} = \frac{30}{31 \cdot 6} = 0 \cdot 9494$$

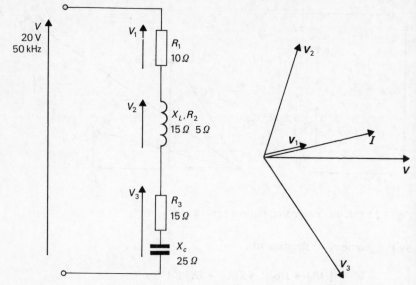

Fig. 6.32

$$\phi = \underline{18 \cdot 5^\circ \text{ lead}}$$
$$V_1 = IR_1 = 0 \cdot 632 \times 10 = \underline{6 \cdot 32 \text{ V}}$$
$$V_2 = IZ_2 = I(R_2{}^2 + X_2{}^2)^{\frac{1}{2}} = 0 \cdot 632(15^2 + 5^2)^{\frac{1}{2}} = \underline{10 \cdot 0 \text{ V}}$$
$$V_3 = IZ_3 = I(R_3{}^2 + X_3{}^2)^{\frac{1}{2}} = 0 \cdot 632(15^2 + 25^2)^{\frac{1}{2}} = \underline{18 \cdot 45 \text{ V}}$$

6.8   Power in an a.c. series circuit

In para. 6.3, we noted that a resistor will dissipate energy at a rate given by

$$P = I^2R$$

It was also noted that energy is not dissipated either by an inductor or by a capacitor but rather is temporarily stored, the peak rate of energy storage being given by —

$$Q = I^2X$$

Finally it was also noted that an a.c. circuit has an apparent power given by

$$S = VI = I^2Z$$

If a circuit comprises both resistance and inductance and/or capacitance, all of the above effects may be seen and this may be better observed by considering the circuit shown in Fig. 6.33.

The power wave has a mean value that is positive, thus indicating that energy is irreversibly transferred from the source to the load, yet at times

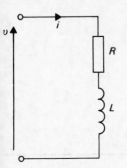

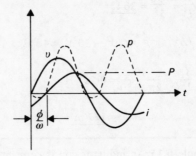

Fig. 6.33 Power in a series circuit

there is a flow of energy from the load to the source as indicated by the power wave having negative values. The overall result is that we may conclude that energy is both being dissipated and being temporarily stored in the load — and this is to be expected since the load chosen has both resistance and inductance. The rate of energy dissipation is still given by I^2R and the reactive power by I^2X. Since $V_R = IR$, it is also possible to observe that $P = V_R I$. This must not be confused with $S = VI$ where V is the voltage drop across the complete circuit.

Example 6.14 An inductor coil is connected to a supply of 250 V at 50 Hz and takes a current of 5 A. The coil dissipates 750 W. Calculate the resistance and the inductance of the coil.

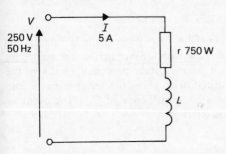

Fig. 6.34

In this example, the symbol r is used to denote the resistance of the coil. It replaces R to draw attention to the fact that the resistance is not a separate component of the circuit but is an integral part of the inductor coil. This device was also used in Example 6.10.

$$Z = \frac{V}{I} = \frac{250}{5} = 50 \ \Omega$$

$$r = \frac{P}{I^2} = \frac{750}{5^2} = \underline{30\ \Omega}$$

$$X_L = (Z^2 - r^2)^{\frac{1}{2}} = (50^2 - 30^2)^{\frac{1}{2}} = 40\ \Omega$$

$$L = \frac{X_L}{2\pi f} = \frac{40}{2\pi \times 50} = 0.127\ \text{H}$$

$$= \underline{127\ \text{mH}}$$

Example 6.15 An inductor coil is connected in series with a pure resistor of 3 kΩ across a 2·4-V, 10-kHz supply. The voltage measured across the coil is 1·8 V and the voltage across the resistor is 1·3 V. Calculate the power dissipated in the coil.

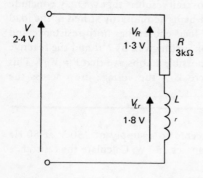

Fig. 6.35

The phasor diagram is constructed by first drawing the phasor I. The resistor voltage V_R is then drawn in phase with I. Since neither the coil phase angle nor the circuit phase angle is known, it is necessary to derive the remainder of the diagram by construction to scale. Circles of radius V and V_{Lr} are drawn radiating from the appropriate ends of V_R. The point of intersection of the circles satisfies the relation

$$V = V_R + V_{Lr}$$

From the diagram,

$$\phi_{Lr} = 79.8°$$

Also $\quad I = \frac{V_R}{R} = \frac{1.3}{3 \times 10^3} = 433 \times 10^{-6}\ \text{A}$

and $\quad Z_{Lr} = \frac{V_{Lr}}{I} = \frac{1.8}{433 \times 10^{-6}} = 4154\ \Omega$

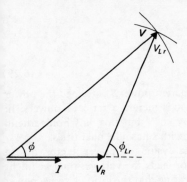

Fig. 6.36

$$r = Z_{Lr} \cos \phi_{Lr} = 4154 \times 0.177 = 735 \ \Omega$$
$$P_r = I^2 r = (433 \times 10^{-6})^2 \times 735 = 138 \times 10^{-6} \ \text{W}$$
$$= 138 \ \mu\text{W}$$

6.9 Power Factor

In Fig. 6.33 we looked at the voltage, current and power waveforms appropriate to a circuit containing both resistance and reactance and it was observed that such a circuit dissipated energy at the average rate given by

$$P = I^2 R$$

and also stored energy at the peak rate given by

$$Q = I^2 X$$

Comparison of Fig. 6.33 with Fig. 6.13 will show that the phase angle ϕ must have a value between 0 and $\pm\pi/2$: should it be 0, then the circuit is purely resistive and only dissipates energy, whilst if ϕ is equal to $\pm\pi/2$ then the circuit is purely reactive and only stores energy. In a circuit containing both resistance and reactance, then the phase angle ϕ may be inferred to determine the ratio of active power P to reactive power Q. This may be analysed by considering again the relation $P = I^2 R$, thus

$$P = I^2 R = I \cdot IR = \frac{V}{Z} \cdot IR = VI \cdot \frac{R}{Z}$$

However Relation 6.15 gives

$$\frac{R}{Z} = \cos \phi$$

Thus $P = VI \cos \phi$ (6.28)

Also relation 6.8 gives

$$S = VI$$

218   Hence substituting in Relation 6.28, then

$$P = S \cos \phi$$

and $\cos \phi = \dfrac{P}{S}$ (6.29)

The ratio of the active power P to the apparent power S is termed the power factor, which is a pure number because it is merely a ratio of powers. In Relation 6.29, the power factor is given by $\cos \phi$ but this only holds true in this instance because we have been dealing with sinusoidal quantities.

It is usual to follow any numerical value of power factor by an indication as to whether the current lags or leads the voltage; thus we might say that a power factor is 0·7 lagging, indicating that the ratio of active power to apparent power is 0·7 and the circuit current lags the supply voltage.

Example 6.16 An inductive coil has a resistance 7·5 Ω and inductance 31·8 mH, and is connected to a sinusoidal supply of 250 V, 50 Hz. Determine:

(a) the current in the coil;
(b) the active power;
(c) the power factor.

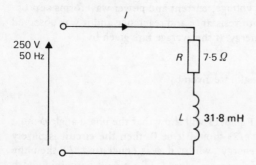

Fig. 6.37

$$X_L = 2\pi fL = 2\pi \times 50 \times 31\cdot8 \times 10^{-3} = 10\cdot0 \ \Omega$$

$$Z = (R^2 + X_L{}^2)^{\frac{1}{2}} = (7\cdot5^2 + 10\cdot0^2)^{\frac{1}{2}} = 12\cdot5 \ \Omega$$

$$I = \frac{V}{Z} = \frac{250}{12\cdot5} = \underline{20\cdot0 \ A}$$

$$P = I^2 R = 20^2 \times 7\cdot5 = 3000 \ W = \underline{3 \ kW}$$

$$\cos \phi = \frac{P}{S} = \frac{P}{VI} = \frac{3000}{250 \times 20} = \underline{0\cdot6 \ lag}$$

In this example it would also have been possible to calculate the power factor first and then the active power.

$$\cos \phi = \frac{R}{Z} = \frac{7 \cdot 5}{12 \cdot 5} = \underline{0 \cdot 6 \text{ lag}}$$

$$P = VI \cos \phi = 250 \times 20 \times 0 \cdot 6 = 3000 \text{ W} = \underline{3 \text{ kW}}$$

Consider again a simple series circuit as shown in Fig. 6.38. We have already seen that the voltage phasor diagram can take either of the forms shown, depending on whether the power factor is leading or lagging. These voltage diagrams are shown in Fig. 6.38 (b). Similar diagrams can be drawn to some other scale if each side is multiplied by a factor I, as indicated in Fig. 6.38 (c). It can then be seen that one side represents the apparent power S since $S = VI$. Also another side represents the active power since $P = VI \cos \phi$. The third side represents the reactive power $Q = VI \sin \phi$.

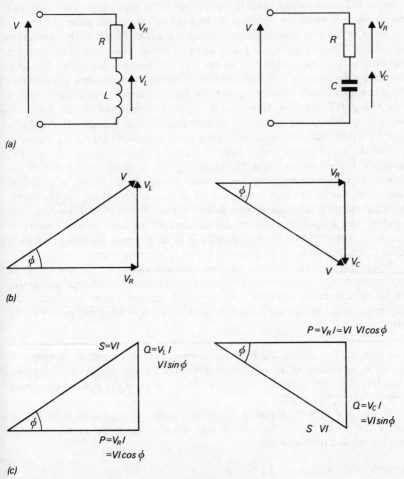

Fig. 6.38 Voltage and corresponding power diagrams

Finally the object of passing a current around a circuit is to transfer energy from one point to another. Consequently much of the emphasis is laid on the active power-content of the apparent power. However, the lower the power factor then the higher is the current necessary to produce the same power. This might be considered to be of little importance until it is remembered that the conductor system for the circuit has some resistance. A cable is rated according to the current it can carry without its temperature exceeding a value appropriate to its insulation. The temperature rise is caused by the I^2R heat loss in the conductor due to its resistance.

On economical grounds, it follows that the power factor is related to the size of cable required. If the power factor is poor (i.e. much less than the maximum possible value of 1) then the current will be greater than the minimum required, i.e. when the power factor is 1; it might then follow that a larger and more costly cable is required. In order to keep the cable size to a minimum, it is therefore necessary to improve or correct the power factor.

There is another reason for improving the power factor in the regulation of voltage. The voltage regulation in a circuit is the change in voltage between the no-load and the loaded conditions. The difference is due to the volt drop caused by the current acting on the impedance of the conductor system. This drop has undesirable effects, e.g. lighting becomes appreciably dimmer with a relatively small volt drop. Generally the less the current, the less the volt drop so again power factor correction is desirable. In this context, it should be noted that the statutory limits of supply voltage variation are ±6·5 per cent.

The degree of power factor improvement is regulated by two factors. The saving in cable cost and also the operating I^2R is offset by the cost of the power factor improvement equipment. There is therefore a point of balance at which the best saving can be obtained. Also many supply tariffs penalise consumers whose power factor is low. This varies throughout the country but English consumers are encouraged to have power factors in excess of from 0·8 to 0·95 if no penalty is to be incurred. Scottish consumers incur a penalty whenever their power factor falls below unity.

Power factor improvement may be achieved either by the use of static capacitors or the application of synchronous machines. Although the power factor improvement equipment changes the reactive power and hence the apparent power and power factor, it does not change the active power of the load.

Example 6.17 A 200-V, 50-Hz a.c. motor is loaded to give an output of 11·2 kW operating at an efficiency 0·80 and a power factor 0·75 lagging. Calculate the reduction in current that would result if the power factor were improved to 0·86 lagging.

If the motor were supplied through a cable of resistance 0·05 Ω calculate the power loss in the cable before and after the power factor improvement is applied to the circuit.

At 0·75 power factor, $P = 11\ 200$ W

$$I_1 = \frac{P}{V \cos \phi_1} = \frac{11\ 200}{200 \times 0.75} = 74.5 \text{ A}$$

At 0.86 power factor, $P = 11\ 200$ W

$$I_2 = \frac{P}{V \cos \phi_2} = \frac{11\ 200}{200 \times 0.86} = 65.0 \text{ A}$$

Reduction in current = $74.5 - 65.0 = \underline{9.5 \text{ A}}$

Initial power loss = $I_1{}^2 R = 74.5^2 \times 0.05 = \underline{278 \text{ W}}$

Final power loss = $I_2{}^2 R = 65.0^2 \times 0.05 = \underline{212 \text{ W}}$

6.10 Sinusoidal waveform assumption

At the beginning of this chapter, it was stated that only sinusoidal waveforms would be considered, and the ensuing theory depends on the validity of this premise. It has been shown that impedance is made up of resistance, inductance and capacitance. Consider each in turn. In the case of resistance, the basic relation is $v = iR$. It is then assumed that the resistance R remains constant regardless of the applied voltage. This is reasonably true of most materials although there are many exceptions. However, for the normal circuit, which does not undergo radical changes of conditions and does not contain any of these special conductors, the assumption of the sinusoidal relation is acceptable.

The circuit component that is the least likely to have sinusoidal relations between voltage and current is the inductance. If the inductance is due to flux linkages in air, then both the voltage and the current will be sinusoidal. However, it is more likely to be the case that the flux linkages pass through a ferromagnetic material. Because of the B/H characteristic, these flux linkages are not proportional to the m.m.f. and hence the back e.m.f. is not proportional to the sinusoidal current. However, if only the linear part of the B/H characteristic is used, this discrepancy is of little importance. Although there is little effect from the error due to the inductance in a circuit, the resulting non-sinusoidal nature of the current may well affect any measurements made by an ammeter. This generally becomes apparent when trying to draw phasor diagrams to scale and it is quite possible to find a phase angle apparently more than $90°$!

Finally there is the case of capacitance which gives the most reliable relations between voltage and current.

Thus it may be observed that the theory of a.c. circuits as presented in this chapter is reasonably valid when applied to most circuits and the most likely source of error in the theory is due to the non-linear proportionality of the voltage and current in an inductor.

Problems

1. A 15-mH inductor is connected to a 50-Hz supply. Calculate the inductive reactance of the inductor.

2. Complete the following table:

Inductance (H)	0·04		0·12	0·008	
Frequency (Hz)	50	50			60
Reactance (Ω)		50	36	4·5	57

3. An inductive reactor allows a current of 15 A to flow from a 240-V, 50-Hz supply. Determine the current that will flow at the same voltage when the frequency changes to:
   (a) 45 Hz;
   (b) 55 Hz.

4. A coil of wire has a resistance 8·0 Ω and inductance 0·04 H. It is connected to an a.c. supply of 100 V at 50 Hz. Calculate the current in the coil.

5. A 200-Ω resistor and a 0·8-H inductor are connected in series to a 240-V, 50-Hz a.c. supply. Calculate:
   (a) the circuit current;
   (b) the power in the resistor.

6. A 200-V, 50 Hz inductive circuit takes a current of 10·0 A lagging the voltage by 30°. Calculate the resistance, the reactance and the inductance of the circuit.
   Sketch, in their proper phase relationships, the waves of the supply voltage, the current and the power.

7. A 10·0-Ω resistor and a 400-μF capacitor are connected in series to a 60-V sinusoidal a.c. supply. The circuit current is 5·0 A. Calculate the supply frequency and the phase angle between the current and the voltage.

8. Find the inductance of a coil of negligible resistance which when connected in series with a non-reactive resistor of 100 Ω reduces the current to one half of its original value, the supply frequency being:
   (a) 50 Hz;
   (b) 5 kHz.

9. A 100-V, 60-W lamp is to be operated from a 220-V, 50-Hz supply. Find what values of
   (a) non-inductive resistance;
   (b) pure inductance;
   would be required in order that the lamp operates at its correct rating; the additional components are to be connected in series with the lamp — which would be preferable?

10. A circuit consists of an inductance 31·8 μH and a resistance 5·0 Ω connected in series. Calculate the resistance, the reactance and the impedance of the circuit if the supply frequency is
    (a) 25 kHz;
    (b) 50 kHz.

11. An 80-μF capacitor takes a current 1·0 A when the a.c. potential difference across it is 250 V. Find:
    (a) the supply frequency;

(*b*) the resistance to be connected in series with the capacitor to reduce
the current to 0·5 A at this frequency.

12. A resistor of 100 Ω is connected in series with a 25-µF capacitor across a 200-V, 50-Hz supply. Find:
    (*a*) the circuit current;
    (*b*) the p.d. across the resistor;
    (*c*) the p.d. across the capacitor.

13. A 100-µF capacitor is connected to a 240-V, 50-Hz supply. Determine the current that will flow in it.
    If a resistor of 100 Ω is connected in series with the capacitor, what will be the new current in the circuit?

14. An r.m.s. voltage of 15 V at a frequency 796 Hz is applied to a circuit consisting of a resistor R in series with a capacitor C. The r.m.s. current flowing is 10·6 mA and the power dissipated is 112·5 mW. Determine:
    (*a*) the resistance of R;
    (*b*) the capacitance of C;
    (*c*) the phase angle of the circuit.
    In a similar circuit in which the capacitor C is replaced by an inductor L, the same current flows and the same power is dissipated. Determine the inductance of L for this circuit.

15. A sinusoidal current of r.m.s. value 8 A and frequency 150 Hz is passed through a circuit containing a non-inductive 10-Ω resistor in series with an air-cored coil of negligible resistance. The total r.m.s. supply voltage is 170 V. Determine:
    (*a*) the coil inductance;
    (*b*) the phase angle of the circuit.

16. The voltage of an a.c. supply is given by $v = 300 \sin 440t$ volts. Determine the frequency and the r.m.s. voltage of the supply and for a series circuit of 33 Ω resistance and 0·1 H inductance, find:
    (*a*) the r.m.s. current;
    (*b*) the power taken from the supply.

17. An air-cored coil is connected across a 250-V sinusoidal supply, the frequency of which can be varied. When the frequency is 80 Hz the current in the circuit is 50 A, and when the frequency is increased to 120 Hz, the current is 40 A. Calculate:
    (*a*) the resistance and the inductance of the coil;
    (*b*) the phase difference between the current and the applied voltage for each frequency.

18. A coil, which has both inductance and resistance, is connected in series with a non-reactive resistor of 30 Ω across a 240-V, 50-Hz supply. The reading on a voltmeter across the coil is 180 V and across the resistor is 130 V. Calculate the power dissipated in the coil.

19. A capacitor of negligible resistance, when connected to a 220-V, variable-frequency sinusoidal supply takes a current 10·0 A when the supply frequency is 50 Hz. A non-inductive resistor when connected to the same supply takes a current 12·0 A. If the two are connected in series and placed across the supply, calculate:

(a) the current taken and its phase angle when the supply frequency is 50 Hz;

(b) the supply frequency when the circuit current is 8·0 A.

20. A ferromagnetic-cored choking coil has a resistance 4 Ω when measured by direct current. When connected to a 240-V, 50-Hz supply, the coil dissipates 500 W, the current taken being 10 A. Calculate the core loss, the impedance, the reactance and the inductance of the coil.

21. A capacitor, a resistor and an inductor of negligible resistance are connected in series. The volt drop across the capacitor is 50 V, across the resistor 80 V and across the inductor 20 V. Find the supply voltage.

22. A coil of inductance 50 mH and resistance 500 Ω is connected in series with a 0·04-μF capacitor and the circuit passes a current of 250 mA. Determine the supply voltage, given that the supply frequency is 5 kHz.

23. A series circuit consists of a capacitor, a resistor and a coil of inductance and resistance, connected in series. When the circuit is connected to a 40-V, 50-Hz supply, it is found that the volt drop across the resistor is 10 V, the volt drop across the coil is 60 V and the volt drop across the resistor and the coil is 65 V. Given that the capacitance of the capacitor is 10 μF, determine the current in the circuit and the inductance and resistance of the coil.

24. A circuit consists of a coil of resistance 100 Ω and inductance 150 mH in series with a 30-μF capacitor. The current is in phase with the 250-V sinusoidal supply voltage. Determine:
(a) the supply current;
(b) the voltage across each circuit component.

25. A ferromagnetic-cored coil connected to a 100-V, 50-Hz supply is found to take a current of 5·0 A and to dissipate a power 200 W. Find:
(a) the impedance;
(b) the effective resistance;
(c) the inductance;
(d) the circuit power factor.

26. A circuit takes a power of 4·2 kW at power factor 0·6 lagging. Find the value of the apparent input power and the peak reactive power.

27. An alternating current flowing through an inductive circuit consists of an active component 7·2 A and a reactive component 5·4 A. The supply voltage is 200 V. Find:
(a) the supply current;
(b) the power factor;
(c) the power dissipated.

28. A circuit consists of a capacitor of 80-μF connected in series with a variable non-reactive resistor across a 120-V, 50-Hz sinusoidal supply. Find the two possible values of the resistance of the resistor such that the power taken by the circuit is 100 W in each case, and determine, the two power factors.

29. A coil takes a current 10·0 A and dissipates 900 W when connected to a 200-V, 50-Hz sinusoidal supply. A second coil takes a current of 20·0 A at a power factor 0·866 lagging when connected to the same supply.

Determine the current and the overall power factor when the coils are 225
connected in series across the same supply.

Answers

1. 4·71 Ω
2. 12·56 Ω, 0·157 H, 47·75 Hz, 89·5 Hz, 0·15 H
3. 16·7 A, 13·6 A
4. 6·71 A
5. 0·75 A, 111 W
6. 17·3 Ω, 10·0 Ω, 31·8 mH
7. 60 Hz, 33·6° lead
8. 551 mH, 5·51 mH
9. 200 Ω, 1·038 H, (b)
10. 5 Ω, 5 Ω, 7·1 Ω; 5 Ω, 10 Ω, 11·2 Ω
11. 7·95 Hz, 433 Ω
12. 1·235 A, 123·5 V, 157·3 V
13. 7·55 A, 2·29 A
14. 1000 Ω, 0·2 μF, 45° lead, 0.2 H

15. 19·9 mH, 61·9° lag
16. 70 Hz, 212·1 V, 3·86 A, 491 W
17. 3·7 Ω, 6·68 mH, 42·2° lag, 53·7°
18. 138 W
19. 7·7 ∠ 39·5° A, 54·6 Hz
20. 100 W, 24·0 Ω, 23·5 Ω, 75 mH
21. **85·4 V**
22. 231 V
23. 116 mA, 1·475 H, 225 Ω
24. 2·5 A, 177 V, 306 V
25. 20·0 Ω, 8·0 Ω, 57·3 mH, 0·4 lag
26. 7·0 kVA, 5·6 kvar
27. 9·0 A, 0·8 lag, 1·44 kW
28. **12Ω, 132 Ω, 0·287 lead, 0·957 lead**
29. 6·92 A, 0·61 lag

Chapter 7

Measuring instruments and measurements

The previous chapters have described and analysed basic electrotechnology. It remains to describe the operation of some of the devices that make these observations possible. Initially, it was sufficient to present a box with a dial on it and to suggest that, connected in the appropriate manner, it would indicate voltage, current and power. Now, by noting the principles of operation of the various devices, it is possible to understand the observations interpreted as they were. It is also possible to note the limitations to the various methods of measurement.

The most reliable, although not the most serviceable, are those devices using comparison methods. Due to their accuracy, they are often used as reference devices whereby other portable instruments may be calibrated, and the most common reference device is the potentiometer.

7.1 Moving-coil instruments

As the name suggests, these instruments have a moving coil which is placed in the magnetic field of a permanent magnet in a manner such that the passage of a current through the coil sets up a torque; the coil is thus displaced rotationally against the restraining torque of a system of control springs to a degree determined by the coil current. This effect can be calibrated and an

typical arrangement is shown in Fig. 7.1.

The coil, usually rectangular, is made from very thin copper wire, which is insulated by a coating of varnish, and is mounted centrally on a spindle. The support for the coil is made from a former of aluminium, usually with a thin layer of insulating material separating the former from the coil. The spindle is mounted either on jewelled bearings or at least needle bearings. These forms of bearing reduce both the friction and the wear.

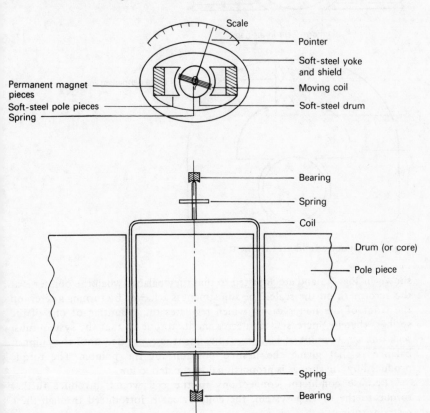

Fig. 7.1 Moving-coil instrument movement

So that the coil experiences a reasonably uniform field, it is free to rotate around a fixed cylindrical core and the pole pieces are shaped in a manner that gives rise to a uniform magnetic field in the air gaps. It will be noted that the field is radially uniform as shown in Fig. 7.2; this diagram also shows an alternative form of pole-piece construction often favoured when the permanent-magnet material is a ferrite.

The restraint is introduced by two spirally wound, phosphor-bronze springs, one at each end of the spindle. They are wound in opposition as

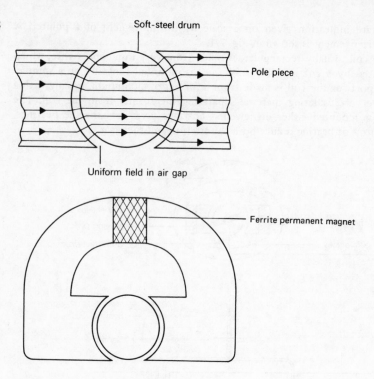

Fig. 7.2 Magnetic field arrangement

shown in Fig. 7.3 and are adjusted so that they balance when the pointer is at the zero mark on the scale. The adjustment is achieved by turning a screw on the front of the meter casing which regulates the mounting of one of the springs, thereby increasing or decreasing its torque so that the system must seek out a new point of balance. Adjustment is continued until the point of balance is that giving the desired position for the pointer. The torque produced by the springs is proportional to the deflection.

Because conductor connections to the coil would introduce further torque to the moving system, the coil current is introduced through these restraint springs.

Over the majority of the indicating scale, the ratio of the angle of deflection to the current giving rise to the deflection remains constant. This ratio is termed the sensitivity of the meter movement. The more sensitive the instrument, the more deflection that results from a given current or alternatively the less current that is needed for a given deflection. If the sensitivity is constant, the torque is proportional to the current and the scale is therefore linear, i.e. there are equal intervals for unit increase of measured quantity. This is illustrated by Fig. 7.4, in which linear and non-linear scales are shown.

In practice, most scales become non-linear at the ends due to the

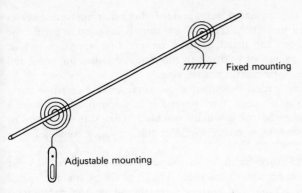

Fig. 7.3 Restraint springs

asymmetry of the magnetic field. This effect is quite small and the instrument is noted for the regular linearity of its scale.

When the instrument movement has a current passed through it, the coil rotates but, in so doing, it attains a certain inertia. If it were only subjected to the influences of the deflecting torque (due to the current in the coil) and the restoring torque (due to the restraint springs), some time would elapse before the movement would come to rest. It is possible that continuing changes in the supply to the meter would keep it continually vibrating about the mean indication. For satisfactory operation, the instrument should quickly move to the mean deflection and there come to rest. This requires a damping torque that opposes motion but ceases to act when the motion ceases. In the moving-coil instrument, electromagnetic damping is used.

It has already been noted that the coil is wound on an aluminium former. The motion of this former through the magnetic field will induce an e.m.f. and hence an eddy current in the former. The effect of this current, as described by Lenz's law, is to oppose the change and therefore the eddy current gives rise to a torque opposing the motion. This damping torque is

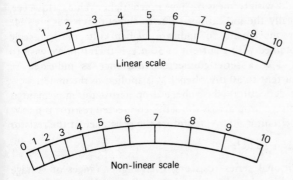

Fig. 7.4 Linear and non-linear scales.

also proportional to the angular velocity and it follows that the torque ceases to exist when the coil movement stops. The former is designed to permit the movement to overshoot the mean position on the first approach, which permits the quickest change of position to the required indication point and also indicates that the instrument is not sticking.

The form of construction described above is reasonably sensitive but a more sensitive form can be made. One method is to suspend the coil from a taut band in which case the coil is usually mounted to one side of the axis of rotation. Such a movement is rather specialist but you may come across it occasionally.

Finally there are other forms of moving-coil instrument that do not involve the use of a permanent magnet. Thus, in describing the meter illustrated in this paragraph, the correct term should be the permanent-magnet, moving-coil meter. However, it is quite usual to omit the reference to the permanent magnet and you may assume that wherever reference is made to a moving-coil meter, then it is the permanent-magnet variety that is intended.

7.2 Moving-coil voltmeter

It has been noted that the moving coil is made from very fine wire wound many times round a former. Such a coil has a resistance that typically is about 2 kΩ. Also, to obtain maximum deflection very little current is required, say 50 μA. Thus such a meter movement requires that a p.d. of $50 \times 10^{-6} \times 2 \times 10^{3} = 0.1$ V be applied to the coil in order that full-scale deflection be achieved. Since the current in the coil is directly proportional to the p.d. applied, it follows that the deflection is directly proportional to the p.d. applied and hence the scale may be marked out in volts.

In the case of the typical meter movement considered above, the full-scale indication would be 0.1 V; thus we have obtained a 0—0.1-V voltmeter.

Such a voltmeter would find a very limited range of application as many voltages which we would wish to measure have much higher values. However, if we remember that really the indication is due to current then it is possible to modify the meter movement to indicate higher voltages. Full-scale deflection (f.s.d.) is obtained with a current of 50 μA; if therefore we wish to measure the range 0—1 V, a series-connected resistance as indicated in Fig. 7.5 will limit the current to 50 μA when 1 V is applied to the meter.

At f.s.d. (full-scale deflection), the voltage drop across the movement is 0.1 V; therefore the voltage drop across the series-connected resistor is 0.9 V. But the current in the circuit is 50 μA; therefore the resistance of the resistor is $\dfrac{0.9}{50 \times 10^{-6}} = 18\ 000\ \Omega = 18$ kΩ.

By means of additional series resistors, even higher ranges of voltage measurement can be achieved and a typical arrangement for a multi-range

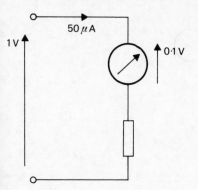

Fig. 7.5 Extension of voltmeter range

moving-coil voltmeter is shown in Fig. 7.6. In this instance, the voltmeter provides various ranges up to 500 V f.s.d.

By examination of Fig. 7.6 it will be seen that the higher the voltage to be measured, the higher the circuit resistance, and at f.s.d. the ratio of circuit resistance to voltage is a constant for each range. This constant is a figure of merit for the instrument and is expressed in ohms per volt. For the movement that has been discussed, the figure of merit is 20 kΩ/V. (If this value is inverted, we obtain the f.s.d. current of $50 \, \mu A = \dfrac{1}{20\,000} \, V/\Omega$.)

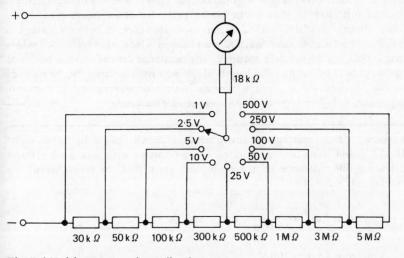

Fig. 7.6 Multi-range, moving-coil voltmeters

A voltmeter is connected across the points of voltage difference to be measured. Thus in the case of the circuit shown in Fig. 7.7, voltmeter V1

232

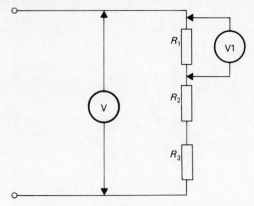

Fig. 7.7 Voltmeter application

indicates the p.d. across resistor R_1 whilst voltmeter V indicates the supply voltage.

Finally the change of voltage range is effected by the series connection of various resistors. Such a series resistor is termed a multiplier. These multipliers are often standard resistors of ±1 per cent accuracy, i.e. a 1-kΩ ±1% resistor has a resistance between 1010 Ω and 990 Ω. Hopefully the resulting voltmeter would correctly indicate the voltage within the range of error ±1 per cent but more usually other factors would double the possible range of error to ±2 per cent. Whilst we shall consider possible errors of measurement later in this chapter, it is worth noting that such resistors are readily and fairly cheaply available for such purposes. However, if better accuracy is required then wire-wound resistors are required which have resistance values that initially are higher than required. The resistance depends on the length of the wire; thus by cutting the length of the wire, its resistance can be reduced to the required value. Such a process is time consuming and is therefore expensive, so higher accuracy involves much higher costs.

Example 7.1 A moving-coil instrument movement has a figure of merit 10 kΩ/V and is to be incorporated in a voltmeter with a range 0−100 V. Calculate the resistance of the multiplier, given that the resistance of the moving coil is 2·5 kΩ

$$\text{Current at f.s.d.} = \frac{1}{10\ 000} = 100 \times 10^{-6}\,\text{A}$$

$$\text{Voltage at f.s.d.} = 100\,\text{V}$$

$$\text{Circuit resistance} = \frac{100}{100 \times 10^{-6}} = 1\ 000\ 000\ \Omega$$

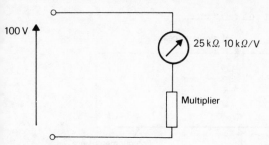

Fig. 7.8

Coil resistance = 2500 Ω
Multiplier resistance = 1 000 000 − 2500 = <u>997 500 Ω</u>

Note that for a normal industrial meter, such a multiplier would consist of a 1-MΩ ±1% resistor since this would cover the value of resistance required.

7.3 Null method of measurement

All of the instruments described so far suffer from one disadvantage — they depend on the assumption that the instrument has been calibrated and that subsequent use has not affected that calibration. With a mechanism involving moving parts that are subject to wear and to friction, we cannot rely on there being no change, although measuring instruments are remarkably reliable.

Nevertheless, we are relying on the instrument to always give the same deflection for the same current. It is less demanding if we do not require the deflection to be calibrated. Such a reduction in demand is possible by the null method of measurement in which we only ask of an indicating instrument that it deflect when a current is passed through it. If there is no deflection, we can assume that there is no current, which is a null condition. Thus the indicating instrument only tells us whether there is or is not a current.

In such a case, should the instrument become worn, etc. it may not deflect so easily but it will continue to fulfil the same function unless it actually sticks.

An instrument indicating a null condition is termed a detector (i.e. it detects current flow) and it is used commonly in d.c. potentiometers and the Wheatstone bridge.

7.4 Direct-current potentiometer

The potentiometer is a piece of apparatus used to compare potential differences. Provided that one of the p.d.s is accurately known, the other may be derived from the comparison. By interpreting the latter p.d., it is also

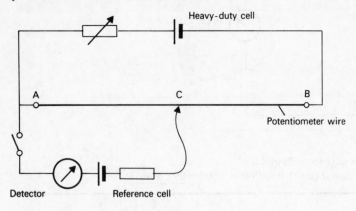

Fig. 7.9 Simple d.c. potentiometer

An elementary form of d.c. potentiometer is shown in Fig. 7.9. The slide wire is a uniform wire stretched between two heavy terminal blocks. A heavy-duty cell is connected across the slide wire and the current is regulated as necessary by a variable resistor. A cell of known e.m.f. is connected between one terminal and a sliding contact which makes a sharply defined point of contact with the slide wire. Into the latter circuit are introduced a switch, a resistor of high resistance and a moving-coil instrument which acts as the detector. This detector has the point of zero deflection in the middle of the scale so that it may indicate deflection in both directions. The switch is closed only when the potentiometer is in use to conserve the reference cell, and the high value of resistance prevents the cell from being short-circuited. The detector indicates the presence of current through the cell.

Because the slide wire is uniform, the voltage drop will be evenly distributed along the wire. It follows that the potential difference between any two points on the wire is proportional to the distance between them.

When the switch is closed, a current flows in the detector, which may also be known as a galvanometer when of the moving-coil variety of instrument. If the p.d. between A and C is greater than the e.m.f. of the reference cell, a current will flow through the reference cell from A to C. The converse is also true. However, it will be noted that the e.m.f. of the reference cell opposes the passage of current due to the heavy-duty cell. If the p.d. between A and C is equal to the e.m.f. of the reference cell, no current will flow. This is the desired condition and it is for this reason that the galvanometer need only show whether there is a current flowing or not, i.e. it indicates the null condition.

From the balance or null condition, i.e. zero current flow, it may be concluded that the e.m.f. of the reference cell is proportional to the length AC. By dividing the e.m.f. by the length AC, the potentiometer may be calibrated in volts per metre. This is termed the constant of standardisation.

It is possible to calibrate the wire directly by setting the sliding contact to a point on the scale equivalent to the reference e.m.f. The slide-wire current is then adjusted by the variable resistor until balance is obtained.

If there is now an unknown p.d. or e.m.f. to be measured, it is exchanged for the reference cell by the operation of the switch — see Fig. 7.11. The potentiometer is balanced, i.e. the null condition is obtained, by movement of the sliding contact and the appropriate length AD, say, is noted. The product of this length and the constant of standardisation gives the value of the unknown p.d. or e.m.f.

Example 7.2 Whilst standardising a simple potentiometer, balance was obtained on a length of 600 mm of wire when using a standard cell of 1·0183 V. The standard cell was replaced by a dry cell and balance was obtained with a length of 850 mm. Calculate the e.m.f. of the cell.

When a 5·0-Ω resistor was connected across the terminals of the dry cell, a balance was obtained with a length of 750 mm. Calculate the internal resistance of the dry cell.

$$\text{Constant of standardisation} = \frac{1 \cdot 0183}{600} = 0 \cdot 001\ 697 \text{ V/mm}$$

$$\text{e.m.f. of dry cell} = 0 \cdot 001\ 697 \times 850 = 1 \cdot 44 \text{ V}$$

$$\text{p.d. across load} = 0 \cdot 001\ 697 \times 750 = 1 \cdot 27 \text{ V}$$

$$E = V + Ir$$

$$= V + \frac{V}{R} \cdot r$$

$$1 \cdot 44 = 1 \cdot 27 + \frac{1 \cdot 27}{5} \times r$$

$$r = \underline{0 \cdot 67\ \Omega}$$

Certain precautions should be taken in operating the potentiometer. The heavy-duty cell must be sufficiently well charged that its e.m.f. remains unchanged throughout the measurement. Also the temperature of the circuit should be permitted to stabilise before any measurements are taken, otherwise the circuit resistances will vary as they increase with temperature rise during the operation.

The reference or standard cell cannot be relied upon if it is permitted to pass any considerable current. The most common cell is the Weston cell which has an e.m.f. of 1·0183 V at 20°C. Usually this e.m.f. is marked on the cell with a correction factor to allow for variation of temperature. It is for this reason that the potentiometer must be standardised before use each time.

When the potentiometer is balanced with a null indication on the detector, it takes no current from the source of the e.m.f. or p.d. which is to be measured. Thus in the case of the battery, it is the open-circuit e.m.f. that is measured. The potentiometer is therefore a measuring device that does not interfere with the circuit in which the measurement is taking place. This eliminates one source of error in the measurement technique.

The accuracy of the potentiometer depends on the length of slide wire used. Most industrial potentiometers obtain the effect of a very long wire by connecting a number of resistors in series with a comparatively short wire. Each resistor has the same resistance as the wire. A simple arrangement giving an increased accuracy of ten times is shown in Fig. 7.10.

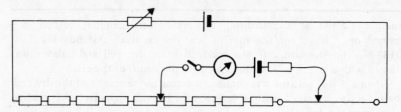

Fig. 7.10 Improved d.c. potentiometer

One important disadvantage of the potentiometer is that it cannot measure a p.d. or an e.m.f. greater than the e.m.f. of the heavy-duty cell. If larger voltages are to be measured, a volt ratio box must be incorporated into the circuit as shown in Fig. 7.11.

The volt ratio box consists of a high-resistance resistor tapped at some known point. The voltage measured is therefore a known fraction of the voltage applied to the box. It should be noted that the potentiometer draws no current from the volt ratio box and therefore the ratio of the box is not affected.

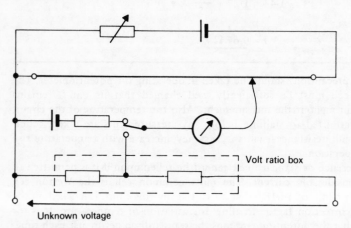

Fig. 7.11 Measurement of voltage with aid of volt ratio box

A disadvantage of the volt ratio box is that it requires a current to pass through it. When measuring an e.m.f., the passage of current means a certain internal voltage drop and therefore the measured value is somewhat less than the true e.m.f. However, if the resistance of the volt ratio box is high enough, the resulting error should be small. The resistance cannot be too high since it would not then allow sufficient current to flow in the detector when the potentiometer is not at balance. A similar problem may occur in the measurement of a p.d.

The potentiometer is a comparatively large piece of apparatus and therefore is not readily portable. It also requires some time to make a measurement. One application, due to the great accuracy possible, is to calibrate portable indicating instruments. A voltmeter can be calibrated by being connected across the volt ratio box of Fig. 7.11 when the box is being energised from a variable-voltage supply. The supply is adjusted until the instrument indicates some desired value. Whilst the supply voltage is held constant, the corresponding p.d. is measured by the potentiometer, from which reading the voltmeter error can be derived. This procedure is repeated for various suitable indications on the voltmeter scale.

The potentiometer can also be modified to measure current. The current is made to flow through a resistor of known resistance and the resulting

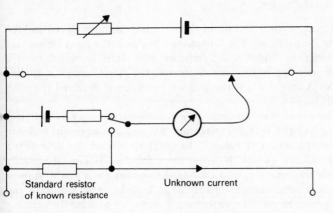

Standard resistor
of known resistance

Unknown current

Fig. 7.12 Measurement of current by potentiometer

voltage drop is measured. The current is then calculated from the values of voltage drop and resistance. The circuit is shown in Fig. 7.12.

The usual application of this arrangement is the calibration of ammeters. The ammeter is connected in series with the resistor and the current is adjusted to give a suitable indication on the ammeter. The current is accurately measured by the potentiometer and hence the ammeter error can be calculated. The method of error calculation will be considered in para. 7.16.

7.5   Wheatstone bridge

Any network made up in the form shown in Fig. 7.13 is termed a bridge network provided that the supply is connected to one pair of opposite terminals and the load is connected to the other pair. The bridge network has already been noted in para. 5.11.

In a measurement bridge such as the Wheatstone bridge, one of the resistive components, described as an arm of the bridge, is variable. By

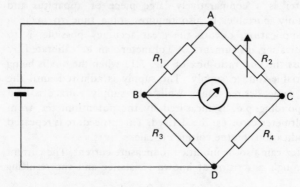

Fig. 7.13 Wheatstone bridge

suitable adjustment, zero deflection of the detector can be achieved and the bridge is said to be balanced. The Wheatstone bridge is the most elementary form of measurement bridge using resistors only. It is energised from a direct-voltage source and in the case illustrated, the direct voltage is applied to the terminals A and D whilst the balance condition is observed from the bridge terminals B and C.

It should be noted that the detector galvanometer only serves to detect the presence of current in the connection BC and consequently seeks to indicate the null condition at balance. In order to protect the detector, a variable shunt resistor (which is not shown in the diagram) is usually connected across the detector, thus causing the current to bypass it to some extent. The shunt resistance is increased as balance is approached and eventually is open-circuited. The protection is necessary because the detector is a delicate instrument being capable of very high sensitivity.

For the bridge shown in Fig. 7.13, let R_1 be the resistor of unknown resistance to be measured; R_2 is a graduated variable resistor (usually a decade resistance box) and R_3 and R_4 are resistors with possible resistances of 1, 10, or 1000 Ω. The operation of the decade resistance box will be described later but it is adjusted until the best possible balance is obtained, i.e. the smallest possible deflection of the detector is obtained with the shunt open-circuited. When the detector gives this null deflection, the potential at B is the same as the potential at C and hence

$$V_{AB} = V_{AC}$$
also $V_{BD} = V_{CD}$

If the current in R_1 is I_1 and the current in R_2 is I_2 then

$$I_1 R_1 = I_2 R_2$$

Because the detector current is zero the current I_1 also flows in R_3 and I_2 flows in R_4, hence

$$I_1 R_3 = I_2 R_4$$

hence $\dfrac{I_1 R_3}{I_1 R_1} = \dfrac{I_2 R_4}{I_2 R_2}$

and $\qquad R_1 = \dfrac{R_3}{R_4} \cdot R_2$

The arms of the bridge containing R_3 and R_4 are termed the ratio arms for reasons indicated by this expression, which is termed the condition of balance.

The decade resistance box may comprise one or more decade switching arrangements as shown in Fig. 7.14. Each decade has a switch which has eleven positions and between each position is connected a resistor of 1, 10, 100, 1000 or 10 000 Ω. Thus by turning the switch, we can connect into the circuit any number of these resistors from none up to all ten. The decades are

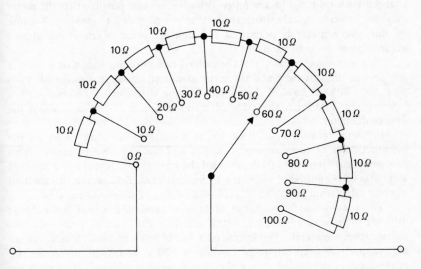

Fig. 7.14 Decade resistance box

connected in series and each is related by a factor of ten to the next decade. To obtain a resistance of 534 Ω, it is therefore a simple matter to turn the 100-Ω switch to position 5, the 10-Ω switch to position 3 and the 1-Ω switch to position 4.

Decade resistance boxes generally have from one to five decades. When incorporated into a Wheatstone bridge, the ratio-arm resistance values are so chosen that all the decades of R_2 are brought into use if possible, thereby giving the best accuracy available. Once balance has been obtained, the resistance of R_2 is read from the switch dials and R_1 is then calculated from the condition of balance relation.

7.6 Calibration accuracy and errors

Much has been made throughout this chapter concerning the errors that may arise during the measurement of voltage, current and resistance. But why should there be error? Error occurs for three reasons:

(i) the limitations of the instrument used;
(ii) the operator is never infallible;
(iii) the instrument may disturb the circuit.

(i) First there are the limitations of the instrument. These may arise from incorrect calibration of the instrument, which does not necessarily mean that the scale indications have been put in the wrong place. It could be that the meter has changed its deflection with age, for instance the springs may not be as stiff as when they were made. The friction of the bearings may have changed with time. So in a number of ways it is quite possible that the meter may not indicate exactly the quantity that it is supposed to measure. Because of this, every meter is permitted a margin of error which is stated as a percentage of the indication.

This is unusual because it is the general case in engineering that you state the desired measurement and the error permitted about that quantity. Thus you may wish to have a shaft made to the diameter of 100 mm with a tolerance of 1 mm, i.e. the error of manufacture is ±1 per cent about the desired diameter.

In meter measurement, however, it is usual to calculate errors on the incorrect basis of the indicated quantity and not the actual quantity. This procedure has no undue effect provided the error is less than about 2 per cent and makes the method of calculation very much easier. However, this method of error calculation must not be used when the error exceeds 3 per cent.

The reason that this change of basis is employed is that it would be difficult to set a supply to, say, 120 V and then read accurately the indicated voltage from the meter whereby the error could be ascertained. Instead we set the supply so that the meter indicates 120 V and then determine by potentiometer or similar means the correct supply voltage. Let this correct voltage be, say, 120·84 V; thus the difference between the indicated voltage and the correct voltage is 0·84 V which is $0·84 \times \dfrac{100}{120} = 0·7$ per cent.

However, the meter gave an indication that was lower than the correct voltage so the error is stated as −0·7 per cent.

Now let the supply voltage be varied so that the meter indicates 60 V.

This time, we may find that the correct voltage as measured by the potentiometer is 59·94 V which means that the meter has overestimated the voltage by 0·06 V, which relative to 60 V means that the error is +0·1 per cent.

Thus we have the following rules:

(*a*) If the instrument error is positive then the indicated quantity is higher than the true quantity.

(*b*) If the instrument error is negative then the indicated quantity is lower than the true quantity.

It would be much more difficult if we were to calculate the errors relative to the correct quantities and the difference would scarcely be noticeable when the errors are so small.

Apart from the causes described, there are other sources of instrument error. Knowing that a range of error is acceptable (and inevitable) it follows that the manufacturer need not seek perfection during construction and can therefore use components which have a range of value, e.g. a multiplier for a voltmeter may acceptably have a resistance of, say, ±1 per cent about its stated value. Also the meter scales can be produced in number and therefore are not exactly matched to the individual instrument. However, even with such sources of possible error, it is relatively simple to make instruments of ±2½ per cent error and even these tend to be much better than the range suggests. A typical range of error is shown in Fig. 7.15, and it will be seen that the error changes over the range of indication.

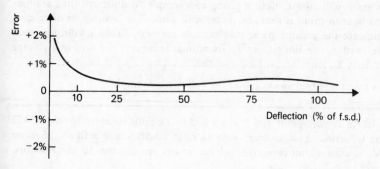

Fig. 7.15 Variation of error with deflection

(ii) However, no matter how well a meter performs, it remains only as good as the operator who can either be careless about reading the scale and thereby cause an error, or there may be a limit as to how accurately the meter may be read to the nearest division with certainty although usually we try to divide up a division into ten parts so that we may give a reading including a fraction of a division. This leads to an unexpected error; let us look at the scale shown in Fig. 7.16.

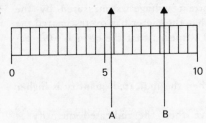

Fig. 7.16 Scale indications

In position A, the pointer is indicating 5·4 which is what many people would take it to be. However, without being careless, some will read it as 5·5 whilst others will see it as 5·3. This is a defect in their judgement and for this reason, no one should place too much reliance on such estimated figures.

Position B illustrates another common reading error. The pointer indicates approximately half way between 8·2 and 8·3. This leads to some reading the indication as being 8·2 whilst others take it as 8·3. It is the human desire to be helpful that causes the error, and not the meter, and we must be aware that this introduces such a source of error.

(iii) Finally there is the error due to circuit disturbance. Meters require a certain amount of power to cause operation. Provided this power is small relative to the power in the measured circuit, then little error will result. However, if the meter power is comparable to the power in the circuit a serious error will result. Before giving an example to illustrate this, another point to bear in mind is that any meter will, within the limitations of calibration, indicate the conditions at its terminals correctly. Thus a voltmeter will indicate, within the limitations of its normal accuracy, the terminal voltage and similarly an ammeter will indicate the current passing through it.

To illustrate these remarks consider the following example.

Example 7.3 A voltage of 100 V is applied to a circuit comprising two 50-kΩ resistors in series. A voltmeter, with an f.s.d. of 50 V and a figure of merit 1 kΩ/V, is used to measure the voltage across one of the 50-kΩ resistors. Calculate:

(a) the voltage across the 50-kΩ resistor;
(b) the voltage measured by the voltmeter.

Let V_1 be the voltage across a 50-kΩ resistor when the voltmeter is not in circuit; thus

$$V_1 = \frac{R}{2R} \times V = \frac{50 \times 10^3}{100 \times 10^3} \times 100 = \underline{50 \text{ V}}$$

Let R_V be the resistance of the voltmeter.

$$R_V = 50 \times 1000 = 50\ 000\ \Omega = 50 \text{ k}\Omega$$

When the voltmeter is connected in circuit, it shunts the 50-kΩ resistor.
If R_e is the resistance of the parallel network, then for two parallel 50-kΩ
resistances, $R_e = 25$ kΩ. The network is thus effectively changed into an
equivalent resistance of 25 kΩ in series with a resistance of 50 kΩ. The
voltage thus measured by the voltmeter is given by

$$\frac{R_e \cdot V}{R + R_e} = \frac{25 \times 100}{50 + 25} = \underline{33.3 \text{ V}}$$

In this instance, clearly the voltage as indicated by the voltmeter is quite
erroneous. The error has been caused by the effect of the voltmeter on the
circuit. Because of the values chosen, the voltmeter takes the same current as
the load whose voltage is being measured. The power taken by the voltmeter
is equal to the power in the measured load.

Even if the resistance of the voltmeter had been ten times as great, the
error would still have been almost 2 per cent. It can therefore be seen that the
meter can affect the circuit to which it is being applied, i.e. the circuit has
been disturbed.

Whilst the sources of error discussed are general, there are further sources
of error that have been introduced but which are specific to the practice of
alternating current, such as change of waveform causing error in certain a.c.
meters. Such problems cause further errors due to limitations of the
instrument in coping with extreme conditions.

Problems

1. Describe, with the aid of a sketch, the essential features of a permanent-
   magnet, moving-coil instrument. In particular describe:
   (i) how the movement is damped;
   (ii) how the controlling torque is provided;
   (iii) why a uniform scale is obtained.
2. A permanent-magnet, moving-coil instrument has a coil resistance 25 Ω
   and 2·0 mA gives full-scale deflection. Determine the resistance of the
   multiplier that would permit the instrument to operate as a 0—10-V
   voltmeter.
3. A 250-V d.c. voltmeter has a resistance of 15 kΩ, and is connected to a
   network with the result that it indicates 240 V. Find the current in the
   voltmeter.
   If the voltmeter indicated full-scale deflection, what current would be
   flowing through it?
4. A type of moving-coil voltmeter in common use has a sensitivity of
   500 Ω/V and 100 V gives full-scale deflection. What is the resistance of
   the meter and what current does it take for full-scale deflection?
5. What is the difference between the deflecting torque and the controlling
   torque in a permanent-magnet, moving-coil instrument?
   When are these torques equal?

6. A potentiometer test is applied to measure the p.d. across a copper conductor and the results are as follows:
   Standardisation data: 0·209 V/mm
   Length corresponding to the p.d. across the copper conductor: 400 mm.
   What is the p.d. across the conductor?

7. A uniform potentiometer wire, AB, is 400 cm long and is of resistance 8·0 Ω. End A is connected to the negative terminal of a 2-V cell of negligible internal resistance, and end B is connected to the positive terminal. An ammeter of resistance 5 Ω has its negative terminal connected to A and its positive terminal to a point on the wire 300 cm from A. What current will the ammeter indicate?

8. A Wheatstone bridge is arranged to measure the resistance of a carbon resistor and it is known that the resistance is between 1000 Ω and 10 000 Ω. The adjustable resistor covers the range 1 to 1000 Ω in 1-Ω steps. A 100-Ω and a 1000-Ω resistor are available for the ratio arms. Sketch a circuit diagram to show how these components should be connected and also where the battery and the galvanometer should be connected.
   If balance is obtained with the adjustable arm set at 400 Ω, what is the value of the unknown resistance?
   The carbon resistor is accidentally short-circuited. What current will flow in the galvanometer? The battery has an e.m.f. 3 V and negligible internal resistance, and the galvanometer has resistance 100 Ω.

9. The ratio arms of a Wheatstone bridge are 100 Ω and 200 Ω respectively, and balance is obtained with the adjustable arm being 250 Ω. The 200-Ω ratio-arm resistor is replaced by a resistor of 500 Ω and balance is obtained with the adjustable arm being 630 Ω. It is known that the 100-Ω and the 500-Ω resistance values are correct but it is believed that the 200-Ω resistance value is incorrect. Determine the resistance of the unknown resistor and hence the correct resistance of the so-called 200-Ω resistor.

10. A d.c. potentiometer is adjusted so that balance occurs when the contact is moved 78 cm from one end and the applied e.m.f. is 1·018 V from a standard cell. This is replaced by the p.d. across a standard 0·1-Ω resistor and balance now occurs at a position 60 cm from the same end of the potentiometer wire. Calculate the current in the 0·1-Ω resistor.
    If an ammeter connected in series with the standard resistor indicates 8·0 A, calculate the error of the ammeter.

11. A d.c. potentiometer and a volt-ratio box are used to check the calibration of a 100-V f.s.d. voltmeter. The ratio of the volt-ratio box is 100:1 and the potentiometer is balanced with a setting of 65·5 cm. If the calibration of the potentiometer is 0·015 V/cm, what is the error of the voltmeter when it is indicating 100 V?

12. The resistance of a resistor is to be determined by measuring the volt drop across it when passing a given current as shown in Fig. 7.17. The instrument indications are 2 mA and 12 V, the ammeter having a resistance of 10 Ω and the voltmeter a resistance of 10 kΩ. Calculate:

(a) the resistance of the resistor as indicated by the instrument readings;

(b) the correct resistance of the resistor allowing for instrument error;

(c) the percentage error of the uncorrected resistance with respect to the corrected resistance.

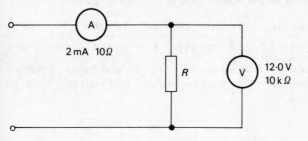

Fig. 7.17

13. With reference to Problem 12, repeat the calculation assuming that the voltmeter and the ammeter had been connected as shown in Fig. 7.18 yet had indicated the same readings as before.

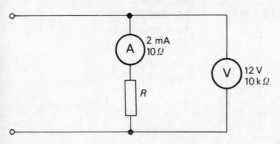

Fig. 7.18

14. For the network shown in Fig. 7.19, determine the correct resistance of resistor R.

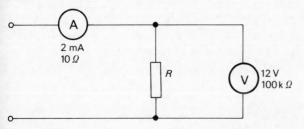

Fig. 7.19

15. Describe the factors that affect the accuracy of an indicating instrument. An ammeter indicates 4·80 mA and this reading is known to be 3·0 per

cent high. The current in the ammeter passes through two series-connected resistors across which voltages of 3·88 V and 4·82 V are measured. At both of these indications, the voltmeter has an error of +4·0 per cent. Determine the resistance of each resistor.

16. A calibration check on a voltmeter gave the following figures in volts:

Voltmeter	0	10	20	30	40	50	60	70	80	90	100
Potentiometer	0	9·5	18·7	29·0	39·1	49·7	60·0	70·4	71·0	90·6	100·4

Obtain a correction curve from these figures and hence determine whether the voltmeter could meet a specification of limit of error to be within ±1 per cent.

Answers

2. 4975 Ω
3. 16·0 mA, 16·7 mA
4. 50 kΩ, 2·0 mA
6. 83·6 V
7. 0·23 A
8. 4000 Ω, 14·3 mA or 13·3 mA
9. 126 Ω, 198·4 Ω

10. 7·83 A, +2·12%
11. +1·75%
12. 6 kΩ, 15 kΩ, 60%
13. 6 kΩ, 5·99 kΩ, 0·17%
14. 6383 Ω
15. 800 Ω, 995 Ω
16. Outwith limits

Chapter 8

Semi-conductor diodes

More than 100 years ago, it was noticed that the junctions of certain materials possessed the property that their resistances depended on the polarity of the applied voltage. This became apparent because current would pass more readily in one direction through the junction than in the opposite direction. Such an action is termed a rectifying action, and the devices that have such a property are generally known as diodes. In recent years most diodes are manufactured from semi-conductor materials such as silicon and germanium.

8.1 Semi-conductors

At normal working temperatures all materials may be electrically classified as conductors, insulators or semi-conductors. This classification depends on their respective values of resistivity, which is indicated in Fig. 8.1.

From the diagrammatic chart, you will observe that the conductors, which are generally metallic in nature, have resistivities in the order of 10^{-8} Ω m. Because of the wide range of the chart, it is difficult to read off precise values, but typical resistivities are those of copper (2×10^{-8} Ω m), aluminium (3×10^{-8} Ω m) and steel (10×10^{-8} up to 100×10^{-8} Ω m).

The insulators have a wider range of resistivities varying from about 10^3 up to 10^{19} Ω m. Typical resistivities of insulators, which are all non-metallic,

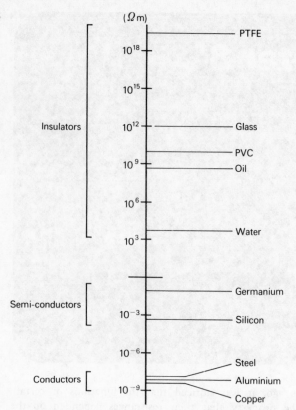

Fig. 8.1 Resistivities of conductors, insulators and semi-conductors

are those of: PVC (10^7 up to 10^{13} Ω m); PTFE (up to 10^{19} Ω m); oil (up to 10^{10} Ω m); and glass (10^{12} Ω m). By comparison, water is a poor insulator with a resistivity of only 10^2 up to 10^5 Ω m in its pure state.

Between these two groups of materials, there lies a third group termed the semi-conductors. The two most important semi-conductors are silicon, which has values of resistivity in the range 1×10^{-3} to 500×10^{-3} Ω m, and germanium, which has values of resistivity in the range 1×10^{-1} to 600×10^{-1} Ω m.

From these figures, it is tempting to think that a semi-conductor is simply a material that is either a bad conductor or a bad insulator. However, if we consider the resistance/temperature characteristics of the three groups of materials, we find that there are other distinctive differences. For the sake of comparison, let us assume that we have three pieces of material each of the same resistance at $0°$ C and let one be a conductor, another an insulator and the third a semi-conductor. By measuring the resistances of each piece over the range of temperature $0-100$ $°$C, the characteristics shown in Fig. 8.2 are obtained.

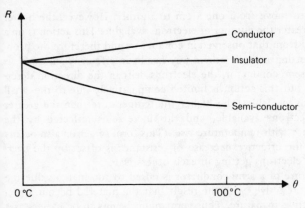

Fig. 8.2 Material resistance variation with temperature

The resistance of the conductor rises with increase in temperature whilst that of the insulator remains more or less unchanged. However the semi-conductor resistance decreases, which indicates that its properties are not confined to remaining somewhere between those of conductors and insulators. To explain these various reactions to change of temperature, it is necessary to briefly consider further the atomic structure of materials.

In conductor materials, the electrons are loosely attached to their parent atoms. Without influence from outside the material, the electrons are so active that they readily move from one atom to another in a random manner. The hotter the material, the greater does this action become. When a p.d. is applied to such a conductor, the electrons drift in the direction determined by the p.d. but this movement of electrons is made difficult by the random action which causes the electrons to get in each others way. The higher the temperature then the more difficult it becomes for electrons to get past each other through the material. This increase in difficulty is reflected by the increase of resistance with temperature rise.

In insulator materials the electrons are tightly attached to their parent atoms. Without influence from outside the material, the electrons remain attached to their parent atoms. Increase of temperature causes almost negligible change to this arrangement and any loose electrons in the material are generally released by impurities in the insulator rather than by the insulator material itself. When a p.d. is applied to such an insulator, the few loose electrons available provide the resulting current and because there are few loose electrons, the material has a high resistivity. However, if the temperature is raised sufficiently to break down the structure of the insulator material or if the applied p.d. is great enough to force electrons away from the parent atoms, then a significant current will flow and the resistivity will fall considerably, but this is often accompanied by the destruction of the insulator material.

In semi-conductor materials the electrons are attached to their parent atoms but, without influence from outside the material, some electrons are sufficiently active to move from one atom to another. However, the hotter the material, the greater the number of electrons available. This action is on a scale much reduced from that observed in conductors and therefore the problem of electrons getting in each others way has little effect. When a p.d. is applied to such a semi-conductor, the electrons drift in the direction determined by the p.d. but this action is limited comparatively due to the small number of electrons available. The higher the temperature then the greater the number of electrons available, and this increase is reflected by the decrease of resistance with temperature rise. (This form of action also occurs in conductors but the effective decrease of resistance is offset by the overcrowded system of electrons getting in each others way.)

If the temperature of a semi-conductor is raised to too high a value the electrons become too active, with the result that the material becomes predominantly conductive in nature. Thus germanium begins to be useless as a semi-conductor at $100\,^\circ$C although silicon does not generally begin to degrade too badly until temperatures in excess of $200\,^\circ$C are reached. This suggests that it might be easier to use silicon rather than germanium because of the higher operating temperature limit but silicon has a higher resistivity with the result that it tends to generate greater i^2R heat losses which require better systems of cooling the material if it is not to overheat.

8.2 Doped Semi-conductors

The introduction of silicon and germanium as semi-conductors was delayed for many decades due to the problem of producing sufficiently pure materials. Curiously, we require to produce pure semi-conductor material in order that we may then introduce impurities into the material. The reason for this strange about-turn will become apparent in the next section but first we must consider the effect of introducing impurities into pure semi-conductor materials.

When impurity atoms are intentionally added, the semi-conductor is said to be doped. Very small amounts of impurity can have remarkable effects on the material, and the ratio of impurity ranges from 1 part in 100 000 000 up to 1 part in 100 000, which is very small either way.

Before the introduction of impurities, silicon and germanium atoms form crystals in which the atoms are arranged in a regular pattern. Because each atom has four valence electrons, then each of the electrons is shared with a neighbouring atom as indicated two-dimensionally in Fig. 8.3. In this manner, the atoms share their valence electrons so each atom feels that it has realised its ambition to fill its valence shell.

In this arrangement, we are only concerned with the effects of the electrons in the valence shell. Each atom has four electrons, thus the fixed core of the atom is equivalent to a fixed positive charge which is equal and opposite to the charge of the four negatively-charged electrons. This is indicated by the +4 marked on each atom whilst each minus dot represents a valence electron. The double lines represent the covalent links between the atoms.

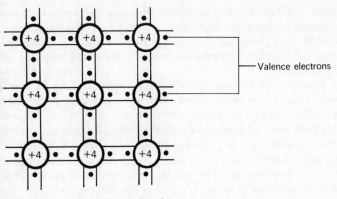

Fig. 8.3 Semi-conductor crystal structure

The diagram indicates the condition of the crystal before it has been energised in order that some of the electrons may be released. However, if an electron receives sufficient energy, it may escape and drift away. An electron may receive such energy by heat or by applied p.d.; in the case of silicon the potential of each electron to be released must be raised by 1·1 V whilst the electrons in germanium require 0·78 V.

The conduction process made possible by the release of electrons from the crystal structure is known as intrinsic conduction. This term differentiates the process from that of extrinsic conduction which occurs with the introduction of impurities.

If an impurity is introduced into a semi-conductor, the resistivity is greatly reduced. One typical form of impurity comprises materials that have five electrons in their valence shell, e.g. arsenic, phosphorus and antimony. An atom of such an impurity has five valence electrons, four of which can take their places in bonds with neighbouring semi-conductor atoms. The fifth valence electron is left free to wander about thus enabling the impure crystal to conduct. Because the impurity atom has given the arrangement a spare electron, it is called a donor atom. This structure is indicated in Fig. 8.4.

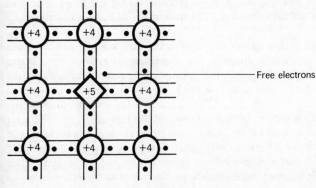

Fig. 8.4 Crystal lattice with a donor impurity

In a material containing donor impurities the spare electrons are freely available for conduction, thus the resistivity is less than that of the pure semiconductor. Because the conduction process is due to the available negatively-charged electrons the impure material is termed n-type, the majority of charge carriers being negative.

Finally it should be noted that even if there is only one donor for every million intrinsic atoms, the number of free electrons is increased many times and the extrinsic conduction is therefore quite distinct.

Another typical form of impurity comprises materials that have three electrons in their valence shell, e.g. boron, aluminium, indium and gallium. An atom of such an impurity has three valence electrons, three of which can take their places in bonds with neighbouring semi-conductor atoms. This leaves an unoccupied place or 'hole' as indicated in Fig. 8.5.

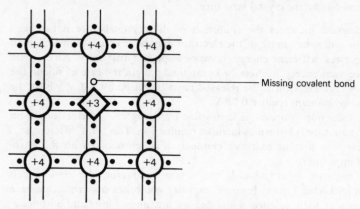

Fig. 8.5 Crystal lattice with an acceptor atom

In this case, the impurity has left room for an electron which it is prepared to accept. It is therefore described as an acceptor impurity. If a voltage is applied to a semi-conductor doped with acceptor atoms, the electrons are attracted towards the positive terminal whilst the holes appear to move towards the negative terminal. The movement of holes is illustrated by Fig. 8.6.

As we go from each stage to the next in the diagram an electron moves along one position towards the left. The movement of each electron leaves behind a space or hole which thus has appeared to have moved towards the right. Having repeated this action several times the eye is not so much attracted to the general movement of the electrons going left, but more to the space or hole which is seen to be moving towards the right.

At normal temperatures these holes move freely through the material and become charge carriers, because very little energy is required to move a valence electron from a neighbouring atom into a hole provided by an acceptor atom. However, a hole attracts an electron and therefore seems to have the properties of a positive charge. Because the conduction process is

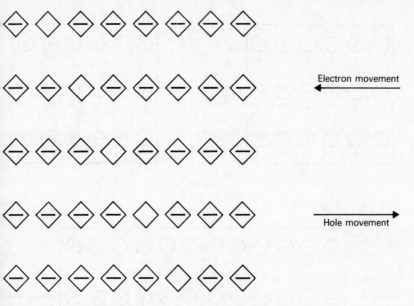

Electron movement

Hole movement

Fig. 8.6 Movement of holes in a semi-conductor

due to the apparently positive holes the impure material is termed p-type, the majority of charge carriers being positive.

Before proceeding to adapt p-type and n-type materials to the construction of diodes and other devices, it must be emphasised that neither material is positively or negatively charged. At the outset each and every atom contained the same number of protons as electrons. The description of the carriers available for the conduction process has referred to mobile charges but these should be related to the fixed charges contained within the fixed parent atoms, which are left behind.

8.3   The p-n junction

The junction of p-type and n-type materials is usually brought about by a form of fusion process. The result is that a crystal if formed in which part of the crystal is doped with acceptor impurities and the remainder is doped with donor impurities. Within the crystal therefore there is a layer of p-type material adjacent to a layer of n-type material.

Although it is not possible to construct a p-n junction in the following way, let us assume nevertheless that we may consider pieces of p-type material and n-type material to be first of separate and then brought together to form a junction. This is shown in Fig. 8.7(a) and (b).

The intrinsic semi-conductor material need not be indicated in these diagrams and it is sufficient to consider only the impurities, the atoms of which are represented by the circles. The p-type material contains the

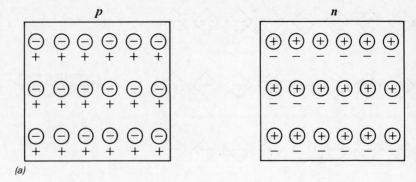

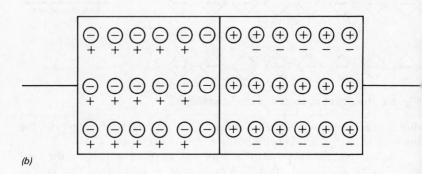

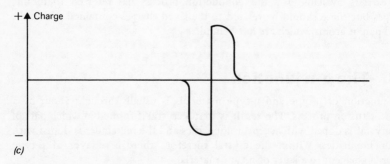

Fig. 8.7 The p-n junction

acceptor impurities which are shown by the circles containing negative signs and associated with these are the holes which are represented by the positive signs.

In the n-type material, there are donor impurities which are shown by the circles within which are negative signs. Associated with these donor im-

purities are the extra valence electrons which are represented by the negative
signs.

As shown when separate, each of the pieces of material is electrically neutral, there being an equal number of protons and electrons in each. When the two materials are brought together, as shown in Fig 8.7(b), there is a redistribution of the charges. Some of the free electrons in the n-type material which were close to the junction migrate across into the p-type material to fill some of the nearest holes. Also some of the holes from the p-type material migrate into the n-type material and absorb the free electrons.

The result of such migration is that the p-type material now contains more negative charge than positive charge and therefore has a net negative charge. Conversely the n-type material has a net positive charge. The final distribution of charge across the junction is indicated by Fig. 8.7(c) and the process by which the charges cross the junction is termed diffusion.

Again referring to Figs 8.7(b) and (c), it will be observed that the diffusion process only affects the region in close proximity to the junction. This region is called the depletion layer and this layer remains quite thin so long as no external potential difference is applied to the junction. Its thickness is determined by the diffusion process which stops as soon as there is a sufficient potential difference across the junction due to the transfer of charge. For instance, it has been noted that the p-type material has become negatively-charged; it follows that this negative charge opposes the transfer of further negatively-charged electrons from the p-type material, i.e. an instance of like charges repelling one another. Similarly the now positively-charged n-type material repels the transfer of further holes and so the diffusion process ceases to continue.

The balance of transfer of charge thus obtained by making the p-n junction remains until a potential difference is applied to the junction. Consider first of all that shown in Fig. 8.8. The direction of resulting electron

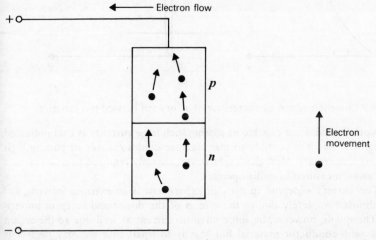

Fig. 8.8 Forward biassing of a p-n junction

256   flow shown in the diagram should not be confused with the direction of conventional current flow normally shown, i.e. electrons flow round a circuit in the opposite direction to that of conventional current.

As soon as the circuit is made the supply positive terminal attracts electrons from the negatively-charged p-type material. This withdraws free electrons from the depletion layer and so more electrons are attracted from the n-type material across the junction. Conversely holes are attracted to the negative terminal of the supply with the consequent result that holes are attracted to cross the junction.

The applied potential difference does not require to be very large in order to overcome the effect of the depletion layer. 0·2 V in germanium and 0·6 V in silicon is generally sufficient to remove the depletion layer and there after the only resistance offered to the passage of current from the source is that of the semi-conductor material.

If we were to measure the various values of current for increasing values of applied voltage we would obtain the current/voltage characteristic shown in Fig. 8.9, which is termed the forward characteristic. The initial part of the characteristic when very little current is flowing is of especial interest and is shown separately in Fig. 8.9(a). At this stage, the depletion layer still plays a significant part in the amount of current permitted to flow in the circuit. Once the depletion layer has been completely overcome, the characteristic becomes almost linear, its rate of rise being almost entirely determined by the circuit resistance. This is shown in Fig. 8.9(b).

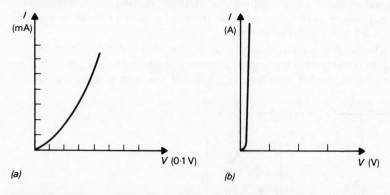

Fig. 8.9 Current/voltage characteristic of a forward biassed p-n junction

Not all diodes are capable of passing such large currents as that indicated by Fig. 8.9, but it is possible to manufacture diodes capable of passing high currents if necessary. Most diodes, however, are only required to pass currents that can be measured in milliamperes.

The current observed in such an experiment is an extrinsic current, i.e. it is almost completely due to the effects of the donor and acceptor impurities. There will, however, be some intrinsic current as well due to the action of the semi-conductor material but this is so small that we may neglect it when considering conduction in the forward direction.

A potential difference can also be applied to a p-n junction as shown in Fig. 8.10. In this connection, the p-type material is connected to the negative terminal of the supply instead of the positive terminal as in the previous instance. Again it should be noted that the flow of electrons and not the flow of conventional current is indicated.

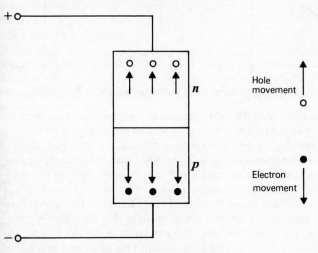

Fig. 8.10 Reverse biassing of a p-n junction

As soon as the circuit is made the positive terminal of the supply attracts electrons from the n-type material, with the result that the positive charge of the material is increased. Also the negative terminal of the supply repels electrons forcing them towards the p-type material, with the result that the negative charge of the material is increased (alternatively this may be described as the attraction of holes from the p-type material towards the negative supply terminal, this also having the effect of increasing the negative charge on the p-type material). The overall effect is that the depletion layer is considerably strengthened to the point that the difference in potential across it is equal to that of the supply. Effectively therefore no extrinsic current can flow in the junction due to the action of the impurity materials.

Nevertheless, if we measure the reverse current in the p-n junction and plot the values against the corresponding voltages, we obtain the reverse characteristic shown in Fig. 8.11. In spite of their lack of extrinsic current, a small current is found to flow. Again the initial part of the characteristic is of especial interest and is shown separately in Fig. 8.11(a).

The current that flows is due to the intrinsic conduction of the semiconductor material. Although there is no extrinsic conduction due to the depletion layer this in no way affects the intrinsic action which particularly responds, as can be seen, to the temperature. Increase in supply voltage has little effect on the number of free electrons thus the current remains almost constant with increase of applied voltage. Such increase in current as there is, is due to leakage along the surface of the junction. Other leakage paths exist

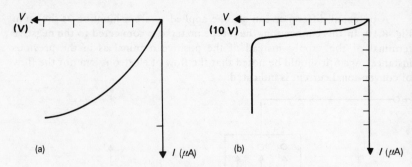

Fig. 8.11 Current/voltage characteristics of a reverse biassed p-n junction

through the mounting material which protects the junction. This current, which is additional to the intrinsic current, is termed the leakage current.

If we apply very high reverse voltages to a p-n junction, the characteristic changes dramatically as shown in Fig. 8.11(*b*). The cause of the change is that the junction is no longer able to remain sufficiently cool. Because the semiconductor material has a negative temperature coefficient, the resistance falls and the current rises which causes the rate of heat generation to increase even further, and the temperature becomes even greater. This condition is sometimes described as a thermal runaway and the junction is said to have experienced a breakdown. The resulting high currents may generate enough heat to destroy the junction, and most p-n junctions have a consequent maximum reverse voltage rating. Finally the high values of current experienced during the breakdown condition are described as avalanche currents.

8.4 Semi-conductor diode

A semi-conductor diode is a device containing a p-n junction mounted in a suitable container made of metal, ceramic or glass. It is packed into the container with a suitable liquid insulator which must conduct readily the heat of the junction away to the container, and which also serves to minimise the leakage current.

The function of any simple diode is to pass current in one direction and not in the other. As we have seen, the p-n junction when forward biassed passes current quite readily, whilst when reverse biassed, it virtually conducts no reverse current. The complete characteristic is shown in Fig. 8.12. It must be noted that the scale of the reverse current is 1000 times greater than that of the forward current.

The p-n junction is not ideal since volt drop occurs across it when conducting in the forward direction, and this causes problems because the diode therefore generates heat which must be dissipated. This is often done by mounting the diode in a metal fin which conducts the heat away rapidly and which provides plenty of area through which the heat may be conducted to the surrounding medium.

Generally the reverse current is of little importance because it is rela-

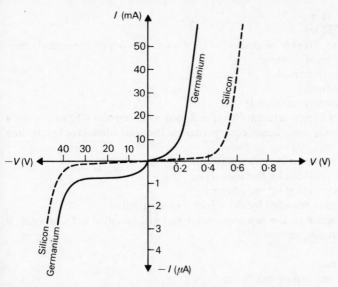

Fig. 8.12 Semi-conductor current/voltage characteristic

tively so small, but it ought not be overlooked. Certain forms of diode make use of the avalanche current for the purposes of stabilisation.

Finally a diode is represented symbolically on a diagram by either of the symbols shown in Fig. 8.13. Essentially the symbols are the same and vary only in detail, and more important, in difficulty to draw. However, in both cases the important point to remember is that the arrow indicates the direction of conventional current flow. This may seem peculiar having completed a chapter almost entirely given over to consideration of the direction of movement of electrons, but the symbol will appear in circuit diagrams which are based on conventional current, hence the symbol reflects the practice associated with conventional current.

BSI recommended symbol 1970   IEE recommended symbol 1978

Fig. 8.13 Diagrammatic symbols for a diode

Problems

1. Which of the following resistivities is likely to be that of a semi-conductor material:
   (a) 10^9 Ω m;
   (b) 10^3 Ω m;

    (c) 10^{-3} Ω m;

    (d) 10^{-9} Ω m?

2. Relative to a highly refined semi-conductor, is a doped semi-conductor:

    (a) more highly refined;

    (b) similarly refined;

    (c) less refined;

    (d) completely unrefined?

3. A piece of highly refined silicon is doped with arsenic. When connected into a circuit, is the conduction process in the semi-conductor crystal due to:

    (a) electrons provided by the silicon;

    (b) holes provided by the arsenic;

    (c) holes provided by the silicon;

    (d) electrons provided by the silicon and the arsenic?

4. With reference to the semi-conductor material specified in Question 3, is the conduction process:

    (a) intrinsic;

    (b) extrinsic;

    (c) both but mainly extrinsic;

    (d) both but mainly intrinsic?

5. In the barrier layer of a p-n junction and within the p-type material, is the charge:

    (a) positive due to fixed atoms;

    (b) negative due to fixed atoms;

    (c) positive due to holes present;

    (d) negative due to electrons present?

6. A piece of doped semi-conductor material is introduced into a circuit. If the temperature of the material is raised, will the circuit current:

    (a) increase;

    (b) remain the same;

    (c) decrease;

    (d) cease to flow?

7. Some highly-refined semi-conductor material is doped with indium. For such a material, are the majority carriers:

    (a) electrons from the semi-conductor;

    (b) electrons from the indium;

    (c) holes from the semi-conductor;

    (d) holes from the indium?

8. With the aid of a suitable sketch, describe the essential features of a semi-conductor diode and also sketch a graph showing the forward and reverse characteristics of a typical silicon diode.

9. Explain, with reference to a semi-conductor material, what is meant by:

    (a) intrinsic conductivity;

    (b) extrinsic conductivity.

10. Discuss the phenomenon of current flow in (i) intrinsic, (ii) p-type, and (iii) n-type semi-conductors, and hence explain the rectifying action of a p-n junction.

Answers

1. (*c*)
2. (*c*)
3. (*d*)
4. (*c*)

5. (*b*)
6. (*a*)
7. (*d*)

Chapter 9

Transistors

A common device in electrical engineering is the amplifier which takes an electrical signal and makes it greater. An example of this action is given by a radio receiver picking up a very small signal by means of its aerial and amplifying it until large enough to produce sound through the loudspeaker. There are many ways in which amplification may be achieved but by far the most popular involves the use of the bipolar transistor.

9.1 Bipolar junction transistor

The bipolar junction transistor is a two-junction, three-layer semi-conductor device which can be made in either the n-p-n or the p-n-p forms illustrated in Fig. 9.1. In either arrangement, the central layer is termed the base and the outer layers are the emitter and the collector.

As with the p-n junction, the three sections of a transistor must form a complete crystal-lattice structure. Effectively the transistor is equivalent to two p-n junctions connected back to back. It has been indicated that the action of the junctions are affected by their respective supply polarities thus the result of the back-to-back connection makes the arrangement bipolar.

In amplifiers similar functions are performed by n-p-n and p-n-p transistors, but one is effectively the mirror image of the other when it comes

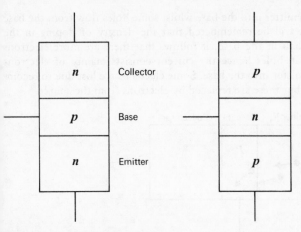

Fig. 9.1 n-p-n and p-n-p transistors

to the detail of their operation. For this reason it is better to consider first the n-p-n transistor and then the p-n-p transistor separately.

Transistors consist of one type of material sandwiched between two layers of the other material. It is tempting to expect therefore that a transistor should be symmetrical and could be used either way round. However, the emitter is usually made smaller than the collector hence there is only one way in which each transistor may be operated in a circuit.

9.2   The n-p-n transistor

At each of the two p-n junctions diffusion takes place causing depletion layers as indicated in Fig. 9.2. The layers of n-type material become positively charged whilst the p-type material of the base becomes negatively charged.

n — type emitter	p —type base	n — type collector
⊕	⊖ ⊖	⊕
⊕	⊖ ⊖	⊕
⊕	⊖ ⊖	⊕
⊕	⊖ ⊖	⊕
⊕	⊖ ⊖	⊕

Fig. 9.2 Depletion layers in an n-p-n transistor

Let us consider first of all the emitter-base junction to be connected to a source of direct voltage as shown in Fig. 9.3. The applied voltage causes the junction to be forward biassed. This results in a considerable forward flow of electrons from the emitter into the base whilst some holes flow from the base into the emitter. It will be remembered that the density of doping in the emitter is greater than in the base; it follows that there are more electrons readily available than holes hence the current consists mainly of electrons moving from the emitter into the base. Some electrons are lost due to recombination with holes but these are replaced by electrons from the source.

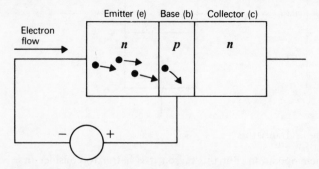

Fig. 9.3 Forward-biassed emitter-base junction

Now let us consider the application of a source of direct voltage to the base-collector junction as shown in Fig. 9.4. The applied voltage causes the junction to be reverse biassed. The depletion layer is thus increased and the majority carrier current flow is prevented. Holes produced by the intrinsic material are swept into the p-type material of the base from which they drift towards the source of the applied voltage; at the same time the electrons produced by the intrinsic material are swept into the n-type material of the collector from which they drift towards the source of the applied voltage. Thus as with other reverse-biassed p-n junctions, the current is only due to the minority carriers.

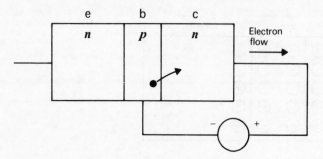

Fig. 9.4 Reverse-biassed base-collector junction

When the transistor is operated as an amplifier, both junctions are biassed at the same time as shown in Fig. 9.5. In this case the emitter-base junction is again forward biassed whilst the base-collector is reverse biassed.

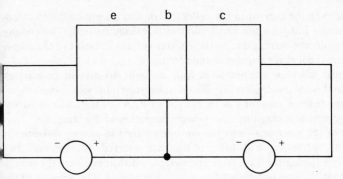

Fig. 9.5 n-p-n transistor connection

In this arrangement, because the emitter-base is forward-biassed, a large number of electrons enter the emitter from the source. This flow of electrons constitutes the emitter current I_e, and it passes through the junction into the base. These electrons can either combine with holes entering the base from the source or they can pass through the base into the collector, being attracted by the higher potential of the collector. For normal transistor action it is essential that most of the electrons from the emitter pass through to the collector and this can only be achieved if the base is made very thin. There are two methods of maximising the number of electrons reaching the collector:

(i) If the base is thin, it provides little space in which the electrons can meet holes and recombine with them. The electrons therefore are less likely to be prevented from reaching the collector.

(ii) If the base is not heavily doped with impurity, there is again less likelihood of the electrons meeting holes and recombination resulting.

Because both of these precautions are observed in the design and manufacture of transistors, most of the electrons in the emitter current succeed in passing through the base into the collector.

Whilst it is only to be expected, from our previous studies, that electrons should pass readily through the forward-biassed emitter-base junction, it is more difficult to grasp the readiness for most of these electrons to continue through the reverse-biassed base-collector junction. A reverse-biassed junction passes no current due to the majority carriers being repelled by the depletion or barrier layer and therefore the reverse current is due to the electrons made available by the intrinsic material, which in a semi-conductor means that very few are available. However, the emitter injects a ready supply of free electrons into the base and these are readily attracted to the collector which is at a higher potential.

Even without the introduction of electrons by the emitter into the base, a reverse current would flow through the base-collector junction due to the applied voltage. In a transistor this current is termed the leakage current I_{cb0}, being the collector-base current under zero emitter current conditions. (Note that this is termed collector-base current, being the conventional current as opposed to the electron flow.) When electrons are injected by the emitter into the base then the current in the collector consists mainly of the electrons from the emitter but with the small additional leakage current. The component of the collector current due to the emitter current is useful to the amplifier action but the leakage current is undesired.

At normal working temperatures I_{cb0} is about 10 μA for germanium transistors and very much less in silicon transistors. In some small-signal transistors the leakage current can be as little as 1 nA but the leakage current cannot be ignored as it may limit the power dissipation of the transistor.

Not all of the electrons from the emitter succeed in passing through the base and some recombine with holes in the base material. This gives rise to a flow of holes entering the base from the source, which is in effect the recombined electrons flowing out through the base connection. The amount of the emitter electron flow diverted to the base is a relatively small proportion of the input flow. In modern bipolar transistors, about 0.95 to 0.995 of the emitter flow succeeds in reaching the collector, thus only 0.05 to 0.005 of the emitter flow is diverted to the base.

The electron and hole movements within an n-p-n transistor are indicated in Fig. 9.6(a) and the resulting currents are shown in Fig. 9.6(b). For convenience in Fig. 9.6(b) it is assumed that αI_e is that part of the emitter current that reaches the collector and therefore $(1 - \alpha)I_e$ is that remaining part of the emitter current in the base connection.

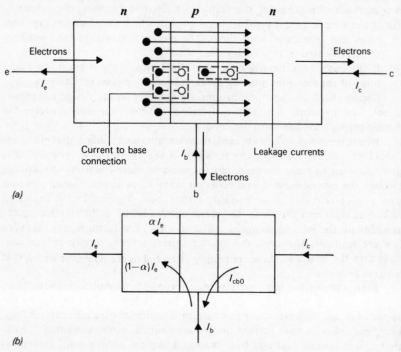

Fig. 9.6 n-p-n transistor action

The action of the n-p-n transistor may be summarised in terms of the currents that we can observe. The crystal is held in a container from which the connecting wires to the emitter, the base and the collector protrude.

The emitter current: the conventional emitter current I_e flows out from the emitter and consists of the electron-flow into the forward biassed emitter-base junction.

The base current: the conventional base current I_b flows into the base, and consists of the electron-flow out of the base due to the electrons which have recombined with holes in the base region and the electron-flow into the base due to the leakage current. This balance can be expressed as

$$I_b = (1 - \alpha)I_e - I_{cb0} \tag{9.1}$$

The collector current: the conventional collector current I_c flows into the collector, and consists of the electron-flow out of the collector due to the electrons which have avoided recombining with holes in the base region and the electron-flow out of the collector due to the leakage current. This balance can be expressed as

$$I_c = \alpha I_e + I_{cb0} \tag{9.2}$$

If we add up all the currents entering and leaving the transistor, the overall balance can be given as

$$I_e = I_c + I_b \tag{9.3}$$

9.3 The p-n-p transistor

As in the n-p-n transistor diffusion takes place at each of the p-n junctions of the p-n-p transistor as indicated in Fig. 9.7. However, due to the interchange of materials the base becomes positively charged whilst the emitter and the collector become negatively charged.

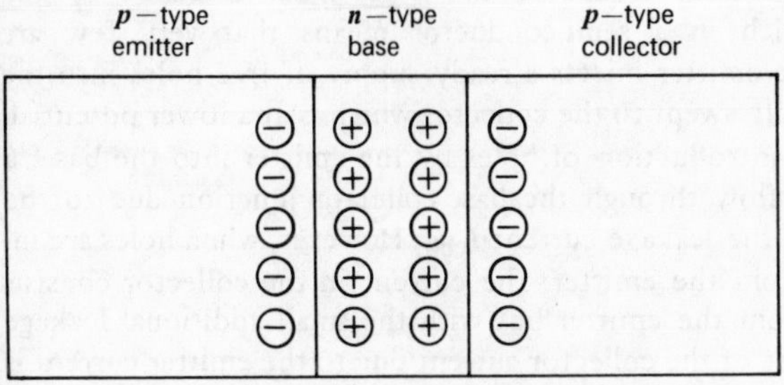

Fig. 9.7 Depletion layers in a p-n-p transistor

Again, in order to forward bias the emitter-base junction, it is necessary to reverse the polarity of the applied voltage to this junction, and the same change of polarity is required to reverse bias the base-collector junction. The necessary applied voltages are indicated in Fig. 9.8.

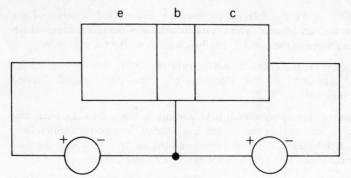

Fig. 9.8 p-n-p transistor connection

The base of a p-n-p transistor has a lower density of doping than the emitter and the collector. This results in there being few electrons which are free in the base compared with large numbers of free holes in the emitter and the collector. The resulting action of a p-n-p transistor therefore depends mainly on the movement of holes rather than on the movement of electrons.

Because the emitter-base is forward biassed, a large number of holes enter the emitter from the source. This flow of holes constitutes the emitter current I_e, and it passes through the junction into the base. These holes can either combine with electrons entering the base from the supply or they can pass through the base into the collector, being attracted by the lower potential of the collector. Because the base is thin and the number of free electrons has been reduced in the base due to there being little impurity material, most of the holes in the emitter current succeed in passing through the base into the collector.

The action of the reverse-biassed base-collector junction again depends on intrinsic conduction. A reverse-biassed junction passes no current due to the majority carriers being repelled by the depletion or barrier layer and therefore the reverse current is due to the holes made available by the intrinsic material, which in a semi-conductor means that very few are available. However, the emitter injects a ready supply of free holes into the base and these are readily swept to the collector which is at a lower potential.

Even without the introduction of holes by the emitter into the base, a reverse current would flow through the base-collector junction due to the applied voltage. This is the leakage current I_{cb0}. However, when holes are injected into the base from the emitter, the current in the collector consists mainly of the holes from the emitter but with the small additional leakage current. The component of the collector current due to the emitter current is useful to the amplifier action but the leakage current is again undesired.

Not all the holes from the emitter succeed in passing through the base and some recombine with electrons in the base material. This gives rise to a flow of electrons entering the base from the source which is in effect a flow of the recombined holes leaving through the base connection. The amount of the emitter hole flow diverted to the base is a relatively small proportion of the input flow. In modern bipolar transistors, about 0·95 to 0·995 of the emitter flow reaches the collector thus only 0·05 to 0·005 of the emitter flow is diverted to the base connection.

The hole and electron movements within a p-n-p transistor are indicated in Fig. 9.9(a) and the resulting currents are shown in Fig. 9.9(b). For convenience in Fig. 9.9(b), it is again assumed that αI_e is that part of the emitter current reaching the collector and therefore $(1 - \alpha)I_e$ is that remaining part of the emitter current in the base connection.

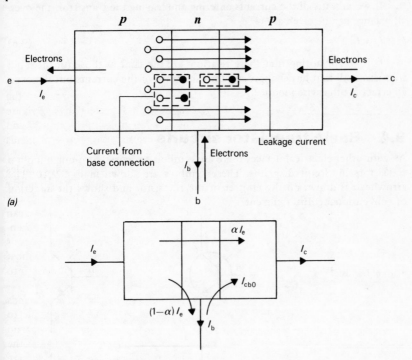

(a)

Fig. 9.9 p-n-p transistor action

The action of the p-n-p transistor may be summarised in terms of the currents that we can observe.

The emitter current: the conventional emitter current I_e flows in to the emitter and consists of the hole-flow into the forward-biassed emitter-base junction. This hole-flow is produced by electrons flowing out from the emitter.

The base current: the conventional base current I_b flows out from the base, and consists of the electron-flow into the base due to the electrons that combine in the base region with holes from the emitter and the electron-flow out of the base due to the leakage current. This balance can be expressed as

$$I_b = (1 - \alpha)I_e - I_{cb0} \tag{9.4}$$

The collector current: the conventional collector current I_c flows out of the collector, and consists of the hole-flow out of the collector due to the holes which have avoided recombining with electrons in the base region and the hole-flow out of the collector due to the leakage current. This hole-flow is produced by electrons drifting into the collector, and the current balance may be expressed as

$$I_c = \alpha I_e + I_{cb0} \tag{9.5}$$

If we add up all the currents entering and leaving the transistor, the overall balance can be given as

$$I_e = I_c + I_b \tag{9.6}$$

It is worth noting that these relations are the same as those for the n-p-n transistor. All that has changed are the directions of the currents but the overall effect is otherwise identical.

9.4 Basic transistor circuits

As with other electrical devices there are symbols to represent n-p-n and p-n-p transistors in circuit diagrams. These symbols are shown in Fig. 9.10. The arrowhead is drawn on the emitter of the transistor and shows the direction of conventional emitter current.

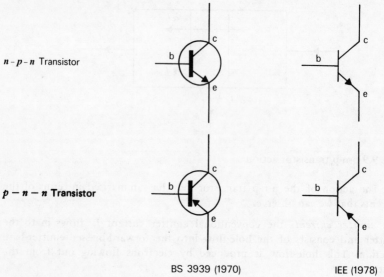

n – p – n Transistor

p – n – n **Transistor**

BS 3939 (1970)　　　　IEE (1978)

Fig. 9.10 Transistor symbols

For the sake of explanation the letters e, b and c have been added to the symbols to differentiate between the emitter, the base and the collector. Normally these letters would not be included as instanced by the remaining diagrams.

The basic transistor circuits including the sources of applied voltages
therefore take the forms shown in Fig. 9.11. The conventional currents and
the electron currents are shown and are those already described in previous
sections.

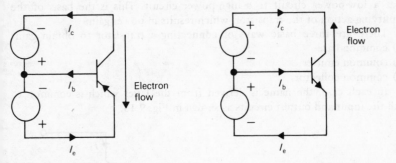

Fig. 9.11 Simple transistor circuits

Before developing the basic arrangement it is worth considering a numerical instance in order that we may appreciate the magnitudes of currents
and applied voltages likely to be encountered. Figure 9.12(a) shows an n-p-n
transistor with 600 mV applied to the emitter-base junction and 5·4 V
applied to the base-collector junction. Being a typical small-signal transistor
the emitter current is likely to be about 1·0 mA of which 0·99 mA reaches
the collector whilst the base current is 0·01 mA. In this case, the leakage
current is negligible.

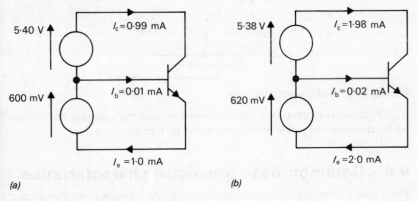

Fig. 9.12 Currents in an operational transistor

The voltage applied to the emitter-base junction is important as in this
instance 600 mV is sufficient to just overcome the depletion layer of a
silicon foward-biassed junction. A further increase of the emitter-base voltage
to, say, 620 mV is likely to produce the currents indicated in Fig. 9.12(b)
whereby all the currents have doubled.

The current in the collector is directly proportional to the emitter current which in turn has been produced by the application of the small emitter-base voltage. The collector current, however, is associated with the much greater base-collector voltage, thus the current has been transferred from a low-power circuit to a high-power circuit. This is the basis of the amplifying action of the transistor, which results in power gain.

There are three basic ways of connecting a transistor to obtain gain:
  (i) common base;
 (ii) common emitter;
(iii) common collector.

In each case, the name is derived from the layer which is common to both the input and output circuits as shown in Fig. 9.13.

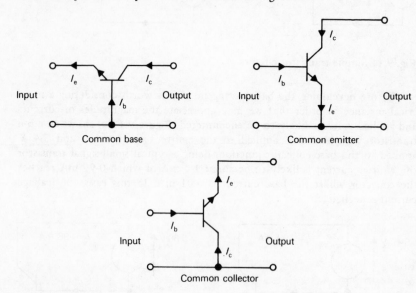

Fig. 9.13 Transistor configurations

Of these configurations the common base and the common emitter are by far the most important and these require further consideration.

9.5 Common-base transistor characteristics

The input to the common-base transistor can be measured in terms of the emitter current and the emitter-base voltage, whilst the output from the common-base transistor can be measured in terms of the collector current and the collector-base voltage. These basic relationships require to be determined in order that we make use of a transistor in this configuration.

It is not reasonable to consider the four variable quantities all at the one time. Some of the variables therefore have to be held constant while the relationships between the others are determined.

First let the emitter current and the emitter-base voltage be held constant while the collector-base voltage and the collector current are varied. If we plot the results of such observations as shown in Fig. 9.14, we obtain the collector characteristic of the common-base transistor.

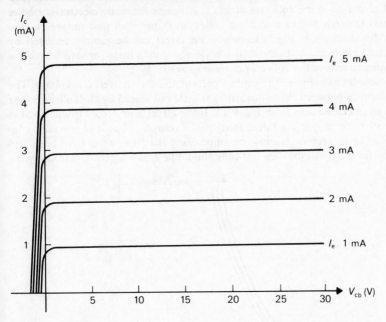

Fig. 9.14 Collector characteristics of a typical common-base transistor

By experimentation it can be shown that a family of collector characteristics are obtained by varying the emitter current, thus we obtain the family of characteristics shown in Fig. 9.14 from several values of emitter current. The family shown is appropriate to an n-p-n transistor, but a family for a p-n-p transistor would be similar except for the reversal of the current and voltage polarities.

From the family of characteristics we should note the following:

(a) When the collector-base junction is reverse biassed, the collector current is almost equal to the emitter current.

(b) When the collector-base junction is reverse biassed, the collector current is almost independent of the collector-base voltage.

(c) When the collector-base junction is forward biassed, the collector current is quickly reduced to zero and then reversed.

As a result of the first two observations we find that the transistor is a current-operated device since the output is almost completely dependent on the input current. Due to the proportional current in the collector we obtain a device giving amplification derived from the emitter current. This factor can permit us to develop the transistor as an amplifier.

Finally you will have observed that the collector current does not cease to flow when the collector is short-circuited to the base, i.e. when $V_{cb} = 0$. This arises because current is still injected from the emitter through the base into the collector; the low level of doping in the base compared with the high level of doping in the collector makes it attractive for many electrons or holes to pass through the base and the collector, rather than pass through a considerable distance in the base only. This effect can be rapidly reversed by injecting electrons or holes at the collector thus a little forward biassing is required to reduce the collector current to zero.

Now let us consider the emitter current and the emitter-base voltage. The relationship between these quantities is little influenced by the collector-base voltage as can be seen from Fig. 9.15. If the effect is neglected it would cause a small error in our considerations of the transistor but it is generally convenient to neglect it. It must be emphasised that the curves have been separated for clarity of drawing but they should be closer together than shown.

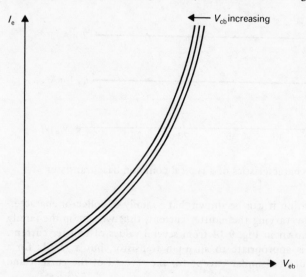

Fig. 9.15 Input characteristics of a common-base transistor

9.6 Common-emitter transistor characteristics

A typical family of collector characteristics for a common-emitter transistor are shown in Fig. 9.16. This shows the relations between the collector current and the collector-emitter voltage for variation of the input current which is the base current.

By comparison with the collector characteristics for the common-base connection shown in Fig. 9.14 the following differences may be observed:

(a) The base current is a controlling factor in the collector current that flows for the common-emitter transistor.

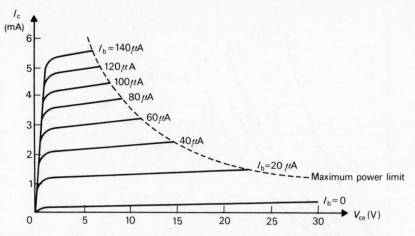

Fig. 9.16 Collector characteristics of a typical common-emitter transistor

(*b*) The collector current is very much larger than the base current.
(*c*) The characteristics of Fig. 9.16 are not evenly spaced. This shows that the collector current is not directly proportional to the base current which is to be expected since it is proportional to the emitter current.
(*d*) The collector current is zero when the output collector-emitter voltage is zero. This is caused by the collector-base junction having the same forward-bias voltage as the emitter-base junction when $V_{ce} = 0$.
(*e*) As the collector-emitter voltage increases, the space between the characteristics also increases. This is due to the value of a increasing with V_{ce}.

Although the response of this family of characteristics is not as linear as that of the common-emitter configuration, it is an important one because of the amplification of the output current (I_c) relative to the input current (I_b). The value of this current amplification is in the order of 30 to 200 which is a considerable increase, from which the common-emitter configuration derives its popularity.

The input characteristics relate the base current to the emitter-base voltage and these take a form similar to that of the common-base transistor; the input characteristics for the common-emitter transistor are shown by a typical family in Fig. 9.17.

The leakage current in the collector-base junction causes one curve of the family to be widely different from the others, i.e. when $V_{ce} = 0$. However, the transistor is not normally operated with small values of V_{ce}.

For other values of the collector-emitter voltage a small emitter-base voltage is required to offset the effect of the leakage current.

Essentially the characteristics shown for the common-emitter configuration contain the same information as those for the common-base configuration, since

$I_e = I_c + I_b$

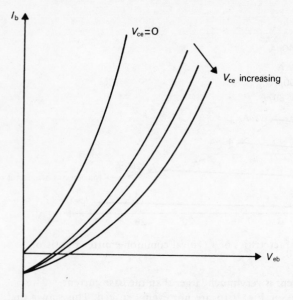

Fig. 9.17 Input characteristics of a common-emitter transistor

However, it is possible to determine the common-emitter characteristics much more accurately. The difficulty with measurements of the common-base configuration are caused by the base current being the difference of two currents as previously noted. Therefore the common-emitter characteristics are usually used to obtain information about transistors.

Transistors are specified to operate within certain parameters or limits. These are defined by the maximum permissible collector voltage, collector current and collector power. Further the power rating must be reduced if the ambient temperature increases. If these conditions are exceeded, permanent damage of the transistor is likely to result. Maximum power limitations are indicated in the characteristics of Fig. 9.16 by the dotted line.

Problems

1. The p-type material of an n-p-n transistor makes up:
   (a) the emitter;
   (b) the base;
   (c) the impurity;
   (d) the collector.

2. With reference to a p-n-p transistor explain what is meant by the forward biassing of the emitter-base junction.

3. In the production of a transistor what precautions must be taken in the specification of the base?

4. In an n-p-n transistor, the leakage current consists of:
   (a) electrons moving from the base to the emitter;
   (b) electrons moving from the collector to the base;
   (c) electrons moving from the collector to the emitter;
   (d) electrons moving from the base to the collector.

5. In a normally operated p-n-p transistor:
   (a) I_c is greater than I_e;
   (b) I_c is equal to I_e;
   (c) I_c is less than I_e;
   (d) I_c is equal to zero.

6. In a transistor:
   (a) $I_e = I_c + I_b$;
   (b) $I_c = I_e + I_b$;
   (c) $I_b = I_c + I_e$;
   (d) $I_e + I_c + I_b = 0$

7. Explain the occurrence of a collector current in a common-base transistor when $V_{cb} = 0$.

8. For the common-emitter configuration of transistor connection, draw the output characteristic relating the collector current to the collector-emitter voltage and comment on the effects of varying the base current.

9. Explain the operation of a p-n-p common-base connected transistor and hence explain why the collector current is almost equal to the emitter current.

10. Explain the occurrence of leakage current in an n-p-n transistor and hence explain the effect it might have on the transistor action when it is connected in:
    (a) the common-base configuration;
    (b) the common-emitter configuration.

11. It would appear that the emitter and the collector of a transistor are interchangeable. Explain why they are not and state the likely outcome of their being interchanged.

12. Draw the input characteristics of a common-emitter transistor and explain the variation of the characteristics as V_{ce} increases.

Answers

1. (b)   5. (c)
4. (d)   6. (a)

Appendices

Appendix A

Relationship between inductance and inductive reactance

In an a.c. circuit, the fluctuating current gives rise to a fluctuating magnetic flux which induces an e.m.f., appearing as an effective voltage drop, in the circuit. The effect of inductance only in a circuit can be considered from the definition of inductance, thus

$$v = L \cdot \frac{di}{dt}$$

Let the current be given by

$$i = I_m \sin \omega t$$

hence

$$v = L \cdot \frac{d}{dt}(I_m \sin \omega t)$$

$$= \omega L I_m \cos \omega t$$

$$= \omega L I_m \sin (\omega t + \frac{\pi}{2})$$

thus

$$V_m = \omega L I_m$$

and

$$\frac{V_m}{\sqrt{2}} = \frac{I_m}{\sqrt{2}} \cdot \omega L$$

In r.m.s. values

$$V = I \omega L$$
$$= I(2\pi f L)$$

$\omega L = 2\pi fL$ is termed the inductive reactance of the circuit and is represented by the symbol X_L, thus

$$V = IX_L$$
and $\quad X_L = 2\pi fL = \omega L \qquad\qquad\qquad (6.3)$

Appendix B

Relationship between capacitance and capacitive reactance

In any circuit, there is capacitance due to the proximity of conductors at different potentials. The effect of capacitance only can be considered in a circuit from the definition of capacitance, thus

$$q = Cv$$

Let the voltage be given by

$$v = V_m \sin \omega t$$
hence $\quad q = CV_m \sin \omega t$

and $\quad i = \dfrac{dq}{dt} = C \cdot \dfrac{dv}{dt}$

$$= C \cdot \frac{d}{dt}(V_m \sin \omega t)$$

$$= \omega C V_m \cos \omega t$$

$$= \omega C V_m \sin\left(\omega t + \frac{\pi}{2}\right)$$

thus $\quad I_m = \omega C V_m$

and $\quad \dfrac{I_m}{\sqrt{2}} = \dfrac{V_m}{\sqrt{2}} \cdot \omega C$

In r.m.s. values

$$I = \omega CV$$

$$V = I \cdot \frac{1}{\omega C} = I \cdot \frac{1}{2\pi fC}$$

$\dfrac{1}{\omega C} = \dfrac{1}{2\pi fC}$ is termed the capacitive reactance of the circuit and is represented by the symbol X_C, thus

$$V = IX_C$$

and $\quad X_C = \dfrac{1}{2\pi f C} = \dfrac{1}{\omega C}$ $\qquad\qquad\qquad$ (6.6)

Index